Introduction to Environmental Studies

Introduction to Environmental Studies

INTERDISCIPLINARY READINGS

First Edition

Edited by Claudia J. Ford, Katherine Cleary, and Jessica Rogers
SUNY Potsdam

Printed in the United States of America.

We dedicate this text to future environmental studies students and their passionate desire to protect the planet.

CONTENTS

Acknowledgments

The authors would like to thank Dr. Heather Sullivan-Catlin, Dr. Matt LaVine, Dr. Becca Berkey, and the SUNY Potsdam students in Introduction to Environmental Studies. We would also like to thank the editors and staff of Cognella Publishing, especially John Remington and Gem Rabanera.

Introduction

Environmental studies is a relatively new discipline. It emerged from the need to understand a combination of several other disciplines and takes some characteristics of each. This is what makes environmental studies an interdisciplinary subject. Combining several disparate disciplines, such as sociology, politics, biology, geology, and communications, is often necessary to be a successful practitioner of environmental studies. Students learning environmental studies need to be able to connect each of these disciplines and synthesize the information in order to advocate for environmental fair use and resource protection. This book was created to help students navigate the most important topics in environmental studies, focusing on the different connections between humans and the environment. We have organized the chapters in a way that builds on each topic and finally looks back to reflect on the journey through the discipline of environmental studies. Because we recognize that environmental studies draws on multiple disciplines to create an integrated field of knowledge, there are themes that continue to emerge and build throughout the text.

This text was designed for an Introduction to Environmental Studies course at the State University of New York at Potsdam. The course most commonly enrolls first-year students, and the readings were chosen with them in mind. One of our goals in writing this book was to prioritize voices outside the white, male canon that we were taught when the field was emerging. We believe that hearing many voices discussing environmental issues enriches our comprehension and communicates the variety of ways that knowledge and understanding can be achieved. Each chapter's introduction summarizes the topic and the included readings. In addition, each chapter's introduction discusses several supplementary key readings and videos that could be recommended to students who wish to learn more about a particular topic. We have tried to include resources that would be available at most institutions of higher education or are publicly available. For any links to recommended readings, videos, or websites, we include the most up-to-date web addresses but we encourage readers to find the titles in a search engine as URLs change over time. Finally, we have included reading and discussion prompts to guide students and instructors through the main themes and ideas in each chapter.

Environmental studies examines the human connection to the environment from many perspectives, including human impacts on the environment and the consequences of those impacts on the global population. The first chapters of this text introduce environmental studies and its companion topic, sustainability. While the topic of sustainability could be, and often is, a complete course on its own, it is necessary to explain the concept of sustainability in the beginning of a discussion of environmental studies before examining all the other facets of humans' influence on the environment. Understanding our impact on the environment, how to decrease that impact, and how to encourage others to follow that example can be powerful tools. **Chapter 1: Environmental Studies** begins by discovering how connections between our own lives and the environment paving the way to becoming an environmentalist. The text makes it clear that understanding the ecological systems of animals, trees, or rivers is insufficient if we fail to acknowledge how these systems interact with humans and the ways in which humans impact the world. **Chapter 2: Sustainability and Consumption** then looks at the connection between humans and the resources we extract from the environment. The five pillars of sustainability—People, Peace, Planet, Partnership, and Prosperity—anchor our connections to environmental studies, and we begin this text by exploring each pillar.

After recognizing our collective and individual impact on the planet, in **Chapter 3: Environmental History**, we look back at the history of environmentalism in North America and how the depiction of the environment from early American colonization to mid-twentieth century environmentalism evolved over time. The colonizers' attitude that elevated humans above nature, coming after Indigenous peoples had lived in constant, sustainable connection with nature, led to the unmitigated destruction of our environment over centuries. It was partly a lack of knowledge about natural processes and biological resources that led to unsustainable use and destructive practices. This connects to **Chapter 4: Biological Resources**, which provides a concise survey of key environmental processes, such as nutrient and energy cycling and the global distribution of biological resources. Knowing how these processes function allows us to harness these cycles without causing long-term damage and gives us the opportunity to correct our current unsustainable trajectory of resource use.

In **Chapter 5: Climate Change, Climate Crisis**, we investigate the most pressing current environmental concern, the global climate crisis, which is linked to all the previous and subsequent chapters and must be at the forefront when discussing our environment. We expand the nutrient cycling discussion from Chapter 4 to look at the consequences of disrupting these cycles as humans have done by increasing greenhouse gasses in the atmosphere as part of industrialization. A significant proportion of those greenhouse gasses comes from the agricultural sector. While the agricultural revolution increased humanity's ability to produce more food using less land, the long-term consequences of modern industrial agricultural practices and food systems are extremely damaging to the environment and human health and are likely to lead ultimately to a decrease in food production efficiency. In **Chapter 6: Agriculture and Food Systems**, we look in detail at the environmental impact of our food production processes and the inequitable impacts of those processes on different countries and groups of people. Examining food as one of the most fundamental human needs and the ways meeting that need has harmed our environment reveals the enormous imbalance in where or who bears those harms. **Chapter 7: Environmental Justice** looks at the broader issue of disproportionate impact and how environmental pollution is harming Indigenous lands, communities of color, and areas of low socioeconomic status. Environmental justice highlights how these groups often lack the power to prevent these insidious, long-term consequences of unsustainable resource use.

The next section of the text examines how we can create change and move forward with new paradigms of human interaction with the environment. Beginning with **Chapter 8: Human Population, Urbanization, and Land Use**, we discuss the ways our current population numbers are affecting the environmental sustainability of our future. Looking at a recurring debate since at least the 1960s, we examine whether our current population growth and resource use trends will lead to a collapse of ecological systems, and what can be done to prevent that. One of the priorities for avoiding collapse is overhauling the means of global energy production. **Chapter 9: Energy and the Environment** focuses on how we can capture economically and environmentally sustainable sources of energy. We live in an era of great change and advocacy around these sustainable energy issues. Energy use and production changes connect deeply to issues of environmental justice as fossil fuel pipelines are often situated on or through Indigenous lands. **Chapter 10: Environmental Law, Policy, and Governance** examines the origins of existing environmental legislation and policies. Policy development is one of the ways environmental studies can effect change on larger scales, advocating for legislation that protects both people and the planet.

The final two chapters of the text ask students to look back and reflect on how the knowledge they have gained throughout the semester has altered (or not) their personal decisions shaping their own ecological impact. **Chapter 11: Environmental Philosophy and Ethics** revisits the earlier discussion of sustainability by looking at the ethical ideas around consumption as well as examining the collective responsibility we all share to stop harming our planet through inaction. It is important for students to acknowledge that Indigenous peoples held and still maintain distinct worldviews about the relationship between humans and the environment, ideas that may have different and more sustainable outcomes. We examine Indigenous environmental knowledge in this chapter. The final **Chapter 12: Environmental Futures** looks toward the future while understanding our current crises. We examine how the 2020 global pandemic was predicted from the many minor outbreaks of disease caused by human incursion into natural wildlife habitats.

The goal of this reader is to provide students with the tools to consider specific environmental issues from a variety of perspectives. The text incorporates readings that consider the social, political, economic, cultural, and biophysical dimensions of a range of environmental challenges and solutions. We want students of environmental studies to understand the interconnectedness of human society with the natural world in order to become a force for change and to prevent problems in the future. We want students to recognize that a paradigm shift is emerging whereby environmental justice, social justice, and thriving sustainable communities must coexist. Knowledge, advocacy, and an ethical approach can reverse the problems that prior generations have caused and allowed to persist. It is up to us to move forward by connecting humans with the environment in sustainable, equitable, and compassionate ways.

CHAPTER ONE

Environmental Studies

Students studying environmental studies need to be able to connect many different disciplines, such as biology, sociology, geology, and political science, and to synthesize information from each discipline to effectively advocate for environmental fair use and protections. This means that students need the broad interdisciplinary education that environmental studies provides in order to capture the nuances and intersections of complex strategies for successful environmental work. In an era of sustainability, environmental justice, and climate change, we need professionals who can draw on multiple streams of knowledge to make recommendations that will incorporate the rights and values of different groups of people as well as the inherent rights of nature. The environmental movement has existed, in some form, for a long time. However, active environmentalism and the struggle for environmental protections began in the United States in the 1960s. The first chapter of this reader sets the stage for the rest of the book, creating a sense of how humans' environmental activities have shaped our world and introducing ideas for how we can mitigate that impact and build a safer, greener, more equitable future.

We begin with a reading on the history of environmentalism by Philip Shabecoff, "Rebuilding the House," a chapter from his book *A Fierce Green Fire: The American Environmental Movement* (2003). We start with Shabecoff showing us how different strands of knowledge come together to fight climate change in order to advocate for those most harmed by its effects. He describes how we already know what needs to be done about climate change, we just lack the will and education to implement those changes fairly and equitably. Shabecoff describes the work that both large and grassroots environmental groups have undertaken to aid society in making these changes along with the different directions and goals these groups pursue. In this chapter, we consider the complexity of the relationship between humans and the environment; Shabecoff describes how balancing environmental protections, improving human health, and fighting poverty have always presented us with strategic challenges. Shabecoff introduces the idea that integration of our economies with our ecosystems does not need to be an either/or contest but can become a both/and measure of success.

READING AND DISCUSSION PROMPTS

1. Shabecoff explores the common misconception that environmentalists are universally opposed to economic growth. Describe some of the ways Shabecoff explains that environmental and economic goals can, in fact, support and advance each other.
2. In order for the environmental movement to become more powerful and more effective, Shabecoff says it must "take up the cause of social justice." How has failure to take up that cause weakened the environmental movement in the past, and how do you think embracing both social and environmental justice will strengthen the movement in the future?
3. Shabecoff spends a considerable amount of time in this piece "debunking myths," that is, he explains why several common ideas about the environmental movement or environmentalists are incorrect. Before reading this article, did you share any of these misconceptions? Which ones? Has your view on them changed since reading the article?

READING 1.1

Rebuilding the House

By Philip Shabecoff

Trend is not destiny.
René Dubos

As a new millennium approaches, time to save and rebuild the environment is running down. Some alarmed environmentalists and scientists fear we have no more than a few decades or so of grace. Still others believe there will be no collapse of our habitat but a long, slow descent into a biological twilight over the next century or two.

René Dubos once observed that "trend is not destiny." The genius that has enabled humankind to master nature and intervene in the process of evolution through technology and social organization can extricate us from the ecological quicksand.

Trend, however, *is* destiny unless that trend is altered. As this is being written, the trend toward a rapidly deteriorating environment is not being altered but accelerated.

The essential message of environmentalism, however, is not catastrophe but hope. Environmentalism, along with science, and even philosophy, has established a broad but clear agenda for us. Wise people in these fields have told us what the solutions are. We are almost awash in answers. We can extricate ourselves from our ecological peril by stabilizing population, conserving resources, preventing pollution, and preserving and restoring nature. Above all, we humans must learn and understand what we are doing to the planet and must adjust our thinking and behavior in response.

We already know in essence what we have to do. All we lack is the wisdom and the will to do it. All that stands in our way is human nature and its works over the last 10,000 years or so.

Environmental historian Donald Worster has pointed out that the nation's economic and social institutions have accommodated the impulse to protect the environment "up to a point." American culture, he said, has always found favor with the ideals of cleanliness and beauty when such ideals did not get in the way of making money.

"But it is altogether premature to assume that such accommodation implies deep cultural change," Worster wrote. "To say the least," he added, "it is highly problematical whether, on balance, there has been a radical change to environmental protection in this society or even whether what has been achieved will survive into the next century."[1]

At the opening of the twenty-first century, Worster's observation seems all too prophetic. American culture is clearly unwilling to accommodate the basic changes required to safeguard the environment for our posterity. Indeed, it is questionable whether the environmental gains achieved in the last third of the twentieth century will survive.

Progress cannot be made with regulatory Band-Aids, blind faith in the invisible hand of the market, or other facile remedies. There will have to be changes in our institutions, in our economic systems, in technology, and in social relationships in ways that reflect our hard-won understanding of the changing balance between human beings and nature. It is, in short, time for society to catch up to the accelerated pace of evolution in the physical world created by human numbers and human power.

To state such goals would appear to set our imperfect society a hopeless task. One has only to look at our economy in disarray, our government under the sway of corporate money, free market absolutists, and the growing power of special interests. Our media are inattentive, and sometimes hostile, to environmental concerns. Our educational system has made strides in some areas but too often, in too many places, struggles to provide a basic education, much less to breed environmental literacy. Poverty and class strife abound. Large segments of the American people are politically passive and show a lack of caring about the future. Americans may worry about the environment, but their concern is deeply submerged beneath the tidal wave of consumerism.

These immense obstacles stand in the way of the broad social changes that are called for by the urgency of environmental problems.

Added to these challenges is the difficulty in bringing the nations of the world together to address the threats to the global environment, not to mention the emotional and intellectual hurdles that we humans, just a few thousand years from huddling around fires in our caves seeking refuge from the terrors of wild nature, must leap in order to readjust our relationship to the natural world.

Differentiating between "hope" and "expectation," the philosopher Ivan Illich said, "I for one see signs of hope in the lifestyles of subsistence peasants or in the network of activists who save trees here, or plant them there. But I admit that I am unable to envisage how, short of a devastating catastrophe, these hope-inspiring acts can be translated into 'policy.'"[2]

That, of course, is what the environmental movement is seeking to do. In the latter part of the twentieth century, the environmental impulse, building on the ideas and leadership of farsighted men and women in the nineteenth and earlier twentieth centuries and expressed through an expanding and popular movement, was the agency of political and social transformation. We have seen how environmentalism led to substantial change in our laws, our institutions, and our personal behavior. It has produced a large cadre of informed, trained activists. If it continued to grow in strength, it could have the potential to become the instrument of a political evolution that would enable us to establish, as Nathan Gardels put it, "equilibrium between man and nature, and between future and present."[3]

Environmentalism provides a way of acting, of overcoming the passivity of individuals in a mass civilization. It is a different way of thinking about such basic issues as what constitutes progress and how people ought to live. By showing us that we can tame our machines and make them useful without being harmful, environmentalism points toward a civilization advancing with the help of careful science and sensible technology. Environmentalism just may be the threshold of a true postindustrial society.

As a nation, we have yet to cross that threshold. At the beginning of the new century it is reasonable to ask if we will ever do so, or do so in time. Support for environmental goals and values remains broad but shallow. The political fallout from short-term crises such as economic downturns, the Persian Gulf war, new threats of war around the globe, or, most dramatically, the terrorist attacks of September 11, 2001 and the subsequent wars in Afghanistan and Iraq, demonstrate how easily the attention of the American people can be diverted from environmental problems, how quickly our concerns revert to short-term self-interest. It is clear that the old industrial order is more firmly in command than ever, not only of the economy but of the political system as well. The environmental movement, despite enormous expenditures of talent and effort and some real progress in limiting pollution and the destruction of resources, has not achieved the fundamental reforms vital to assure our ecological security over the long run.

It also is apparent that the environmental movement in the United States, while still vital, is running up against the limits of its ability to achieve social change using its traditional tools. Congress and the courts can no longer be counted on as allies; increasingly, they are obstacles to environmental progress. To achieve the basic reforms necessary to reach its goals, the environmental movement itself will have to evolve. There must be a fourth wave of environmentalism, bigger, richer, more skillful, powerful, and assertive.

For much of recent decades, the movement has been functioning as an ecological emergency squad, responding to crises and seeking to plug a leaking statute here or fill a regulatory gap there. In the future, instead of simply lecturing, lobbying, demonstrating, haggling, or litigating to protect public health and natural resources, the environmentalism activists almost certainly must move forward to acquire the *power* necessary to achieve fundamental change. To do so, they will have to tap the latent support that is repeatedly demonstrated by the opinion polls to build an effective political base—a base strong enough to counter the financial power wielded by those interests that oppose environmental reform. Political leaders must be presented with a clear choice between addressing our environmental ills and being replaced.

Little has changed since Gifford Pinchot commented a century ago that "there is no reason why the American people cannot take into their hands again the full political power which is theirs by right and which they exercised before the special interests began to nullify the will of the majority."[4]

Gus Speth, then president of the World Resources Institute, predicted in 1990 that the environmental movement was moving toward a political breakthrough. "I believe that the United States is going to have what we really haven't had yet. We talk about the greening of technology, and the greening of this and the greening of that. We really haven't had a greening of politics in the United States."[5]

As yet, fundamental change has yet to materialize. Polls show that most Americans are tired of the entrenched political system and no doubt would welcome a change of direction. But the public has not been educated, mobilized, and energized to make the profound change that is necessary, certainly not by environmentalists or environmentalism.

If environmentalism is to be an agent of the necessary social transformation, it will have to first transform itself. It will have to acquire the political, economic, and moral strength to counter the seemingly overwhelming forces arrayed against it.

To begin with, ways must be found to close the gap between the large national environmental organizations and the grassroots groups whose members comprise an army of millions ready to be mobilized in the war for political power. As Lois Gibbs pointed out, the community-based groups often succeed where the national organizations fail. They do so, she insisted, by rejecting the "soft path" of negotiation and compromise with governments and corporations and instead taking the harder path of direct political confrontation.[6] Negotiation and compromise can be more useful tools for the environmentalists when they can come to the table with strength equal to that of their opponents.

The national organizations have the knowledge, professionalism, and experience in the niceties and not-so-niceties of national, regional, and statewide politics. They can reinforce the grassroots activists with an array of skills that can be used where direct political confrontation would be unproductive overkill. They bring their own substantial and relatively affluent membership into the political arena.

A step in this direction was made in 1990 when the "Gang of Ten," an informal but exclusive club of major national environmental groups, disbanded and its members sought to enlarge their outreach to a wider segment of the movement. But it was a small step on a long journey.

When the national and grassroots environmentalists forge themselves into a unified force—if they ever do—they would constitute a formidable new presence on the national political stage. Parties and elected officials would be required to pay more respectful attention to their issues. But even a unified environmental movement would be far from possessing the commanding political power requisite for attaining fundamental social reform. A much broader coalition is required.

To make the political breakthrough necessary to achieve their goals, the environmentalists *must* make common cause with other sectors of our society that have a stake in changing the political and economic status quo. Potential allies include the poor, minorities, women, the elderly, industrial workers, and other vulnerable groups whose vital interests demand significant social change. The movement surely should explore joining forces with businesses that require a clean environment and efficiently used resources to prosper and with conservatives fed up with the corporate socialism that is the hallmark of today's PAC-financed realpolitik.

It will not be easy. It cannot happen overnight. But a new majority coalition, with the environmental movement as one of its major building blocks, is not an impossibility.

First, however, the environmental organizations must put their own houses in order. One great failure of much of the national movement in recent years, in my opinion, has been its unwillingness or inability to take up the causes of social justice in the United States. This failure is all the more dismaying because one of the deepest roots of contemporary environmentalism lies, as we have seen, in the activist civil rights/peace/women's tradition of the 1960s.

Opponents of the environmental movement often brand it as "elitist." For example, William Tucker's book *Progress and Privilege*, published in 1982, called environmentalism "the politics of aristocracy." Tucker described the environmental movement as "essentially a suburban agrarianism" espoused by those who have achieved a high level of comfort and security and want to preserve their privileged position by blocking further economic and technological progress.[7] Such arguments, deliberately or out of ignorance, overlook the fact that almost all Americans, particularly the poor and under-privileged, are the victims of environmental degradation. It is a point of view that fails to recognize that pollution is a serious public health concern and that misuse of resources is a threat to our national security. It is a perspective that is out of touch with reality.

It is true that the leadership of national environmental groups *is* largely white, male, well educated, and relatively well heeled, with incomes above the national average. This description, however, would fit activists in many if not most social movements. As one study concluded, "people who are politically active, whether in environmental or any other issues, tend to be uniformly drawn from the upper middle class."[8] While relatively well-to-do, few of today's national environmental activists could be considered rich. The tradition of wealthy, highborn amateurs of the early conservation years is long since gone. Sociologists Denton Morrison and Riley Dunlap point out, moreover, that "the *opponents* of environmentalism come much closer to being an elite than do core environmentalists. Most of the most vocal, coordinated opposition comes from top levels of corporate management. Such objections to environmental reform are hardly above suspicion as representing upper-class interests, even if frequently couched in a rationale of concern for general, including underclass, welfare."[9]

The imbalances in the social composition of the leadership and staffs of the national environmental organizations cannot, however, be simply dismissed. One of the reasons that there are not more representatives of minority groups is that the leaders of the groups have not, until recently, taken the trouble to reach out to those communities. I am not sure of the reasons for this, but I doubt that they reflect racism. I suspect that many of the environmentalists are so confident that they are doing the Lord's work that it does not occur to them that they have other obligations to society.

Most of the environmental organizations have made some effort to change "the whiteness of the green movement," but one senses they are doing so basically out of a sense of obligation or in response to criticism. In reality, the environmentalists need the knowledge, talent, street smarts, practical experience, political energy, and militancy of angry outsiders from minority communities more than the minorities need the environmentalists.

Early in 1990, leaders of civil rights and minority community organizations wrote to the major national environmental groups asking them not only to change their hiring practices but also to play an active role in addressing the environmental evils afflicting the poor and oppressed. "You must know as well as we do," the letter said, "that white organizations isolated from our Third World communities can never build a movement." Since then, the champions of environmental justice for all have forged a vital and growing, if internally contentious, movement by merging the goals and ideals of environmentalism and civil rights. The national environmental organizations would do well to learn from the environmental justice activists and enlist in their cause. For their part, the environmental justice activists will have to welcome the mainstream groups instead of maintaining a wall of resentment and suspicion.

Environmentalists are often charged with opposing economic growth that creates jobs and economic projects, including housing, that helps the poor. They are also accused of selfishly blocking economic development of public lands that could benefit all of society.

Some members of groups on the radical fringe are no-growth advocates, but modern environmentalism does not seek to halt economic growth; on the contrary, one of its overriding goals is to be sure that economic growth can be sustained over the long run. It therefore presses for an economy that makes prudent use of natural resources and production methods that do not pollute the commons. The corporate critics who charge elitism are often those whose practices pollute and waste resources and thus compromise the nation's long-term economic prospects, who themselves eliminate thousands of jobs by moving their plants to foreign countries where the cost of labor is low, or who abandon block after block of inner-city housing.

Many of the environmentalists, however, are too often insensitive to the economic consequences of their programs, particularly as they affect workers, minorities, and the poor. During the 1990 congressional debate over amendments to the Clean Air Act, for example, the environmental lobbyists in Washington, D.C., only belatedly and weakly supported economic assistance for miners in the high-sulfur coal industry whose jobs would be eliminated by the new rules for reducing acid rain. Much the same could be said about the environmentalists' campaign to save the endangered spotted owl and the ancient forests of the Northwest that are the bird's only habitat. While pursuing their worthy goal, they provided only late and inadequate proposals for protecting the jobs of workers in the timber industry and preserving the logging communities that depended on the old-growth forest for their livelihood.

Environmental regulation as now practiced does have a negative, if relatively small, effect on the gross national product and on the creation of jobs over the short term—although there is disagreement among economists about that conclusion. But as Morrison and Dunlap assert, "there is no inherent reason why environmental protection and social justice must constitute conflicting social goals. The challenge is to develop social policies which promote *both*."[10] It is a challenge the environmental movement must accept.

Today's environmentalists are not indifferent to injustices such as poverty and racism. Many have a deep personal concern. But involved in the pressing, sometimes overwhelming task of dealing with environmental crises, they push aside the issues of social and economic equity as someone else's immediate business. At least some of the organizations hold back from broader social activism because they fear it would jeopardize their funding from corporations or government sources or alienate their more conservative constituencies.

Environmentalism will not be able to claim full legitimacy for its aims, however, until it addresses the even graver social ills of poverty, hunger, prejudice, and economic inequity. Bertold Brecht said it in *The Threepenny Opera*: "First feed the face and then talk right from wrong." It is not enough for the environmental groups to demand that the old-growth forests of the Northwest be preserved to save the spotted owl or call for an end to the burning of high-sulfur coal to reduce acid rain. It is also incumbent upon them to come up with carefully worked-out, politically acceptable, economically viable, and timely programs for preserving the communities that depend on logging and for making sure that displaced coal miners are protected against economic disaster. Environmentalists need not put jobs, housing, discrimination, drugs, or homelessness at the top of their list of priorities. But they need to recognize that these problems are important parts of their agendas.

Near the end of the twentieth century, some environmentalists began to integrate their conservation goals with the economic and cultural needs and practices of local communities. Ecotrust in the Pacific Northwest was a pioneer in this endeavor. The environmental community, however, still has far to travel down this road.

It is unlikely that the comprehensive reforms needed to protect the environment can ever be achieved without redressing those wider social problems. Environmental degradation and social injustice, as we have already seen, arise from essentially the same flaws in our social structure.

Political power cannot be built on a base of dispirited, impoverished people struggling to stay alive in crime-ridden urban ghettos, in barrios or rural slums. As the Reverend Jesse Jackson, the indefatigable herald of the Rainbow Coalition, said: "You cannot separate environment from empowerment. Toxic waste dumps are put in communities where people are the poorest, the least organized, the least registered to vote. If you are poor you are a target for toxic waste. If you are unregistered to vote you are a target."[11]

Preserving open spaces and public lands is vital, but conservationists must try to assure that those amenities are broadly available to all Americans. Of course, the claim by those who wish to profit from the public lands and develop every inch of green space that only rich elitists oppose them is hypocritical and false. The national parks and forests and other public lands are used for enjoyment today chiefly by middle- and working-class vacationers, while the well-to-do can go to the parks or to Acapulco, St. Moritz, or their summer homes on Martha's Vineyard. But these lands must also be open to the children of Watts and Harlem, for whom a forest or a meadow is today an all too exotic sight.

Widening their agenda in this way will be difficult for the national environmental organizations. Many of them draw much of their membership and financial support from the more well-to-do people or from corporations, where support for social activism tends to be thin or negative. Some fear being categorized as an amorphous general interest organization rather than a group dedicated to their specific environmental missions.

But environmentalism could be a potent democratizing force. If the house that shelters us all is crumbling, we can unite to try to save and rebuild it. The ground must be made fertile for the planting of entirely new political seeds, making it possible to raise a formidable popular coalition able to win elections at the local, state, and national levels and to push environmental issues to the forefront of the national agenda.

The old progressive coalition that arose with the New Deal is gone and cannot be revived. But there are broad elements of American society desperately unhappy with the nation's political course at the beginning of the twenty-first century. They may constitute a powerful new political movement waiting to be born. Now, however, they are an inchoate, leaderless, and virtually powerless impulse. The environmental movement, with its broad membership base and even broader support of its goals, could provide the leadership to weld these diverse elements into a political force to be reckoned with. But first it must raise its line of sight.

Broadening its vision to encompass larger social goals and joining forces with the environmental justice movement and other sectors of society with a vital stake in changing the current direction of politics in the United States is part of the transformation the environmental movement as a whole must make to acquire sufficient power to achieve its goals. Among other things, the movement will have to acquire the skills and tools and tactics needed to win at the political game in the United States.

Most important, perhaps, is learning to become effective at political organizing at the local, state, and national level. Money is currently the dominant variable in American politics, and that is not going to change in the near future. Despite efforts to reform the campaign financing process, the environmentalists can expect to be continually outspent by degrees of magnitude by their foes. The environmentalists can counter with a sustained campaign to educate the public on the importance of their issues and then to enlist them in the effort to reassert democratic control of the electoral process.

If they are to succeed, they might draw on an unlikely model: The Christian right has been able to play a decisive role in the political process far beyond its actual numbers by such painstaking organizing. The fundamentalists have built their strength by electing members of school boards, local selectmen, and state representatives and, in so doing, have imposed their own agenda on the Republican Party. The environmental movement has at least as firm a moral platform as well as a wider, if not deeper, political base on which to build its strength.

Such a campaign will require a cadre of trained organizers to work with local groups across the country. Lois Gibbs's Center for Environment, Health and Justice is doing that now, but with extremely limited resources. The environmentalists will have to expand their ability to communicate to the public. They will have to acquire more resources to participate in the electoral process and to use those resources more effectively. They will have to stop playing at politics and go to war to force their goals to a much higher rung on the national agenda and to elect representatives at all levels of government to carry out that agenda.

Then what? Assuming that the environmental movement attains the will, the means, and the strength to exercise decisive power over American politics and government, how does it use that power? How does it try to build an ecologically rational as well as socially just society?

Certainly wiser budget choices, enacting more effective laws, ensuring honest and rigorous enforcement of those laws, and appointing dedicated public servants to oversee them are vital to the protection of the environment. But laws and rules, as the last twenty years have demonstrated, are insufficient by themselves. Waste, inefficiency, avarice, shortsightedness, indifference, cannot be legislated out of existence.

A new group of economists, under the banner of ecological economics, suggests that the starting point must be a reevaluation of some of our economic assumptions. Anyone who has followed environmental problems over the years can hardly fail to trace many of their causes to flaws in our day-to-day economic practices. A key step in our effort to save the environment, the ecological economists argue, is dealing with those shortcomings.

Free-market capitalism has proven to be a resilient and effective system for producing and distributing goods and services. In practice, however, markets are frequently managed and manipulated, and their "freedom" is illusory. Only a cursory look at the United States economy—with its huge budget and trade deficits, its unemployment, its badly skewed distribution of wealth, its savings and loan debacles, its Enron-style scandals, the boundless greed of many corporate executives, its irrational subsidies, and other malfunctions—demonstrates that it is far from a perfect system. A rising tide, contrary to popular wisdom, not only often fails to lift all ships, it can also cause extensive damage to coastal ecosystems. One can believe in and support the free market without regarding it as an object of worship to be defended by a holy war at any word of criticism or suggestion of reform.

One failure of the system is that it does not reasonably account for ecological values. Environmental degradation and resource depletion are issues that are largely unaddressed by our economic yardsticks. Today's market indicators do not assign a negative value to pollution or the expenditure of natural resources. They do not place a fair or realistic value on unspoiled natural systems or human health. If we are to preserve the environment from destruction, we must get the costs of production and consumption right and then adjust prices to reflect the true costs.

One way to get at this dilemma is "full-cost pricing," an approach that in recent years has been getting increased scrutiny from economists and even many businesspeople. The idea would be to add the costs of pollution and the depletion of resources to the selling price of any product. An example offered by energy expert Amory Lovins would be to impose a surcharge on autos that guzzle gasoline and to offer rebates on fuel-efficient cars.

An ecologically sound society must also reexamine the prevailing economic notion of progress. One need not oppose economic growth to ask: Growth for what? Growth for whom? The gross national product (GNP)—the gross production of goods and services—is a highly doubtful measure of national and human welfare. Does a healthy economy really require the continual expansion of the production of goods and services without regard to the necessity and utility of those products and their impact on health and the natural environment? Does it make sense for us to spend well over $100 billion a year to repair the ravages of pollution and then count that sum as growth, as progress, because it adds to the GNP?

An ecologically sound economy should adopt policies that encourage not growth for its own sake, but growth that provides for the real needs of its citizens with an absolute minimum of waste and pollution.

Progress is not achieved solely by stimulating consumer wants and accumulating profits. Are not many of our economic goods really economic bads? Is our mass economy really making us happier as individuals, more stable and secure as a society? Are not the degradation of our environment, social inequity, and social ills such as drugs and crime related to the failures of our economic and social systems?

We need different definitions of economic growth to measure progress. Instead of using the GNP as our most sacred indicator, we must substitute new measures of national well being that account for the depletion of resources, the destruction of nature, the welfare of human beings, and real national progress over the long run. Ecological economists such as Herman Daly have proposed a new Index of Sustainable Economic Welfare, and many other efforts are ongoing.

The idea is not to abandon our economic system but to strip it of those parts that threaten not only the long-term health of the environment but the long-term health of the economy as well. Sustainable development may now be regarded as a cliché, but it is really an expression of responsibility for and faith in the future.

Our mullahs of free-market orthodoxy who condemn long-term economic and environmental planning as sacrilege are shortsighted and are voices of generational selfishness. "Their eyes are fixed upon the present gain and they are blind to the future." By looking indifferently at the pollution of the commons and the exhaustion of resources, those indifferent to the true costs of environmental protection could be the gravediggers of American capitalism if they have their way. Those who demand economic policies that can be sustained in future generations are the true champions of the free market.

With proper planning and prudence, there need be no limits to economic growth. We are not truly constrained by what Kenneth Boulding called a "spaceman" economy, one that can expand so far and no farther in a hermetically sealed system. As Barry Commoner and others have pointed out, the earth enjoys a constant supply of new energy from the sun. If we use the earth's resources wisely to put this energy to use, there is no reason that we cannot have a constantly rising standard of living into the foreseeable future.

The new economics will reward husbanding dwindling resources, recycling existing resources, and restoring land, water, and other natural systems that have already become degraded and unproductive. Progress will be redefined to mean reducing poverty and providing a steadily rising quality of life for a stable or diminishing population. The wealth that is created out of natural resources must be shared more equitably. Provision will be made for preserving open space, biological diversity, and the beauty of nature, all of which will be recognized as representing long-term economic as well as aesthetic value. The natural systems that sustain life will have to be protected through careful and constant stewardship.

Revised economic goals will require changes in the way we operate financial markets and in the role of corporations. Our financial practices customarily discount long-term investments. Developing and exploiting resources as quickly as possible thus make the highest returns. Professor Colin Clark, who teaches applied mathematics at the University of British Columbia, noted that "if dollars in banks are growing faster than a timber company's forests, it is more profitable (indeed, more economical) to chop down the trees, sell them, and invest the proceeds elsewhere."[12]

American corporations are, almost by definition, in thrall to the "tyranny of the immediate," particularly the tyranny of the money and securities markets. Even those corporate executives who want to do the right environmental thing are constrained by the need to produce the best bottom line in the near term to satisfy their shareholders and to make the best use of the money markets. Voluntarism cannot do the job. A giant company such as Du Pont can change policy to reward its managers for environmental as well as economic performance, or a company like Dow can pledge to reduce toxic emissions unilaterally, only because they are in exceptionally strong market positions. But many companies that would like to adopt responsible environmental policies cannot do so because they would then be at a competitive disadvantage with businesses in their industry that choose to plunge ahead in seeking profit and ignoring the environmental consequences.

Economic incentives, of course, are one way to influence corporate behavior. If corporate managers were required to include in their annual balance sheets heavy taxes paid on air or water they have polluted, they would no doubt think twice before letting their emissions into the environment. Eliminating subsidies for environmentally destructive developments that are bad for public health, such as oil drilling or coal mining on public land, superhighway construction, and tobacco production, and making these activities subject to the discipline of the marketplace would also help.

In recent years, there have been an increasing number of proposals to restructure our tax system by partially replacing taxes on wages and profits—that is to say, taxing work and capital formation—with taxes on pollution and resource depletion. Such a policy would have some problems—a pollution tax would be regressive and require rebates to lower income families. But it would also raise revenues by taxing harmful things, such as pollution and resource depletion, rather than productive things, such as work and investment.

To achieve meaningful, lasting changes in corporate behavior, however, it probably will be necessary to make substantial changes in the structure and values of the corporations themselves. This could be done by revised securities laws that would require companies to achieve defined levels of environmental performance. Another possibility is the mandatory rewriting of corporate charters to reflect a set of values similar to the Valdez Principles, a code of behavior that calls on companies to address the impact of their operations and products on their employees, their communities, their customers, and the environment. Corporate behavior may eventually be regulated by the principle—codified by law—that the health of the common environment takes precedence over the rights of private property. Punishments for violation of this principle would have to be certain and severe. When industry tells us that for the good of society we must accept the level of risk its operations and products generate, it should be required to justify the claim. It must prove that there is no commercially practicable alternative that can reduce or eliminate risk. It must show clearly who benefits and who suffers as a result of the risk.

Certainly the legal principle, dating to the nineteenth century, that corporations are persons guaranteed the same constitutional rights as individual citizens is bad fiction and should be revisited. Big corporations, with all of their financial, technical, manpower, and other resources, can exercise their "rights" with overwhelmingly more effect on society than individuals and often do so at the expense of the general good. The framers of the Constitution did not intend to create an Orwellian *Animal Farm* where some animals are more equal than others.

But within the framework of new legal and ethical norms, corporations would also have to be given the freedom to achieve their production, financial, and environmental goals as flexibly as possible, without detailed, day-to-day prescription by government regulators.

Corporations required to adhere to environmental as well as financial standards would, perforce, have to adopt new criteria for developing and deploying their technologies. No longer could a General Motors announce one week that it had developed the prototype of a virtually pollution-free electric car and the next week attack stiffer tailpipe emissions standards proposed in clean air legislation as unattainable. Experience has shown that companies forced by environmental rules to adopt new technologies generally find themselves in a better competitive position after modernizing.

At present, such changes in the way the market functions and the way corporations behave would seem to be unattainable. The old production-consumption paradigm has a tighter hold on the country than ever, and corporate influence over the economy, backed by a government dedicated to the perceived interests of business and industry, is unshakable, at least for the time being.

Some within the environmental movement believe that the only way to change the economic status quo is for environmentalists to become capitalists and corporate executives and to reform the system from within. Allen Hershkowitz of the Natural Resources Defense Council, who is a leading proponent of active participation by environmentalists in the industrial economy, asserted that "We can no longer be supplicants to the corporate sector. We have to be managers of the corporate sector." The environmental activists, he believes, will have to become not critics but supporters of industrial development. It would be, however, a different kind of development. "The industrial system we have now is not sustainable," he asserted. Hershkowitz believes that by becoming corporate directors, managers, and shareholders and by creating their own businesses, environmentalists would be able to build a new industrial ecology that does not deplete and destroy the environment but sustains and enriches it.[13]

Hershkowitz himself tried an ambitious experiment in ecological entrepreneurship when he joined with a local community group in the South Bronx to try to build a major waste paper recycling plant on an abandoned railroad yard. The project would have addressed New York City's massive waste paper problem as well as provided jobs and economic revitalization in one of the poorest parts of the city. The experiment failed for a number of reasons, but it did create a vision for a new industrial ecology in which environmentalists and communities participate.

One of the major goals for a benign industrial ecology would be to replace the inappropriate technologies designed solely to maximize efficiency, production, and profits. Technologies such as high-compression fossil fuel-driven engines, cancer-causing and mutagenic pesticides and other chemicals, hormonal additives to foods, surface removal mining, and many others are putting us into ecological jeopardy. Appropriate technology—designed and used with the well-being of humans and the preservation and enhancement of the environment as necessary goals—can be one of the roads out of our predicament. The mainstream of environmentalism embraces technology that does not destroy the garden but quietly and unobtrusively helps cultivate the land and grow safe and healthy crops.

We need not cling to a blind faith in science and technology to realize that if we are to escape ecological degradation we will need the tools that only science and technology can provide. But we must think through very carefully all the consequences of using our machines. We must ask ourselves, for example, if we wish to continue to have machines replace human labor when joblessness causes so much human suffering. We must reject technology that destroys life and the means of sustaining life. As Lewis Mumford stated, "For those of us who are more hopeful both of man's destiny and that of the machine, the machine is no longer the paragon of progress and the final expression of our desires: it is merely a series of instruments which we will use in so far as they are serviceable to life at large, and which we will curtail where they infringe upon it or exist purely to support the adventitious structure of capitalism."[14]

To make sure we are served by our machines and not injured by them, we must assert some democratic control over decisions involving where to put our scientific resources and where and how and for what purpose we deploy our technologies. These decision cannot be made exclusively for the purpose of making profit.

The power of computers and the Internet to store and communicate knowledge gives us a strong push down the road to an environmentally sustainable technology. The space program can help monitor the earth and may someday carry humans to the other planets. Other technologies—new energy sources such as photovoltaics, a panoply of energy-saving appliances, vehicles, and other devices, genetic engineering, durable new materials and new methods of reusing old materials, superconductors, perhaps safe nuclear fusion, and many other feats of wizardry—will be pulled out of the hat to serve both the economy and the environment.

Freeing ourselves of the machinery of the industrial age and replacing it with a technology that serves both organic nature and human society is today's mission into the wilderness. It will be a demanding task. Our choices must be careful ones.

"For each specific technology," the futurist Hazel Henderson admonished, "we might ask whether it is labor-intensive, rather than capital- and energy-intensive, and how much capital is required to create each workplace. Does it dislocate settled communities and cultural patterns, and if so, at what social cost? Is it based on renewable or exhaustible resource utilization? Does it increase or decrease societal flexibility? Is it centralizing or decentralizing? Does it increase human liberty and widen the distribution of power, knowledge and wealth in societies or concentrate them? ... What risks does it pose to workers, consumers, society at large and future generations?" If a technology produces irreversible and intergenerational risks it should be "assumed socially unacceptable until proven otherwise. The very shifting of burdens of proof to the producers of technological hardware in itself constitutes an important paradigm shift toward greater human maturity and responsibility for future generations."[15]

This shifting of the burden of proof has come to be called the "precautionary principle," and it is being embraced by a growing number of ethicists, physicians, and scientists as well as environmentalists. But it is still a political nonstarter, shunned by most of the corporate world as well as by many in the general scientific community.

The environmental enterprise, along with most other human activity, has in recent years become irreversibly globalized. No country can go it alone to protect its citizens and their habitat. Understanding, mutual respect, and cooperation among nations is imperative to preserve the systems that support life on earth and to make that life worth living for its inhabitants. Unfortunately, U.S. diplomacy at the present time ignores that reality. The current government in Washington, abusing America's status as the sole superpower, is acting as the global bully, rejecting environmental treaties, ignoring human rights and disarmament responsibilities, and causing rising dismay and hostility across the planet. A far different diplomacy is called for today.

Social justice, political power, economic reform, corporate accountability, and technological evolution—these are the building blocks of an ecologically sound society in the United States. But the edifice cannot be raised without a deeper devotion of the American people to environmental goals and values. As former EPA administrator Lee M. Thomas said, our response to the environmental threats that confront us "must involve a personal commitment from each of us to live environmentally ethical lives—not because it is a requirement of law but because it is an essential component of our inherent responsibility to ourselves, our neighbors, our children and our planet. In fact, environmental laws will not be effective unless they are supported by a widely accepted environmental ethic."[16]

That time does not yet appear to be at hand. But perhaps it is approaching. A restless, discontented, increasingly fragmented American people is, I think, groping for new values, a new center to our lives. That center has shifted several times over the course of our nation's history. The first Europeans came here to plant a garden in the freedom of a fresh new world. That dream was replaced by belief in Manifest Destiny and the optimism and opportunity of the frontier. Then came the industrial revolution, which elevated mass production, consumption, the corporation, and the worship of the machine into a paramount position in our value system.

Consumerism now seems to be growing increasingly stale and dissatisfying as a value around which to build our lives. At the same time we are becoming more and more aware of the peril created by our own works and of how far we have distanced ourselves from nature. Environmentalism has shown us that the world need not be this way. And it is pointing us in a new direction, toward a new set of values that would lead us to live more gently on and harmoniously with this planet.

In *Man and Nature*, George Perkins Marsh asked, "Could this old world, which man has overthrown, be rebuilded, could human cunning rescue its wasted hillsides and its deserted plains from solitude or mere nomad occupation, from bareness, from nakedness, and from insalubrity, and restore the ancient fertility and healthfulness … ?" His answer was that such rebuilding "must await great political and moral revolutions in the governments and peoples…."[17]

More than a century and a quarter later, those political and moral revolutions have yet to take place. But given the grave dangers our current course will impose on our posterity, those changes may yet materialize, although not necessarily in timely fashion. The critics of environmentalism, the Julian Simons and Herman Kahns who contended that we need not fear ecological disaster because human intelligence, resourcefulness, and ingenuity will find the solutions, may have been right—but right in a way they did not intend. Many humans *are* responding to the devastation that human works have created. They are doing it by creating a new system of values and a new cultural movement called environmentalism. In the United States, this movement is advancing—slowly and sporadically—on a broad front. Its ranks are open enough to include radical Earth First! tree huggers and patrician big-game hunters, militant community activists and cool intellectuals cloistered in think tanks, hard-nosed lobbyists and dreamy bird-watchers. It has captured the interest and sympathy of a wide segment of the American public, the pained attention of our business community, and the rhetorical if not actual support of our public officials.

Despite its potential, the environmental movement has yet to exercise its strength decisively. Possibly it may never do so. The forces that oppose it—a minority, to be sure, but one that possesses enormous wealth with which it can exercise control over the nation's political and economic affairs—have given ample evidence that they will not lightly surrender their power. At the beginning of the new century, that power appeared to be driving back many of the gains made by the environmental revolution.

In a sane world, the values of environmentalism should prevail. The alternatives are clearly unacceptable to a rational and democratic society. If we do not cleanse, replant and rebuild, we bequeath to our children a bleak and dubious future on a crowded, hungry, poisoned, and unlovely planet. And that might not be the worst. As William Ruckelshaus and others have warned, the exigencies of supporting human life in an increasingly degraded, unproductive, and threatening environment could impose pressures on our free institutions heavy enough to break them.

Rachel Carson told us there is another road that offers "our last, our only chance to reach a destination that assures the preservation of our earth."[18] In recent years, we have taken the wrong fork. We are again careering blindly down road toward an ecological dead end. As a people, we have still to recognize what the philosopher Hans Jonas described as "our fundamental ethical obligations to the human and natural future."[19]

But the history of this country is a history of regeneration, of continual social reconstruction. As James Oliver Robertson reminds us, "American destiny was informed, in myth, by one central principle: America is a fresh place, a new beginning, an opportunity."[20] America can still be that place. Today, the frontier, the new beginning, is the challenge of restoring and safeguarding our environment, of recreating a "fresh place."

If we are to find our way back to that other road and create not only a cleaner, safer, more pleasant environment but also a sustainable economy, a more just and democratic society, and a safer world, the environmental enterprise will have to succeed. At the beginning of the twenty-first century it confronted the possibility of failure. But the story is not finished.

NOTES

1 Donald Worster, "Conservation and Environmental Movements in the United States," in Bailes, op. cit., pp. 258–59.

2 Ivan Illich, interview in *New Perspectives Quarterly*, Vol. 6, No. 1 (Spring 1989), p. 23.

3 Nathan Gardels, "A New Ecological Ethos," *New Perspectives Quarterly*, Vol. 6, No. 1 (Spring 1989), p. 3.

4 Quoted by Michael Frome in *Defenders*, Vol. 63, No. 4 (July–August 1988), p. 6.

5 James Gustave Speth, interview with author.

6 Lois Gibbs, interview with author.

7 William Tucker, *Progress and Privilege: America in the Age of Environmentalism* (Garden City, N.Y.: Anchor Press/Doubleday & Company, 1982).

8 Paul Mohai, *A Case for Environmental Non-Elitism: An Analysis of Social Movement Participation through Integration of Social Psychological and Resource Mobilization Perspectives* (Department of Forest Resources, Utah State University).

9 Denton E. Morrison and Riley E. Dunlap, "Environmentalism and Elitism: A Conceptual and Empirical Analysis," *Environmental Management*, Vol. 10, No. 5 (1986), pp. 581–89.

10 Ibid.

11 Jesse L. Jackson, "The Right to Breathe Free," speech prepared for Earth Day tour, March 30–April 3, 1990.

12 Quoted by Sandra Postel, "Toward a New 'Eco'-Nomics," *WorldWatch*, Vol. 3, No. 5 (September–October 1990), p. 23.

13 Allen Hershkowitz, interview with the author.

14 Mumford, op. cit., p. 365.

15 Hazel Henderson, *The Politics of the Solar Age: Alternatives to Economics* (Indianapolis: Knowledge Systems, 1988), p. 353.

16 Lee M. Thomas, "Speaking Frankly," *EPA Journal*, Vol. 14, No. 4 (July–August 1988), p. 9.

17 Marsh, op. cit., p. 44.

18 Carson, op. cit., p. 277.

19 Strachan Donnelley, "The Legacy of Hans Jonas," *Hastings Centre Report*, Special Issue, 1995, p.2.

20 James Oliver Robertson, *American Myth, American Reality*, New York: Hill & Wang, 1980), p. 29.

BIBLIOGRAPHY

Carson, Rachel. *Silent Spring.* 25th anniversary ed.; Boston: Houghton Mifflin Company, 1987.

Henderson, Hazel. *The Politics of the Solar Age: Alternatives to Economics.* Indianapolis: Knowledge Systems, 1988.

Marsh, George Perkins. *Man and Nature*, ed. by David Lowenthal. Cambridge: Harvard University Press, 1965.

Morrison, Denton E., and Riley E. Dunlap. "Environmentalism and Elitism: A Conceptual and Empirical Analysis," *Environmental Management*, Vol. 10, No. 5 (1986).

Mumford, Lewis. *Technics and Civilization.* New York: Harcourt, Brace & World, 1962.

Robertson, James Oliver. *American Myth, American Reality.* New York: Hill and Wang, 1980.

Tucker, William. *Progress and Privilege: America in the Age of Environmentalism.* Garden City, N.Y.: Anchor Press/Doubleday & Company, 1982.

Worster, Donald. "Conservation and Environmental Movements in the United States," in Kendall E. Bailes, ed., *Environmental History.* Lanham, Md.: University Press of America, 1985.

CHAPTER TWO

Sustainability and Consumption

Humans are part of natural systems, and for much of our evolution, we existed in sync with these systems, using locally available resources and learning to manage these natural resources so that they would be available in the future. In the Western world, our relationship with the natural world changed significantly during the Industrial Revolution in Europe and the US during the eighteenth and nineteenth centuries when we began to use fossil fuels to power growing economies. Harnessing fossil fuels allowed us to improve standards of living and expand our economies, but it also had dire consequences: the moment we started basing our economies on fossil fuels, we started living on borrowed time. This is because fossil fuels come from organisms that lived and died millions of years ago, organisms that got the vast majority of their energy from the sun. Since the Industrial Revolution, we have been living in part on sunlight from the past, and the amount of sunlight from the past is both fixed and declining.

Powered by energy from past sunlight, global resource consumption grew throughout the nineteenth and twentieth centuries, and an increasing number of people began to realize that perhaps we were consuming the planet's resources faster than they could be replenished. But how much faster? Without a clear idea of how much energy the planet gets from the sun each year and a clear estimate of how much people were consuming, it was not possible to say. In 1992, researchers at the University of British Columbia introduced a conceptual solution to this problem: the "ecological footprint." An ecological footprint is defined as the amount of land required to produce all the resources to support a single person (or a region, a country, or the whole world; it can be calculated at any level). Several organizations now offer an online calculator to estimate your personal ecological footprint, one of which is highlighted in the recommended viewing section of this chapter. According to researchers, humanity first went into ecological overshoot in 1970. This means that starting in 1970, every year we use more wood, freshwater, soil, and other natural resources than the planet can regenerate in a year. As of 2020, humanity was consuming resources 1.6 times faster than the planet can produce them, and this number will continue to grow if we do not change our resource use patterns[1].

By the time we went into ecological overshoot, there was already a growing awareness of the dangerous impact of human activities on the planet. In 1987, a United Nations (UN) panel formed to address our resource use issues and formally defined "sustainable development" as "development that meets the needs of the present without compromising the ability of future generations to meet their own needs." Based on this definition, the UN partner countries established a set of 17 "Sustainable Development Goals" (SDGs) that embrace the five pillars of sustainability: Peace, People, Planet, Partnership, and Prosperity. You can learn more about the SDGs in the recommended reading.

The SDGs will help us move high-level global policy toward sustainability, but the transformation to a more sustainable society will not occur without individual people making changes in their behavior. In a nutshell, we need to reduce our consumption of everything. We live on a finite planet, yet we consume material resources as if they were infinite. The primary reading selected for this chapter by Norman Myers and Jennifer Kent, "Sustainable Consumption: How to Get from Here to There" from *The New Consumers: The Influence of Affluence on the Environment* (2004), provides a guide for thoughtful reflection on how your own lifestyle might be tweaked to help wean yourself off unsustainable patterns of consumption. The goal of all of the readings is to provide students with the tools and awareness to look forward to the coming transitions, not with fear but with understanding, excitement, and hope.

RECOMMENDED READING

United Nations Department of Economic and Social Affairs. 2020. *Sustainable Development Goals.* Retrieved from: https://sdgs.un.org/goals.

RECOMMENDED VIEWING

Global Footprint. 2019. *Footprint Calculator.*
WATCH AT https://www.footprintcalculator.org/.

1 Global Footprint Network, https://www.footprintnetwork.org/our-work/ecological-footprint.

Leonard, A. 2007. *The Story of Stuff.* Free Range Studios.

WATCH AT https://www.storyofstuff.org/movies/story-of-stuff/.

READING AND DISCUSSION PROMPTS

1. What is the difference between material consumption and knowledge consumption? Why does knowledge consumption have a lighter ecological footprint?
2. Check out the ecological footprint link in the recommended viewing and take a minute to calculate your own ecological footprint. What part of your lifestyle is increasing your footprint the most?
3. Reflect on your own patterns of consumption. Do you think you personally consume too much or not? How does your own pattern of consumption affect your happiness, your relationships with other people, and the way you feel about nature?

READING 2.1

Sustainable Consumption

HOW TO GET FROM HERE TO THERE

By Norman Myers and Jennifer Kent

And so to the final chapter, with a look into a revolutionary future where consumption is transformed from an activity "like there's no tomorrow" into a activity like there's endless tomorrows. It is not so much that current consumption is too high, rather it should be modified for certain areas such as food, energy, raw materials, and water, plus a lengthy shopping list (so to speak) of costly incidentals. To reiterate a pivotal point: what counts is not only quantity of livelihood but also quality of life.

Consider food, an item we consume several times a day. We have seen that fast food leads to fast fat and can even end in fast death. Reader: when you've moved on from high-calorie meats, try eating locally. You'll enjoy food that is fresher, tastier, and healthier than food from afar. A typical meal item in the United States has traveled an average of at least 1500 kilometers before it reaches your dinner plate, one-quarter farther than in 1980. If the full cost of all those fossil fuels for transportation, including their pollution costs, were added onto the supermarket price, a California lettuce on a New Yorker's table would require tens of times as much fossil-fuel energy as it provides in food energy.[1] And why not enjoy the variety of seasonal fruits and veggies? Or couldn't we live without strawberries in February?

Consider the cautionary tale of a carton of strawberry yogurt marketed as "Made in Stuttgart" in southern Germany. The strawberries originate from Poland, whereupon they combine with yogurt from north Germany, jam from west Germany, sugar beet from France, and corn and wheat flour from the Netherlands. Only the milk and carton are produced in Stuttgart.[2] During the last 40 years while population has doubled, the value of international trade in food has tripled, and the weight of food shipped between countries has quadrupled.[3]

By contrast, note the explosive growth of farmers markets, being weekly gatherings when local consumers buy directly from local farmers. Money spent at these markets stays within the community, cycling through to create jobs and raise incomes as well as to support smallholder farmers. Every $10 spent at a farmers market is worth $25 for the local area, compared with $14 when it is spent in a supermarket. Such markets in the United States have grown from nearly 300 in the mid-1970s to well over 10 times as many today. Some three million people visit these markets each week and spend more than $1 billion each year. Since the mid-1970s, too, the global retail market for organic produce has jumped by three-quarters to reach $18 billion derived from 170,000 square kilometers of organically managed farmland, an expanse equivalent to Florida.[4]

MAKING A PERSONAL DIFFERENCE

What shall we do about runaway consumption? While this book addresses those people who are mainly enjoying grandscale consumption for the first time, they will be reluctant to do anything different until the long-rich people change gear. Let's look, then, at what that superconsumer society, America, could consider. The same applies of course to other highly consumerist societies (though not on the scale of America's), such as Britain, Germany, Japan, and the lengthy like.

Every American can make that famous difference, supposing he or she is one of the two out of three who say they would do more to conserve energy and protect the environment in dozens of other ways if they felt their individual actions would make a worthwhile impact.[5] They must slay the dragon of rampant overconsumption—or at least put the dragon on a diet. Every last citizen can help, and every last one is needed like crazy. Here's how.

Make a start by introducing a few personal adjustments to your lifestyle. Even a single adjustment can make a notable difference. Skip one 30-kilometer car trip each week by telecommuting, biking, or combining errands, whereupon you will reduce your annual CO_2 emissions by half a tonne—and save at least $130. Replace one beef meal a week and thereby save more than 30 kilograms of grain and 40,000 gallons of water a year—as well as putting another $75 into your pocket. Reduce household electricity by replacing traditional light bulbs with energy-efficient fluorescent bulbs and moving the thermostat a few degrees Fahrenheit down in winter and up in summer, thus preventing well over 1 tonne of CO_2 emissions annually—and saving $165 a year. Install efficient showerheads and low-flow faucet aerators, and the household avoids more than 30,000 gallons of water and prevents 800 kilograms of CO_2 emissions each year—plus saving $50. Total saved per year: $425. If a family undertook a list of other similar actions as set out by the Center for a New American Dream's "Turn the Tide" program, (www.newdream.org/turnthetide), they would save enough to pay for a year-end vacation.[6]

Finally, inspire two friends to join you with these simple activities, and then get them to persuade two others in turn, and so on. If they all managed this every day (okay, a bit much), they would reach the entire United States within a month or so.

Next, consider something you can probably do every day, and again with sizeable clout. Shop carefully, and thus use your dollar votes to support the good-guy manufacturers, being the ones who try to be efficient with raw materials, who don't overexploit scarce natural resources, who aim for cradle-to-cradle products, who are miserly with energy, who plan for products manufactured with zero emissions, and all the other things that please Planet Earth. How do you learn which manufacturers are on the side of the angels? Check www.responsible-shopper.org or www.buygreen.com. Or if you are religious, take a look at "The Responsible Purchasing Guide for Faith Communities" (www.newdream.org/faith). Or you could try *Shopping for a Better World* from the Council for Economic Priorities in New York. Then too there is Vicki Robin's *Your Money or Your Life* at the New Road Map Foundation (www.newroadmap.org). Perhaps best of all is to check your own eco-footprint by consulting the website of Redefining Progress at www.rprogress.org.

Go for it—and remember that you live not only in a political democracy but an economic democracy too, the second allowing you to vote several times each day. Recall as well that if you don't go for it, you are unwittingly but effectively voting for the same dysfunctional world we are stuck with right now. Let's change it with every dollar bill.

Don't be surprised to find that as you do your bit to change the world, your actions are changing you. A big bonus of getting on with the task is that it will save you from that dread sense of paralysis in face of proliferant problems on every side. In addition to the shopping list of antishopping items that the counterconsumption crusader will readily think up, make yourself a promise that once a year you will plant a tree. True, if a million people were to do as much, it would not soak up enough carbon dioxide to make a difference to global warming. But it will make a difference to the way you feel about yourself. Go and dig in the ground, get your hands dirty, offer long life to a sapling, and you'll be registering a vote for yourself as well as the planet.

Or keep on recalling the protester who was told by the politician that carrying a placard would not make the politician become like him. "No," came the response, "but it will stop me becoming like you."

How else to make your difference? You could try your hand at volunteer work to support the environment or to otherwise offset your lifestyle impacts (nobody treads the planet with zero impact). In the Netherlands the work of volunteers equals 450,000 full-time jobs—and that in a country with a labor force of only six million. These activities are worth around $14 billion a year, or almost $1000 per citizen. In South Korea—a new-consumer country—nearly four million people volunteer more than 450 million hours per year, worth more than $2 billion, or $40 per citizen. In Brazil—another new-consumer country—at least one adult in six volunteers some part of his or her free time.[7] If you want to join the band, check www.parti.org/how-you-can-help/volunteer.com. On December 5 each year, designated the International Volunteer Day, you can seek out a rallying point for organizations and individuals to express support for the Millennium Development Goals, in which environmental activities are prominent.[8] Of if you want to go straight to organizations that recruit volunteers for the environment, try the World Wildlife Fund, Earth-watch, Raleigh International, Greenforce, or the David Suzuki Foundation.

If you feel you want to do still more, consider a grand strategy known as voluntary simplicity.[9] In popular parlance it is often referred to as downshifting, or shifting to a more simple and relaxed, albeit less affluent, lifestyle; in other words, leaving the rat race to those sleek overcompetitive rats.[10] Way back in the early 1990s millions of American workers, including every tenth executive or professional, went to their employers and said they would like to work fewer hours, and of course they would take home less pay. They could then spend more time with their spouses, children, friends, and neighbors, and they could enjoy more time on a martini or a sunset. Many of them liked it so much that next year they went back to their employers and requested still fewer hours at work.[11] For sure, they still total a small share of the U.S. populace. But then, those Americans who struggled for civil rights or an end to the Vietnam War once numbered only a small share of all Americans.

The same is happening in Britain where millions of people have given up well-paid jobs as a rejection of the "culture of endless getting and spending," despite increasing pressures to earn and spend more.[12] In mid-2003 a senior government minister became the third top-flight official to abandon a highly promising career (he was viewed as a potential prime minister) to spend more time with his family.

Want to know more about the voluntary simplicity movement? Try organizations and publications such as Real Simple, Live Simple, the Simply Living Network, the Frugality Network, the Center for a New American Dream, Alternatives for Simple Living, the *Simple Living Resource Guide*, the Simple Family Life, the Lifestyle Movement, Simple Abundance, Fringe Wisdom, Living and Having More with Less, Living without a Car, Voluntary Simplicity Overview, or the *Journal of Voluntary Simplicity*.

Voluntary simplicity ranks high among many of the people known as "cultural creatives." There are 50 million of them in the United States, every fourth adult, and even more of them in Europe where they make up every third adult. They espouse strong environmental viewpoints, they highlight relationships, they are generally committed to psychological development and even spirituality, they are turned off by large institutions (including both the extreme left and right in politics), and above all they reject conspicuous consumption. They focus on renewable energy and resource-efficient products, alternative transportation, nature protection, organic products, alternative health care, socially responsible investments, eco-tourism, and lifelong education. They watch only half as much television but listen to twice as much radio as does the general public; they read as many books as magazines; and they are Internet addicts. They include the 30 million Americans who practice yoga, up from 4 million in 1990. Two-thirds of the cultural creatives are women, and they walk their talk.[13]

THE AUROVILLE EXPERIMENT

What, dear reader, are you saying that despite all the above, human nature cannot change? That people are, on the whole, hardwired to want more and waste more and that consumption patterns are set in concrete? Well, note that in the recent past at least 60 million Americans have given up smoking. At the start of the period they were under social pressure to light up, and at the end of it they were under social pressure to stub out. It has been a cultural earthquake, almost overnight.

You may still respond that this is an isolated item and says nothing about the bigger picture. Consider a community in southern India that has foresworn consumption from top to bottom. Auroville, meaning "city of the dawn," is a highly innovative community, as this book's first author has invariably noted on his repeated visits there (where he served on the International Advisory Committee) (www.auroville. org). Started in 1968, it contains 1500 residents, 500 of them Indians and the rest from 40 countries around the world. Their eventual aim is to build up to 50,000 members. They are not hippy-type "do nothings"; they are mostly educated and enterprising people bent on making their planet-saving lifestyles function in the Monday-morning world. When the first pioneers arrived, they were armed with little more than their ideals for a new model of life on Earth, centered on simplified living, self-reliance and environmental know-how. They could hardly have been assigned a more unpromising place. They were allotted 10 square kilometers of land so degraded that it was officially declared "unfit for human habitation." There were only a few dozen trees, there were scant streams and no rivers, and there was next to no topsoil. Today the soil cover has been restored, rivers flourish, and there are two million trees.

Auroville's agriculture supplies half of its food while depending on organic fertilizers and pesticides. The community uses solar and wind power for much of its energy. It employs photovoltaics to supply electricity to light buildings, to pump and heat water, and to cook food. The township's use of solar energy in so profitable that it has become a demonstration model for the whole of India. It exploits wind power too, through several dozen windmills, some of which pump water from 30 meters down. In addition, Aurovilleans are pioneers in ecotechnologies for water reclamation, agroforestry, soil conservation, and land rehabilitation.

In still more striking ways, Auroville's lifestyles epitomize the goal of "living lightly on the face of the planet." Members agree to a cash income of only $100 per month, together with subsidized food, housing, water, clothing, and other basic needs, plus permanent employment, worth $250 per month. This makes a total of little over $4000 per year. Simple living with a vengeance, and with endless satisfaction—as I have witnessed during my frequent sojourns onsite.

Bottom line: it is Auroville's philosophy as well as its eco-technologies that make the system work. To cite the late prime minister of India, Indira Gandhi, Auroville is "an exciting project for understanding the environmental needs for people's spiritual growth."[14] Auroville's vision is an ambitious goal—and one that is essential if the world's communities are to live in a way that suggests they plan to remain on Earth forever rather than act as visitors for a weekend.

THE BIGGEST QUESTION

This book has raised many questions about where we are now, where we want to go, and how we get from here to there. Now for the biggest question of all: what do we truly want from consumption, and is it delivering?

The answer might seem so obvious that it is not worth stating. Hundreds of millions of people proclaim the consumerist message through their actions every day of their lives, and many more want to join the throng. Politicians of every sort and stripe, in every land, view it as what every voter wants above all else. The marketplace urges it as a glorious given. To question it suggests the questioner comes from outer space.

And yet, and yet. There are murmurings if not rumblings in many a quarter to the effect that consumption as generally practiced may not always be up to its job. Perhaps, just conceivably, we are sometimes confusing means with ends. We pursue consumption to make our lives better: that is its clear purpose. It has become so widespread and deep-seated that it is squeezing out any other means of achieving the ultimate purpose. To question it is not just heresy, it is nonsense. It is to close one's eyes to the way the world works, to what makes individuals tick.

Let us take a big deep breath and ask if the end invariably justifies the means. In fact there are quite a few people taking that breath, and they are not idle layabouts, they are some of the brightest and best among us. There is an emergent trend in the long-rich countries whereby certain people are increasingly asking if greater wealth, whether of the economy or the citizen, must inevitably lead to greater well-being. There is evidence a-building in the United States and Europe that the road to riches is far from a necessary road to fulfilment—or, if we dare to use a big word, happiness. If there is any substance to this line of thinking, it might prompt the new consumers to pause and consider the upshot of endless consumption.

Many people sense that consumption gives them a fine feeling in the right place, so ever-more consumption should give them ever-greater happiness. But does it? Absurd as this question may have sounded a few years ago, it is gaining a hearing in many quarters. Whereas the British economist guru John Keynes once asserted that consumption is the primary purpose of humankind, there are cold-eyed economists today who contest this in certain respects. They include Nobel Prize–winner Daniel Kahneman,[15] Richard Layard of the London School of Economics,[16] and many other economists in the boom industry of what is known in the trade as happiness research. The new view is even gaining attention from top-level officialdom. The British government has recently published a report on life satisfaction with hints that personal fulfilment may soon become "the new money." Already there is a pioneering effort on the part of a little country with big ideas, Bhutan in the Himalayas. Its government looks beyond Gross National Income to assess Gross National Happiness, based on the four principles of economic development, environmental protection, cultural promotion, and good governance—all to be sustainable.[17]

In sum, happiness is not simply a peaches and cream affair. After all, people who run marathons (no minority sport) may not feel much conventional pleasure, but they sense satisfaction so deep that they can hardly find it elsewhere. But what "real world" evidence is there to support the idea that consumption is less than a never-ending pleasure trip? It seems that when people reach an individual income level of around $10,000 a year, being enough to meet their basic material needs, they find that more income does not always lead to more happiness in the sense of lifestyle fulfilment.[18] During the last half century people in rich countries have not only become much more affluent but they are healthier, they live longer, they work less, and they travel more widely on longer vacations. Yet they feel they are no happier. Consider, for instance, how rushed and frazzled we have become. Technocrats have brought us one time-saving device after another, notably washing machines, clothes driers, microwave ovens, blenders, and push-button phones among a host of such items. Despite the time that these items have saved, we now find ourselves with less of "our" time than before.[19] Not even enough time to sleep; a morning rush-hour train or bus can be full of passengers snoozing. Many business people commute for more than an hour at each end of the day, never seeing their children awake throughout the working week. Some of them are starting to say they would prefer more sleep to more salary.[20]

Recent research shows that only one-third of Americans feel "very happy," no more than in 1950.[21] During much the same period, Britons have achieved twice as much income in real terms, yet their perceived quality of life has not increased; two-thirds of them would rather see the environment improve than have more economic growth and personal spending money.[22] In fact, a "happiness index" places Britain 32nd and the United States 46th out of 54 countries assessed, ranked behind such "poor" countries as China and Philippines.[23] In Europe generally, there has been no long-term rise in happiness except in Italy and Denmark. Japan features no change in its low level of happiness despite a sixfold increase in per-capita income in just three decades.[24] Most new consumers in Russia sense frustration with their supposed well-being.[25]

To this extent, affluence appears to be far from the answer to all problems. What people most want is a lifestyle with solid satisfaction through things like personal relationships, good health, and valued work.[26] Indeed, many people say they suffer from a kind of psychic and emotional poverty, largely due to excessive and misplaced consumerism, plus community decline and environmental rundown.[27] To cite Dr. Laurie Michaelis, of the former Oxford Commission on Sustainable Consumption, "Consumption is about belonging with other people, not being better than other people. Belonging is what people are really hungry for. Once basic material needs are met, what really makes people happy are decent relationships or an interesting job."[28]

This line of thinking could be what lies behind an even more heretical notion—that many people enjoy consumption primarily when it is conspicuous consumption and a source of personal prestige, whereupon they often find it brings outer contentment but at a cost of inner satisfaction.[29] It is "keep up with the Jones's" again, or even "keep ahead of the Jones's." As Will Rogers once said, many people spend money they don't have on things they don't want in order to impress people they don't like.

Such consumers can also suffer from the stress of overmany possessions, together with debt and waste. The number of individuals in Britain declaring themselves bankrupt has topped 100 people a day at a time when personal borrowing continues to surge at record speed. The proportion of these bankruptcies due to consumer debt has risen by two-thirds in the past eight years.[30] Despite the highest income levels ever known in Britain, well over half of all citizens feel depressed periodically. These people are twice as likely to say they sometimes buy things that they later regret.[31] In fact, people whose values center on material goods seem to face a greater risk of depression, a reaction that applies regardless of age, income, or culture.[32] Despite the all-singing advertisers in Britain who suggest that consumers are one big happy family, well over half of citizens are depressed from time to time, ostensibly because they buy things they cannot afford and things that often fail to supply satisfaction.[33] In high-income countries, depression now ranks second in the world table of diseases, more widespread than cancer. Yet depression drives many sufferers to seek retail therapy at the shopping mall. Materialism causes unhappiness, and unhappiness causes materialism.[34]

Here's still more evidence. In Britain three-fifths of people say they cannot afford to buy everything they really need, yet almost 9 out of 10 people think British society is "too materialistic [with] too much emphasis on money and not enough on the things that really matter."[35] In the top two income brackets, 4 people in 10 say that if they had a choice, they would take more vacation rather than a pay raise. Nearly the same number want to spend more time with family and friends, while almost 3 in 10 want to enjoy nature more. Only 1 in 7, mainly young people, say that a greater priority lies with shopping. This contrasts strongly with the image of a modern world peopled by couch potatoes and television addicts. Only 1 British person in 50 wants to be remembered as wealthy and materially successful.[36] Who on their death bed wishes they had earned more in order to consumer more?

All this reflects, of course, the consumption pressures of the rich countries, with societies that have long exceeded the bounds of acceptable consumption. For them consumption has often spilled over into mis- and overconsumption. The new consumers for the most part have yet to reach that stage, with the exception of their emphasis on meat-based diets and ever-more cars. They might take heed, however, of the insidious allurements of consumption for its own self-consuming sake.

BEYOND TODAY'S CONSUMPTION

A final question arises, stemming from the backlash effects of runaway consumption. Could we be on the verge of one of the greatest revolutions in human history, when people leave behind 10,000 years of fixation on all-out consumption and shift their lifestyle priorities to something different and better? With over-the-top consumption out of the way, people would have space to try out new this and sample fresh that. It would amount to a big exploration, a huge adventure.

It would be a seismic shift, and virtually instantaneous within human history—a shift in spending, a shift in thinking. It could rank as one of the biggest shifts ever. However hard it may be to envision at this stage, recall the management guru Peter Drucker's words, albeit with reference to humankind's planetary impact writ large: "Every few hundred years in Western history there occurs a sharp transformation. Within a few short decades, society rearranges itself—its world view, its basic values, its social and political structure, its arts, its key institutions. We are currently living through such a transformation."[37]

Not that the transformation would mean an end to consumption. Quite the opposite. It would mean an advance to consumption of a basically different sort, what we might call "consumption of knowledge and experience." Thus far we have mainly contented ourselves with the manufactured products of industry, notably cars, washing machines, fridges, houses. All these can be consumed by only one individual or household at a time, and they are used until they are used up. Nobody else shares in their consumption (which is part of their appeal). By contrast, the "new consumption" would focus on "knowledge products" such as sports, the arts, outdoors trips, and exploratory travel. These can be not only consumed but possessed and shared with many other consumers. Compare, for instance, a car to a concert, whether classical or pop. The car can be owned, whereupon its enjoyment is denied to others (who may actually lose through road congestion and traffic pollution). Conversely all knowledge products, which are fortunately multiplying in kinds and numbers, can be copied many times over. They can be enjoyed by consumers without end, and they remain available for future consumption without end.[38]

Suppose, however, that a shift to knowledge products rather than material goods meant a shift in the economy. It need not mean an end to the ever-growing economy, rather an end to the economy that we have known. Knowledge products have their role in the marketplace, making for an economy akin in some ways to the service economy that in many countries is displacing the material-goods economy. In any case, the growth economy needs to give way to the "development economy" directed at human development, just as we do not need to grow the Earth in order to develop the Earth.

A shift to a sustainable form of consumption would be a revolution indeed. Daunting as may be the prospect, it is unavoidable if only for abundant environmental reasons. We shall undertake the change either by default or by design. But the revolution will run up against a profound trait of our species: resistance to change. It is not that we don't like change, it is rather that we don't like things to be different. To cite a perceptive observer, Sir Crispin Tickell: "It takes time to learn to think differently. If policy lags behind change of mind, and practice behind policy, little will change unless and until we think differently. The power of inertia is immensely strong, especially in the functioning engine room of society—the middle ranks—whether in government, business or elsewhere. For change we need three factors: leadership from above, pressure from below, or some exemplary catastrophe."[39]

We live in a time of change anyway: change on every side, change without parallel in history, and change that will leave our futures unrecognizable. The world is changing outasight, and what is changing most is the speed of change. Yet one thing does not seem to have changed much, and that is our capacity to recognize change. For instance, when we make our way to our workplaces each day, do we sense that we are traveling through an atmosphere that is changing climatically more than in 100,000 years? We can't see the change, we can't smell it, we can't taste it, even though it is one of the most potent forces in our world. Yesterday the world's population increased by one-quarter of a million people, as much as would have taken almost two weeks in 1900: who of us could tell the difference? We seem to be programmed to dismiss change, to tune it out. "I've smoked for thirty years, so what harm will another year do?"—even though we know that sooner or later that extra year could mark a terminal change. Recall the man who fell out of a twentieth storey window, and said as he passed the tenth floor, "Nothing new so far."

How to set about the consumption challenge, being one of the biggest changes that human societies have ever encountered? If it doesn't bear thinking about, it therefore demands a great deal of thinking. Fortunately, and as we have seen in this book, there are experts aplenty who believe we can do it. Whether we will actually do it—whether we will devise the eco-technologies, make the philosophic shifts, and so on, backed by the right public opinion and political leadership—is another matter. We may find that the most valuable resource, and the one in shortest supply, will be our willingness to change our understanding of how best to live on our limited planet. If we feel daunted by this supersize prospect, we should bear in mind (again) that we do not face a choice between change and no change. Rather it is between change that we choose or change that we suffer as a result of nonchoice. Shall we choose to choose?

Clincher factor: however hard it will be to live with the profound changes ahead, it will not be so hard as to live in a world profoundly impoverished by the environmental devastation of current consumption. The question is not "can we afford to consume sustainably?" Rather it is "how can we afford not to?" Let us bear in mind the insight of the leader of the Rio Earth Summit, Maurice Strong: "History demonstrates that what seems unrealistic today becomes inevitable tomorrow."[40]

Sign-off thought: could the time come when we shall hail the country that, by leading the way to the New Consumption, has become a lifestyle leader—or even a lifestyle superpower?

NOTES

1 B. Halweil, *Home Grown: The Case for Local Food in a Global Economy* (Washington, DC: Worldwatch Institute, 2002).

2 C. Aslet, "Clocking Up Food Miles," *Financial Times* (London), February 23, 2002.

3 Halweil, *Home Grown: The Case for Local Food in a Global Economy.*

4 Ibid.

5 Center for a New American Dream, "Turn the Tide: Nine Actions for the Planet" (www.newdream.org/tttoffline/actions.html) (2003); J. Getis, *You Can Make a Difference* (Boston: McGraw-Hill, 1999).

6 Center for a New American Dream, "Turn the Tide: Nine Actions for the Planet"; see also Population Coalition, *Our Choices Matter* (Redlands, CA: Population Coalition, 2002); P. R. Ehrlich and A. H. Ehrlich, *One with Nineveh: Politics, Consumption, and the Human Future* (Washington, DC: Island Press, 2004).

7 United Nations Development Programme, *Human Development Report 2002* (New York: Oxford University Press, 2002).

8 United Nations Volunteers, "Volunteerism and the Millennium Development Goals" (www.worldvolunteerweb.org/development/mdg/volunteerism/UNV_mdg.htm) (2003); United Nations Development Programme, *Human Development Report 2002.*

9 S. B. Breathnach, *The Simple Abundance Companion* (New York: Warner Books, 2000); S. Mills, *Epicurean Simplicity* (Washington, DC: Island Press, 2002); J. M. Segal, *Graceful Simplicity: The Philosophy and Politics of the Alternative American Dream* (Berkeley: University of California Press, 2002).

10 G. M. Bellman, *Your Signature Path: Gaining New Perspectives on Life and Work* (Williston, VT: Berrett-Koehler, 2000); P. Ghazi and J. Jones, *Downshifting: The Guide to Happier, Simpler Living* (London: Coronet, 1997); Getis, *You Can Make a Difference;* R. J. Leider and D. A. Shapiro, *Repacking Your Bags: Lighten Your Load for the Rest of Your Life* (Williston, VT: Berrett-Koehler, 1996); R. K. Leider, *The Power of Purpose: Creating Meaning in Your Life and Work* (Williston, VT: Berrett-Koehler, 2000); J. Schor, *The Overspent American* (New York: Basic Books, 1998).

11 The Harwood Group, *Yearning for Balance: Views of Americans on Consumption, Materialism, and the Environment* (Takoma Park, MD: Merck Family Fund, 1995); see also A. Etzioni, "Voluntary Simplicity: Characterization, Select Psychological Implications, and Societal Consequences," *Journal of Economic Psychology* 19 (1998): 619–643; C. Handy, *The Hungry Spirit: Beyond Capitalism; A Quest for Purpose in the Modern World* (New York: Broadway Books, 1998).

12 C. Hamilton, *Downshifting in Britain: A Sea-Change in the Pursuit of Happiness* (Canberra: The Australia Institute, 2003); C. Hamilton, *Growth Fetish* (Sydney: Allan and Unwin, 2003); Ghazi and Jones, *Downshifting: The Guide to Happier, Simpler Living.*

13 P. H. Ray and S. R. Anderson, *The Cultural Creatives: How 50 Million People are Changing the World* (New York: Three Rivers Press, 2000); Conscious Media, Inc., *About LOHAS* (Broomfield, CO: Natural Business Communications/Conscious Media Inc., 2002). About LOHAS (Lifestyles of Health and Sustainability) on the LOHAS Web site (http://www.lohasjournal.com/app/cda/nbp_cda.php?command=Page&pageType=Ab out) (accessed 2003).

14 Gandhi statement March 25, 1969 (www.auroville.org/organisation/supp_statements_india.htm).

15 D. Kahneman, E. Diener, and N. Schwarz, eds., *Well-Being: The Foundations of Hedonic Psychology* (New York: Russell Sage Foundation, 1999).

16 R. Layard, *Happiness: Has Social Science a Clue?* (London: London School of Economics, 2003).

17 R. Rosenblatt et al., *Consuming Desires: Consumption, Culture, and the Pursuit of Happiness* (Washington, DC: Island Press, 1999); L. J. Y. Thinley, "Gross National Happiness and Human Development—Searching for Common Ground," *Gross National Happiness* (1999): 7–11 (Thimphy, Bhutan: The Centre for Bhutan Studies, 1999).

18 A. J. Oswald, "Happiness and Economic Performance," *Economic Journal* 107 (1997): 1815–1831; T. Princen, M. Maniates, and K. Conca, eds., *Confronting Consumption* (Cambridge, MA: MIT Press, 2002); Rosenblatt et al., *Consuming Desires: Consumption, Culture, and the Pursuit of Happiness.*

19 E. Ayres, "Out of Touch," *World Watch* 15(5) (2002): 3–4; Ehrlich and Ehrlich, *One With Nineveh: Politics, Consumption, and the Human Future.*

20 N. Myers and J. Kent, *New Consumers*, report to the Winslow Foundation, Washington, DC, 2002.

21 R. Layard, *Towards a Happier Society* (London: London School of Economics, 2003); see also D. G. Myers and E. Diener, "Who is Happy?" *Psychological Science* 6 (1995): 10–18.

22 R. M. Worcester, "More than Money," in I. Christie and L. Nash, eds. *The Good Life* (London: DEMOS, 1998), 19–25; see also N. Pidgeon, *Is the Consumer Bubble Set to Burst?* (Norwich, UK: Centre for Environmental Risk, University of East Anglia, 2003).

23 C. Chandy, *The Dissatisfaction Syndrome* (London: Publicis, 2001).

24 G. McCormack, *The Emptiness of Japanese Affluence* (Armonk, NY: M. E. Sharpe, 2001); see also B. S. Frey and A. Stutzer, *Happiness and Economics: How the Economy and Institutions Affect Human Well-Being* (Princeton: Princeton University Press, 2002).

25 C. Graham and S. Pettinato, *Happiness and Hardship: Opportunity and Security in New Market Economies* (Washington, DC: Brookings Institution Press, 2002).

26 Ehrlich and Ehrlich, *One With Nineveh: Politics, Consumption, and the Human Future*; see also D. A. Crocker and T. Linden, eds., *Ethics of Consumption: The Good Life, Justice and Global Stewardship* (Lanham, MD: Rowman and Littlefield, 1997); Leider, *The Power of Purpose: Creating Meaning in Your Life and Work*; Bellman, *Your Signature Path: Gaining New Perspectives on Life and Work*; Handy, *The Hungry Spirit: Beyond Capitalism; A Quest for Purpose in the Modern World.*

27 N. Robins and A. Simms, "Opinion Poll: British Aspirations," *Resurgence*, July/August 2001(201) (www.resurgence.gn.apc.org/issues/robins201. htm); M. Seligman, *Authentic Happiness* (New York: Free Press, 2002).

28 L. M. Michaelis, "Drivers of Consumption Patterns," in R. B. Heap and J. Kent, eds., *Sustainable Consumption: A European Perspective* (London: The Royal Society, 2001), 75–84.

29 R. de Yong, "Some Psychological Aspects of Reduced Consumption Behavior: The Role of Intrinsic Satisfaction and Motivation," *Environment and Behavior* 28 (1996); N. R. Goodwin, F. Ackerman, and D. Kiron, eds., *The Consumer Society* (London: Earthscan, 1997); Hamilton, *Growth Fetish*; The Harwood Group, "Yearning for Balance: Views of Americans on Consumption, Materialism, and the Environment."

30 Robins and Simms, "Opinion Poll: British Aspirations"; R. E. Lane, *The Loss of Happiness in Market Economies* (New Haven: Yale University Press, 2000); J. B. Twitchell, *Living It Up: Our Love Affair with Luxury* (New York: Columbia University Press, 2002).

31 C. Chandy, *The Dissatisfaction Syndrome*; S. A. Saunders and C. Roy, "The Relationship Between Depression, Satisfaction with Life and Social Interest," *South Pacific Journal of Psychology* 11 (1999): 9–15; T. Jackson and L. Michaelis, *Policies for Sustainable Consumption* (London: Sustainable Development Commission, 2003); R. Levett, I. Christie, M. Jacobs, and R. Therivel, *A Better Choice of Choice: Quality of Life, Consumption and Economic Growth* (London: The Fabian Society, 2003).

32 T. Kasser, *The High Price of Materialism* (Cambridge, MA: MIT Press, 2002); R. E. Lane, *The Loss of Happiness in Market Economies*; Seligman, *Authentic Happiness*.

33 Chandy, *The Dissatisfaction Syndrome*; Layard, *Towards a Happier Society*; Pidgeon, *Is the Consumer Bubble Set to Burst?*.

34 Kasser, *The High Price of Materialism*; J. de Graaf, D. Wann, and T. H. Naylor, *Affluenza: The All-Consuming Epidemic* (San Francisco: Berrett-Koehler, 2001); Robins and Simms, "Opinion Poll: British Aspirations"; Seligman, *Authentic Happiness*.

35 C. Hamilton, *Overconsumption in Britain: A Culture or Middle-Class Complaint?* (Canberra: The Australia Institute, 2003).

36 Layard, *Towards a Happier Society*.

37 P. Drucker, *Post-Capitalist Society* (Cambridge, MA: HarperBusiness, 1992).

38 S. B. Breathnach, *The Simple Abundance Companion*; D. Elgin, *Voluntary Simplicity* (New York: William Morrow, 1993); Etzioni, "Voluntary Simplicity: Characterization, Select Psychological Implications, and Societal Consequences"; B. Schwartz, *The Costs of Living: How Market Freedom Erodes the Best Things in Life* (New York: Norton, 1994).

39 C. Tickell, "Sustainability and Conservation: Prospects for Johannesburg," speech to the Society for Conservation Biology, Canterbury, Kent, U.K., July 15, 2002.

40 M. Strong, statement at the hearing of the United States Senate Committee on the Environment and Public Works and the Committee on Foreign Relations, July 24, 2002.

CHAPTER THREE

Environmental History

In this chapter on environmental history, we begin by looking at a description of ideas about nature in order to understand how these views have shaped current environmental issues and challenges. We are especially concerned with the beliefs people hold about nature and how the meaning of nature shifts over time and is different for different groups in society. When we study environmental history, we are reviewing the relationship of human society to nature over time. In this text, we examine the ways that the society-to-environment relationship affects both people and nature.

In North America, the most profound shift in the relationship between human society and nature happened when European settlers arrived and slowly replaced Indigenous relationships to the natural world with ideas that were primarily European and Western. Settlement of North America marked a profound shift in how land and natural resources were viewed and consumed, a shift that created and accelerated many of the conservation and biodiversity challenges we face today. Despite the more extractive mentality of European settlers, many of them also expressed a profound appreciation of the stunning beauty of the North American landscape. Over time, settlers who were motivated by consumption and exploitation of natural resources began to prioritize conservation and preservation of large tracts of wilderness for their intrinsic worth and human appreciation. There were significant efforts for land preservation and conservation at the turn of the twentieth century by presidents and early environmentalists.

Aldo Leopold emerged from these times and became an important figure in shaping an American idea of human relationship to land, calling it "The Land Ethic" which he wrote about in his book *A Sand County Almanac* (1949). We recommend that students read an excerpt from this book in which Leopold speaks poetically of the ecological balance between humans, landscape, and wild species. Promoting this concept of balance made Leopold well known within environmental studies, but it is important to note that the idea of living in balance with nature was a fundamental tenet of Indigenous environmental knowledge long before Europeans arrived in North America. We return to this idea of a "land ethic" toward the end of the book when discussing the ethical use of nature in Chapters 11 and 12.

The first article selected for this chapter addresses environmental history in the US by reviewing Leopold's work and the work of other important figures in the environmental movement, such as Rachel Carson and Robert Bullard, both of whom you will learn more about in subsequent chapters of this text. In "A Garden Planet," the introduction to her book *Reinventing Eden* (2003), environmental philosopher Carolyn Merchant describes recent environmental history in the US through opposing progressive versus declensionist narratives. These narratives present two different ways to see the relationship between human society and nature. In the progressive narrative, human advancements over the past two centuries have recreated Christianity's Garden of Eden and provided a life of plenty and ease for all. Of course, as Merchant points out, the new Garden of Eden is not equally available to all people; the true cost of creating a life of ease and plenty for the few is borne by the many, a concept we explore under environmental justice in Chapter 7. According to the declensionist narrative, human activities over the past two centuries have damaged and degraded the planet's resources to a point almost past recovery. Merchant reflects on the trajectory of environmental history rather than a review of the dates and names that mark milestone events. In the recommended viewing section, you will find resources to guide your learning on some of these milestones not mentioned by Merchant.

The selected reading in this chapter from Dorceta Taylor's book *Environment and the People in American Cities: 1600s–1900s: Disorder, Inequality, and Social Change* (2009) reminds us that environmental history includes examining the challenges of urban areas, not only the stories of parks, wilderness, and vast tracts of unused land. This text from Chapter 8 on urbanization and population growth provides further details about land use in cities. In the recommended reading section, Carolyn Finney's article "This Land is Your Land, This Land is My Land: People and Public Lands Redux" (2010) compliments Taylor's chapter by reminding us that environmental ideas, especially opinions about public and protected lands, were prioritized for white Americans but not for other Americans. Through a powerful personal story, Finney asks us to consider who cares deeply about the natural world, which communities get the chance to participate in environmental decision-making, and whose stories about land are told.

RECOMMENDED READING

Finney, C. 2010. "This Land is My Land: People and Public Lands Redux." *The George Wright Forum* 27(3): 247–254.

Leopold, A. 1949."Thinking Like a Mountain." In *A Sand County Almanac*, 129–133. Oxford, UK: Oxford University Press.

RECOMMENDED VIEWING

Bradbury, M. J. 2016. C. M. Russell Museum. "Women Naturalists of the Turn of the Twentieth Century" (33:32).

WATCH AT https://www.youtube.com/watch?v=sQr8Q_uy-XI.

Johnson, S. 2014. National Park Service. "The Conservation Legacy of the Buffalo Soldier" (2:32).

WATCH AT https://www.youtube.com/watch?v=qa5RMvn2V6k.

Lyons, O. and Hill, S. 2015. Tree Media. "Doctrine of Discovery" (5:59).

WATCH AT https://www.youtube.com/watch?v=V3gF7ULVrl4.

READING AND DISCUSSION PROMPTS

1. Which point of view from Carolyn Merchant's work about environmental history do you most agree with, the progressive or the declensionist narrative? Why? What circumstances convince you that environmental history points toward progress or toward decline?
2. Review the reading by Dorceta Taylor from her book *Environment and the People in American Cities 1600s–1900s*. What are some of the ways Taylor describes how the environmental movement has improved the quality of life for people in cities? Has this environmental improvement been equally distributed among all urban residents? If not, who has benefited less, and who has benefited more?
3. On your own, you should watch the video "The Doctrine of Discovery." In your own words, define the Doctrine of Discovery. What effect do you think this policy had on the way European settlers arriving in the Americas treated Indigenous peoples and their land over the past 500 years?

READING 3.1

A Garden Planet

By Carolyn Merchant

Life
Like a spider
Spins its web
In cyclical melodies
Telling enigmatic, sacred tales
To deaf, dumb, blind me.
Carolyn Merchant, 1998

A lush garden. Pathways wander invitingly among rolling lawns and fragrant flowers. Lilies, roses, and herbs send forth a sweet ambrosia. The air smells continuously fresh. Peacocks strut among the trees in the near distance and doves make their distinctive three-note coo. A cottontail, appearing unconcerned, nibbles at grass nearby, while lambs suckle at their mother's teat. Nearly hidden among the taller and more distant cedars, a doe and fawn munch at the undergrowth. A small grove of fig trees can be glimpsed down a side path. A couple strolls arm in arm toward a fig grove near the middle of the garden, where a waterfall gushes over rocks fed by a clear bubbling stream. At the garden's very center are two trees known simply as the tree of life and the tree of the knowledge of good and evil.

Where is this Eden? It is not in the Mesopotamian lands of the pre-Christian era. It is the new downtown square on the promenade in Anytown, California. The square is replete with fountains, grassy knolls, meandering streams, and benches for passersby. Along each side of the river flowing through the square are the shops of the revived cityscape. Gracefully arched bridges connect the two sides of the street, and the shops face the greenbelt along the river. The stores are those found in hundreds of towns across the nation: Borders Books, Starbucks Coffee, Cost Plus World Market, Noah's Bagels, Banana Republic, The Gap, Crate and Barrel, and Jamba Juice. This is the new American Eden. [1]

The Garden of Eden story has shaped Western culture since earliest times and the American world since the 1600s. We have tried to reclaim the lost Eden by reinventing the entire earth as a garden. The shopping mall, the "new main street," the gated community, and the Internet are the latest visions of a reinvented Eden. From Christopher Columbus's voyages, to the search for the fountain of youth, to John Steinbeck's *East of Eden*, visions of finding a lost paradise have motivated global exploration, settlement, and hope for a better life.

The Recovery of Eden story is the mainstream narrative of Western culture. It is perhaps the most important mythology humans have developed to make sense of their relationship to the earth. Internalized by Europeans and Americans alike since the seventeenth century, this story has propelled countless efforts by humans to recover Eden by turning wilderness into garden, "female" nature into civilized society, and Indigenous folkways into modern culture. Science, technology, and capitalism have provided the tools, male agency the power and impetus. Today's incarnations of Eden are the suburb, the mall, the clone, and the World Wide Web.

As with any mainstream story, however, a counternarrative challenges the plot. Recent postmodern and postcolonial stories reject the Enlightenment accounts of progress. Many environmentalists see the loss of wilderness as a decline from a pristine earth to a paved, scorched, endangered world. Many feminists see a nature once revered as mother now scarred, desecrated, and abused, and women as the victims of patriarchal culture. Similarly, many African Americans and Native Americans see their history as one of colonization by Europeans who "explored," "discovered," and took over their lands and viewed their bodies as animal-like and close to nature. But even as they call for new pathways to a just society, these counterstories of a slide downward (or declension) from Eden buy into the overarching, metanarrative of recovery. Both storylines, whether upward or downward, compel us to find a new story for the twenty-first century.

Narratives form our reality. We become their vessels. Stories find, capture, and hold us. Our lives are shaped by the stories we hear as children; some fade as we grow older, others are reinforced by our families, churches, and schools. From stories we absorb our goals in life, our morals, and our patterns of behavior. For many Americans, humanity's loss of the perfect Garden of Eden is among the most powerful of all stories. Consciously at times, unconsciously at others, we search for ways to reclaim our loss. We become actors in a storyline that has compelled allegiance for millennia.

But "mastering" nature to reclaim Eden has nearly destroyed the very nature people have tried to reclaim. The destruction of nature in America became clearly apparent in the late nineteenth century. The railroad, the steam engine, the factory, and the mine began to demolish forests, blemish landscapes, and muddy the air and water. Romantics reacted sharply. They began to tell a new story of what went wrong—a story of decline from pristine nature. Explorers, writers, poets, and painters proclaimed their love for untouched wilderness. The early conservation movement attempted to redeem both nature and humanity by saving places of pristine beauty.

Yet the new parks, the modern suburbs, and the garden cities reclaimed nature at a cost. These Edenic spaces ostracized those "others" of different classes and colors who did not fit into the story. The green veneer became a cover for the actual corruption of the earth and neglect of its poor; that green false consciousness threatened the hoped-for redemption of all people. The middle class appropriated wild nature at the expense of native peoples by carving national parks out of their homelands. The new suburbs existed at the cost of poor minorities who lived with polluted wells, blackened slums, and toxic dumps. Today, many people of color look back to an apparent Edenic past before slavery and colonization changed their lives forever.

The narrative of reinventing Eden, told by progressives as well as environmentalists, raises fundamental questions about the viability of the Recovery Narrative itself. Do not the earth and its people need a new story? What would a green justice for the earth and humanity really look like? Why do people tell stories, and whose ends do they serve? Both the modern progressive and declensionist stories, however compelling, are flawed. They are products of the linear approach of modern scientific thinking and also reflect the oppositional polarities of *self* and *other*. New kinds of stories, new ways of thinking, and new ethics are required for the twenty-first century.

A narrative approach raises the question of the fit between stories and reality. There is a reality to the progressive story. Great strides have been made in many people's struggle for survival and ease of life. There is also a reality to the Decline from Eden narrative. The environmental crisis and its connections to overdevelopment, population, consumption, pollution, and scarcity are critical issues confronting all of humanity. Through these contrasting stories, we can see both progress and decline in different places at different times. Progressives want to continue the upward climb to recover the Garden of Eden by reinventing Eden on Earth, while environmentalists want to recover the original garden by restoring nature and creating sustainability.

The two stories seem locked in conflict. Played out to its logical conclusion, each narrative negates human life: the mainstream story leads to a totally artificial earth; the environmental story leads to a depopulated earth. Pushed to one extreme, the recovered Eden would be a completely reinvented, totally managed, artificially constructed planet in which shopping on the web would replace shopping at the mall, the gated community the urban jungle, and greenhouse farms the vicissitudes of nature's droughts and storms. Pushed to the opposite extreme, the recovery of wilderness implies a humanly depauperate earth. The tensions between the two plots create the need for a new story that entails a sustainable partnership with nature.

We interpret our hopes and fears through such powerful cultural stories. We act out our roles in the stories into which we were born. The American dream holds out a promise, dangling its rewards for those who work hard and are lucky enough to find its treasures. For those who fail, dire consequences may result. These larger stories propel those who act within them to reinvent the planet as a new world garden. Rich and poor alike buy into the mainstream recovery story and act it out over their lifetimes.

The environmental crisis of the 1960s showed that all was not well on the "garden planet." Rachel Carson's *Silent Spring* alerted the nation to the disruptive effects of pesticides on the food chain,[2] while the testing of nuclear weapons raised the specter of the widespread effects of radiation on biotic, especially human, life. In 1967, historian Lynn White Jr.'s classic article "The Historical Roots of our Ecologic Crisis" laid the blame for environmental disruption on an idea: Christian arrogance toward nature. "God … created Adam and, as an afterthought, Eve to keep man from being lonely," White wrote, "Man named all the animals, thus establishing his dominance over them.… Especially in its Western form, Christianity is the most anthropocentric religion the world has seen." White's assessment was, "We shall continue to have a worsening ecologic crisis until we reject the Christian axiom that nature has no reason for existence save to serve man," and the article brought forth cries of criticism over its assignment of the ecological crisis to a single cause. Critics such as Lewis Moncrief responded that a more complex scenario was needed that included capitalism, industrialization, the American frontier, manifest destiny, urbanization, population growth, and property ownership. Others argued that the rise of science and technology contributed to the ability of humanity to dominate nature and to the idea that mechanistic science promoted the separation of humans from nature.[3]

The complexity of causes leading to environmental degradation as well as efforts to conserve nature and its resources helped to spawn the field of environmental history. In the 1970s and 1980s, an array of books documented the loss of wilderness, the erosion of soils, increased urban pollution, and the decline of biotic diversity. The early successes of environmental history helped to create an overarching narrative of environmental decline as one of the dominant themes in the field. By the mid-1980s, Donald Worster, William Cronon, and others identified the plots of many environmental histories as "declensionist." Cronon compared two different narratives by two different authors about the 1930s Dust Bowl of the Great Plains, both with virtually the same title (*The Dust Bowl* and *Dust Bowl*), and both published in the same year (1979)—one a story of progress, the other a story of decline. Cronon wrote, "Although both narrate the same broad series of events with an essentially similar cast of characters, they tell two entirely different stories. In both texts, the story is inextricably bound to its conclusion, and the historical analysis derives much of its force from the upward or downward sweep of the plot." The question raised was one of the fit between stories and reality. How accurately did these or any histories fit the events in question? Who were the characters in the stories? Who was omitted? Was all environmental history declensionist history? And even if that were the case, did this insight in any way undercut the value of environmental history's insights into historical change?[4]

By the 1990s, chaos and complexity theory further challenged ecology and environmental history. The new approaches disrupted the idea of a balance of nature that humans could destroy but also restore. Humanity was not the only major disturber of an evolved prehuman ecosystem. Natural disturbances, such as tornadoes, hurricanes, fires, and earthquakes could in an instant wipe out an old-growth forest, demolish a meadow, or redirect the meander of a river. Humanity was less culprit and more victim; nature more violent and less passive. Environmental history moved away from assigning all destructive change to humans and toward chance and contingency in nature.[5]

My own view is that both progressive and declensionist stories reflect real world history, but from different perspectives. Both open windows onto the past, but they are only partial windows depending on the characters included and omitted. The linearity of the upward and downward plots also masks contingencies, meanderings, crises, and punctuations. Including nature and its climatic and biotic manifestations, however, adds complexity and contingencies to the unidirectional plots of progress and decline. Droughts, freezes, "little ice ages," domesticated animals and plants, invasive nonnative species, bacteria, viruses, and humans are all actors who are often unpredictable and unmanageable. They inject uncertainties into the trajectories of progress and decline. As environmental historian Theodore Steinberg argues, "it is quite simply wrong to view the natural world as an unchanging backdrop to the past. Nature can upset even the best-laid, most thoroughly orchestrated plans.... We must acknowledge the unpredictability involved in incorporating nature into human designs and, in so doing, bring natural forces to the fore of the historical process."[6]

My view is that the new sciences of chaos and complexity not only reinforce the role of natural forces in environmental history, they also challenge humanity to rethink its ethical relationship to nature. The new sciences suggest that we should consider ourselves as partners with the nonhuman world. We should think of ourselves not as dominant over nature (controlling and managing a passive, external nature) or of nature as dominant over us (casting humans as victims of an unpredictable, violent nature) but rather in dynamic relationship to nature as its partner. In the following pages I present a new perspective on the history of humanity's relationship to nature. I draw on the framework of progressive and declensionist plots, on the roles of men and women in transforming and appreciating the environment, on ideas of contingency and complexity in history, of nature as an actor, and of humanity as capable of achieving a new ethic of partnership with the nonhuman world.

In *Reinventing Eden*, I begin by naming the powerful, overarching story of modern history as a Recovery Narrative. I show how the new millennium presents a major turning point for both the progressive Enlightenment stories and the counternarratives told by women, minorities, and nature itself. I look at the origins of the Recovery Narrative as it arose through biblical, ancient, and medieval history and then set out its political and environmental codification during the Scientific Revolution and European Enlightenment. I focus on the role of Christianity in the formation of the Recovery Narrative and do not attempt to include the influence of Judaism or the Hebrew interpretation of the Genesis stories. Although I am aware that a very large and important literature on biblical interpretation exists, my goal is not to reinterpret biblical scholarship, to write a history of religion, or to examine the development of religious movements, denominations, and sects; nor do I attempt to review or assess the vast literature on Eden in Western culture or Edenic ideas in other cultures and throughout the world.[7]

I then examine the impact of the mainstream Recovery Narrative as it comprises European culture's development and transformation of the New World. American stories—from John Winthrop's Puritan garden to Thomas Hart Benton's manifest destiny—follow and re-create the progressive Recovery storyline. This powerful story of reclaiming and redeeming a fallen earth by human labor becomes the major justification for the westward movement and the effort to remake indigenous Americans in the image of European culture. Eastern wilderness and western deserts are turned into gardens for American settlers.

Throughout the ensuing chapters, I also examine the second story, or what went wrong—the story of Earth in decline. From Plato to Henry David Thoreau, writers have noted the destruction of nature and the problems of vanishing forests and fouled waters. I set out the nineteenth century origins of the romantic counternarrative, the conservation movement, and the late-twentieth-century narratives of environmental crisis. The effects of development on nature, women, and minorities are part of a larger counterstory of the loss of an evolved, earthly abundance and human equality. Despite nuances, hopeful advances, and upward trends, these counternarratives of decline and loss relate the all-too-real experiences of large numbers of people. The continued downward spiral leads to an impoverished earth where diversity is decreasing and environmental health is declining. This also is a story in which we live. It too affects our lives. Over time the Recovery

Narrative with its two storylines—one of progress, the other of decline—has shaped the earth's landscape as well as human hopes, desires, and lives.

Within the broad arc of the Recovery Narrative, nature itself has played a major role in affecting outcomes. Despite the efforts of humans to control the natural world, contingencies and crises have occurred. Lurches, advances, and dips disrupt the apparent linearity of the narrative. Natural disturbances inject unpredictability and question the foundations of the narrative within the trajectory of modernity itself. From Noah's flood in Genesis 7 to the volcanic destruction of Pompei during the Roman Empire (C.E. 79), to the Lisbon earthquake of 1755 and Hurricane Gilbert in 1988, nature has shaped human actions and limited possibilities. Nature's actions along with new sciences that incorporate contingencies and complexities into their very assumptions suggest new ways for humanity to relate to the material world.[8]

Since the 1960s, I have witnessed enormous contention within the trajectories of progress and decline. Developers and wilderness advocates are in continual conflict. One group presses for ever greater profits at the earth's expense; the other struggles to save what remains of wilderness on the planet. In the final chapters of the book, I explore possibilities for new narratives about nature. I examine new ways of thinking about the human–nature relationship suggested by postmodern and postcolonial thinking, as well as the implications of recent theories of chaos and complexity. I offer some new ways to think about a multiplicity of stories and introduce ideas about nonlinear plots.

Throughout the book, I suggest possibilities for alternatives to domination based on a partnership between humanity and nature. Finally, I propose an environmental ethic based on a partnership between humans and the nonhuman world: rather than being either dominators or victims, people would cooperate with nature and each other in healthier, more just, and more environmentally sustainable ways. I show how complex interconnections can weave us into cyclical melodies and envelop us within new enigmatic, sacred tales.

NOTES

1 Issues concerning the corporatization of new American downtown strip malls appear in T. J. Sullivan, "Cookie Cutters Shaping U.S. Cities," *Ventura County Star*, Jan. 3, 1999, A1, A8.

2 Rachel Carson, *Silent Spring* (Boston: Houghton Mifflin, 1962).

3 Lynn White Jr., "The Historical Roots of Our Ecologic Crisis," *Science* 55 (1967): 1203–7, reprinted in Ian G. Barbour, ed., *Western Man and Environmental Ethics: Attitudes Toward Nature and Technology* (Reading, Mass.: Addison-Wesley, 1973), 18–30; quotations on 25, 29. Lewis Moncrief, "The Cultural Basis of Our Environmental Crisis," in Barbour, ed., *Western Man and Environmental Ethics*, 31–42. See also Carolyn Merchant, The *Death of Nature: Women, Ecology, and the Scientific Revolution* (San Francisco: Harper Collins, 1980).

4 William Cronon, "A Place for Stories: Nature, History, and Narrative," *Journal of American History*, 4, no. 4 (1992): 1347–76, quotation on 1348. Cronon compared the plots of Paul Bonnifeld, *The Dust Bowl: Men, Dirt, and Depression* (Albuquerque: University of New Mexico Press, 1979) and Donald Worster, *Dust Bowl: The Southern Plains in the 1930s* (New York: Oxford University Press, 1979).

5 Donald Worster, "Ecology of Order and Chaos," *Environmental History Review* 14, nos. 1–2 (1990): 14–16; James Gleick, *Chaos: The Making of a New Science* (New York: Viking, 1987); M. Mitchell Waldrop, *Complexity: The Emerging Science at the Edge of Order and Chaos* (New York: Simon and Schuster, 1992).

6 Theodore Steinberg, *Down to Earth: Nature's Role in American History* (New York: Oxford University Press, 2002), 284.

7 On ideas of Eden and the golden age in cultures throughout the world, see Richard Heinberg, *Memories and Visions of Paradise: Exploring the Universal Myth of a Lost Golden Age*, rev. ed. (Wheaton, Ill.: Quest Books, 1995). Heinberg states, "Our search has taken us from Mesopotamia to Iran, Egypt, India, China, Australia, North America, and Africa. Everywhere, we have encountered essentially the same myth—the story of a primordial era when humanity and Nature enjoyed a condition of peace, happiness, and abundance.... If a single source did exist, the diffusion from that source must have occurred so long ago that the process of borrowing is now impossible to trace. The myth can just as easily be interpreted as having originated independently in many locations" (54); and further, "Two of these traditions the Hebraic and the Greek continue to shape Western values and ideals" (49). On tropical Edens, see Richard Grove, *Green Imperialism: Colonial Expansion, Tropical Island Edens, and the Origins of Environmentalism, 1600–1860* (New York: Cambridge University Press, 1995).

8 See Norman Cohn, *Noah's Flood: The Genesis Story in Western Thought* (New Haven, Conn.: Yale University Press, 1996); William B. B. Ryan, *Noah's Flood: The New Scientific Discoveries About the Event that Changed History* (New York: Simon and Schuster, 1998); and T. D. Kendrick, *The Lisbon Earthquake* (London: Methuen, 1956).

READING 3.2

Selection from Environment and the People in American Cities, 1600s–1900s

DISORDER, INEQUALITY, AND SOCIAL CHANGE

By Dorceta Taylor

CONCLUSION

Three centuries ago America was on the brink of urbanization. Since then cities have proliferated and undergone tremendous changes. The urban population grew rapidly and cities expanded outward and upward to accommodate them. Cities also became industrialized. During the eighteenth century and the nineteenth, urban population growth quickly outpaced cities' abilities to cope with the demands placed on them. Rural out-migration fueled the growth of many European and American cities, but American cities also grew because of massive immigration from Europe. Though European cities were forced to wrestle with the consequences of overcrowding earlier than American cities, American cities had a new wrinkle to contend with: in addition to the class tensions that characterized European cities, American cities such as New York had a much wider range of racial and ethnic groups crammed together.

American urbanization was accompanied by enormous social stratification and escalating class, racial, and ethnic tensions. Ethnic and racial groups that had little or no prior contact with each other found themselves stacked on top of each other in deplorable housing, competing fiercely for horrid low-wage jobs, drinking each other's wastes from contaminated water sources, and sifting through each other's trash to eke out a living. At the same time people were trying to understand and cope with their new life circumstances in this volatile mix, cities seemed to be exceeding their ability to accommodate large numbers of people. Consequently environmental issues such as sewage and garbage disposal, clean water, decent and affordable housing, navigable roads, and clean air became urgent problems that cities had to deal with. Resolving these problems required a massive outlay of cash, a centralized planning system, civic governance, and forethought. Cities were woefully lacking in these, and as a result were frequently ravaged by epidemics and wracked by social unrest. Cities lurched from one crisis to another as civic leaders tried to figure out how to make them work.

From the beginning cities had religious, political, economic, and policy elites who played the role of civic leaders and reformers. These reformers covered the ideological spectrum from conservative to progressive. While they were more inclined to frame problems in moral and religious terms at first, it became evident that the resolution of the problems required more than religious reform. Increasingly reformers came to realize that many of the problems were environmental in nature and that their resolution required an environmental approach. Hence by the middle of the nineteenth century environmental activists were very involved in reform work.

The cities have been at the forefront of environmental activism for a long time. Urban environmental activists embarked on initiatives to improve sanitation, waste disposal practices, and public health; provide clean water and recreational opportunities; develop safe and affordable housing and comprehensive zoning; and create a legacy of urban parks and open space. In short, urban activists laid the foundation for many of the environmental campaigns and strategies that were used by wilderness and wildlife activists later on.

Today American cities, like many in Europe, are more racially and ethnically diverse than ever. Class as well as racial and ethnic tensions still pose a challenge to stability. At the same time, civic leaders are stronger, the infrastructure for governance is more powerful, social control is more institutionalized, and civil society is more developed. Urbanites are more tolerant of each other's differences, and there is greater understanding of how to achieve the common good. In addition to stronger governments cities now have better physical infrastructure to serve the populace and are now far more capable of responding to social, political, and economic crises than they were even a century ago. City leaders spend more time forecasting and planning so that urban centers can anticipate and prepare for crises rather than simply react to them.

Modern cities rely on environmental professionals in local, regional, state, and federal agencies to set, monitor, and enforce regulations and plan and develop environmental contingencies. Environmental agencies have budgets to undertake initiatives. Though millions of environmental activists from thousands of environmental organizations still play important roles in policy making the context in which they operate has changed. During the nineteenth century early environmental activists operated in a social and political context in which the activists themselves diagnosed the problems and prescribed the solutions. There was a tremendous vacuum in leadership in government on these issues. Activists often had no regulations or guidelines to support their cause or guide them. Governments were slow to identify and solve problems, and there was little or no institutional infrastructure for dealing with environmental affairs. Things have changed. While government entities are still targets of action for environmental activists and sometimes act slowly, contemporary activists interact with existing government agencies that are charged with overseeing a broad range of environmental concerns.

When eighteenth- and nineteenth-century urbanites consumed water mixed with their neighbors' wastes, the results were devastating outbreaks of diseases. Today American cities are cleaner and the epidemics of the past have all but vanished. Thanks to dramatic improvements in sanitation and a more sophisticated understanding of how diseases are transmitted, people in industrialized countries drink water already used and disposed of by their upstream neighbors without triggering outbreaks of deadly epidemics.

But American cities still face significant problems. Though municipalities no longer dump their trash and sewage in open gutters along the sides of city streets, water pollution is a significant problem in some areas. Today the water is more likely to be contaminated with pesticides and other toxic chemicals than with fecal matter, entrails, or trash. Solid waste disposal is still a problem as many cities run out of landfill space and citizens oppose new facilities.[1] The politics of locating waste dumps and other noxious facilities in cities follows a familiar pattern. As early as the seventeenth century noxious facilities expelled from white neighborhoods were relocated to black communities. Such facilities were allowed to foul the air and water with impunity. In contemporary times there is an increased likelihood that such facilities are located in poor, inner-city neighborhoods inhabited by blacks and other minorities.[2]

While cities try to resolve their waste disposal problems by shipping their wastes to poor, rural, out-of-state (often minority) communities or developing countries, most people realize that these are not long-term viable or sustainable options.[3] Though yellow fever and cholera no longer pose a threat to American urbanites, cancers and other illnesses have supplanted them. In short, the air, water, solid waste disposal systems, housing infrastructure, transportation systems, and public open space are still issues that environmental reformers wrestle with in the twenty-first century.

In general, housing conditions have improved dramatically and laws are in place to protect tenants. However, neighborhoods are still segregated, and there are still pockets of substandard housing that would make nineteenth-century reformers cringe. Most notably the public housing projects that reformers fought long and hard for became uninhabitable in the 1990s. Some of the same conditions that reformers fought to eradicate a century ago—low wages, limited skills, high unemployment, limited employment opportunities, low educational attainment—still plague residents of housing projects. Contemporary housing reformers are pinning their hopes on programs like HOPE (Home Ownership and Opportunity for People Everywhere) VI, which is replacing dilapidated public housing with mixed-income developments to which some former residents of the housing projects have access. Residents of HOPE VI developments have an option to rent or buy.[4]

At the other end of the spectrum the wealthy have not lost their desire to cloister themselves in exclusive residential enclaves. In bustling downtown areas they live in well-guarded condominium complexes and luxury high-rises. In the ruralized suburbs idealized by the likes of Downing, the well-to-do build gated communities or sprawling mansions on rapidly disappearing farmland. The quaint suburbs of the mid-nineteenth century such as Olmsted's Riverside have been enveloped by cities, becoming either a part of the city proper or an inner-ring suburb. Those wishing to bask in the solace of the long, lazy days of summer that Emerson cherished have to drive much farther into the countryside to find such bucolic surroundings.

Cities still struggle to control land use. Such groups as the Fifth Avenue Association were effective in influencing early comprehensive zoning laws and in maintaining the character of Upper Fifth Avenue. The avenue still has the feel of an exclusive mixed commercial and residential district. Chicago's "Magnificent Mile" on Michigan Avenue has also been successful in capturing the essence of this type of urban neighborhood.

Workplace health and safety are still a challenge. Though we have made great strides in understanding the causes of occupational illnesses and reducing workplace hazards, many workers are still being killed or injured on the job. On average, 9,000 U.S. workers sustain disabling injuries on the job each day. In 2004 there were 4.3 million nonfatal injuries and 249,000 job-related illnesses in private industry workplaces; there were 4.4 million nonfatal injuries and illnesses in 2003, a rate of 4.8 cases per 100 equivalent full-time workers. In 2003 the rate was 5.0 per 100. Data from niosh show that annually $145 billion is spent on injuries and $26 billion on diseases. The number of work-related fatalities has been declining steadily since 1992, but the 2004 figures showed a 2 percent increase over 2003 figures. In 2004 there were 5,703 fatal work injuries in the United States; the number was 5,575 in 2003. Ninety percent of work-related fatalities occur in private industry. Fatal work injuries occurred at a rate of 4.1 per 100,000 workers; this is a slight increase over the rate of 4.0 recorded for 2002 and 2003. The highest rate recorded since 1992 was 5.3 per 100,000 in 1994.[5]

To respond to these issues environmental activism has grown tremendously over the past century. For several decades this was a heavily middle-class movement, but the movement has grown more diverse in the past three decades.[6] Around the time large numbers of low-income grassroots environmental groups were mobilizing against toxins and other environmental hazards during the 1980s, there was widespread public perception that some of these hazardous conditions posed a large threat to individuals. For instance, in 1989, 69 percent of the respondents in a national poll felt threatened by the disposal of hazardous wastes; 65 percent by contamination of underground water supplies; 60 percent by the pollution of lakes, rivers, and oceans; 60 percent by food additives and pesticides; 58 percent by pollution caused by business and industry; and 52 percent by vehicular pollution. All the figures showed an increase over the 1987 figures.[7] Moreover 82 percent of the respondents in a 1988 Roper poll thought severe air and water pollution would create a "serious problem" twenty-five to fifty years hence.[8] In 1990, 55 percent of respondents thought pollution would be a "very serious threat," and 46 percent thought the quality of their drinking water had worsened in the past five years.[9] In 1998, 53 percent of the respondents in a cbs poll thought the environment would worsen over the next century, while only 15 percent thought it would improve.[10] More than 66 percent of respondents thought that hazardous waste disposal; contamination of ground water supplies; pollution of lakes, rivers, and oceans; and general air pollution posed a "large threat" to the environment.[11]

Despite the large number of environmental groups operating in working-class communities and the increasing effectiveness of those groups in taking action to improve environmental conditions in poor communities, those communities are still threatened by industrial pollution, degraded air and water, hazardous wastes, chemical spills, accidental toxic releases, and explosions, to name a few. Throughout the country contaminated sites abound. More than thirty-five thousand hazardous waste sites have been evaluated by the Environmental Protection Agency since Superfund came into existence in 1980. In 2006, 970 Superfund sites had already been cleaned up, and scores more were in the process of being cleaned up. Yet 1,300 sites still remain on the National Priorities List, a list of the most hazardous sites. It is estimated that it will take an average of $35 million to clean up each site. Superfund sites are found in each state, but New Jersey, Pennsylvania, and California have the largest number. About 57 percent of the sites are related to various industries and businesses, 28 percent are landfills or waste dumps, 11 percent are government sites, and about 4 percent are related to mining operations.[12]

Cities are still trying to keep pace with the demand for adequate access to open space. In the past 150 years urban park administrators have come full circle in the way they think about acquisition of land for and the funding of open space. While earlier government entities considered it their role to fund and administer public parks, since the 1970s there has been a shift away from this position. Increasingly, local governments are slashing park budgets and looking to the private sector to finance public parks. Once again this raises serious questions about access and equity. One hopes that public awareness of these trends will stimulate vigorous debates that will help provide some answers about the nature of public goods such as urban parks and the role of government in safeguarding these goods.

Tempting though it was to write a simpler book, one written solely from a classic environmental perspective, the more I researched the topic, the greater my sense that such a book would do a grave injustice to the topic. The environmental challenges cities face are inextricably connected to their demographic context, social classes, labor market dynamics, and politics. I hope that this account of how American cities confronted and dealt with environmental problems will provide some deeper insights into the problems, broaden our perspective, and help us approach contemporary problems with a greater awareness and understanding of the issues.

NOTES

1 Louis Blumberg and Robert Gottlieb, *War on Waste: Can America Win Its Battle with Garbage?* (Covelo, Calif.: Island Press, 1989).

2 See, for instance, United Church of Christ, *Toxic Wastes and Race in the United States: A National Report on the Racial and Socioeconomic Characteristics of Communities with Hazardous Waste Sites* (New York: United Church of Christ, 1987); Paul Mohai, "The Demographics of Dumping Revisited: Examining the Impact of Alternative Methodologies in Environmental Justice Research," *Virginia Environmental Law Journal* 14 (1995): 615–53.

3 Conner Bailey, Charles Faupel, and James Gundlach, "Environmental Politics in Alabama's Blackbelt," in *Confronting Environmental Racism: Voices from the Grassroots*, edited by Robert Bullard (Boston: South End Press, 1993), 107–22; Bill D. Moyers, *Global Dumping Ground: The International Traffic in Hazardous Wastes* (Washington, D.C.: Seven Locks Press, 1990).

4 Popkin et al., *The Hidden War*; U.S. Department of Housing and Urban Development, "Hope VI," 2006, at http://www.hud.gov.

5 NIOSH, *National Occupational Research Agenda*, 4; Bureau of Labor Statistics, *News: National Census of Fatal Occupational Injuries in 2004*, press release, August 25, 2005, 1; Bureau of Labor Statistics, *News: Workplace Injuries and Illnesses in 2004*, press release, November 17, 2005, 1.

6 D. E. Taylor, "The Rise of the Environmental Justice Paradigm," 508–80.

7 Cambridge Reports, "Trends and Forecasts," 1989, press release, 4–6; Cambridge Reports, "The Rise of the Green Consumer," 1989, press release.

8 Roper, "Research Supplement," June 1989, 1.

9 Cambridge Reports, "Trends and Forecasts," 4–6; Cambridge Reports, "The Rise of the Green Consumer."

10 "Environment a Worry," CBS News Poll, March 1–2, 1998.

11 Cambridge Reports, "Trends and Forecasts," 4–6; Cambridge Reports, "The Rise of the Green Consumer."

12 Mark Crawford, introduction to *Toxic Waste Sites: An Encyclopedia of Endangered America* (Santa Barbara: abC-ClIo, 1997), vii–xii; U.S. Environmental Protection Agency, "National Priorities List: NPL Site Totals by Status and Milestone," February 24, 2006, at http://www.epa.gov/superfund/sites/npl; U.S. Environmental Protection Agency, "Superfund National Accomplishments Summary, Fiscal Year 2003," November 3, 2003, 1–2, at http://www.epa.gov/superfund; Dave Ryan, "Superfund: 40 High-Priority Superfund Sites Cleaned Up," 2003, press release, U.S. Environmental Protection Agency.

CHAPTER FOUR

Biological Resources

One of the pillars of environmental studies is the natural sciences. Understanding the underlying systems and cycles of resources on our planet is crucial in order to make decisions about how best to preserve them, to use them sustainably, and to restore them. The readings in this chapter focus on the different levels of the architecture of the planet from individual species and populations to ecosystems and biomes.

The selection "Ecosystem Properties as a Basis for Sustainability" from *Investing in Natural Capital: The Ecological Economics Approach to Sustainability* by AnnMari Jansson and Bengt-Owe Jansson explains each of the planetary organizational levels by looking at different species interactions and how those interactions are based on the transfer of energy from the sun to plants and consumers up a food chain. As environmentalists, when we understand the different types of interactions between the abiotic and biotic environments, we can make decisions about how to use natural resources such as forests and rivers, how to manage our lands to create the most sustainable systems for the long term, and how to mitigate or remove threats to those resources. This selected reading uses language from the field of economics to describe our natural resources as "capital" that we can draw upon and need to protect. Often the threats to natural resources come from our desire for immediate economic gain without concern for maintaining our reserves of natural capital. Jansson and Jansson discuss how biodiversity protection leads to long-term stability and resiliency. This ensures that we achieve the main goal of conservationists, protecting our planet for the long term. This reading looks at the issue of natural capital as it connects to sustainability as reviewed in Chapter 2.

The recommended reading from the "Executive Summary" of the *Global Biodiversity Outlook 3* produced by the Secretariat for the Convention on Biological Diversity (2010) gives us a sense of current threats to biological resources. We understand that one of the decisions we are forced to make is where to devote our financial resources toward protecting nature. One of the methods for targeted conservation, among many, that is proposed by Norman Myers et al. in the recommended reading article, "Biodiversity Hotspots for Conservation Priorities" from *Nature* (2000), is to protect biodiversity "hotspots" to get the most "bang for our buck" and protect the most important species that we can. This work on hotspots has been extensively expanded and reviewed over the past 20 years to support more comprehensive conservation strategies.

When making conservation decisions, another crucial consideration for all environmental studies students, as you have and will see throughout this text, is the human connection to the issues raised. The "Stillheart Declaration" by Global Exchange (2014) helps make these connections clear by connecting the *use* of nature to the *rights* of nature and to the rights and practices of Indigenous peoples on their lands as explained in Chapters 7, 9, and 11. Connecting the strands of different paradigms of thought about how we view nature is crucial to achieving the goal of sustainable biological resources use and conservation. This chapter on biological resources allows us to understand the underlying functioning of the environment as discussed throughout the text, such as how climate changes (Chapter 5) and how that change must and can be mitigated. Lessons about the cycle of energy help us understand why certain types of pollution can be catastrophic throughout an ecosystem even if some individuals are barely harmed as seen in Rachel Carson's *Silent Spring* (Chapter 10). In addition, acknowledging the rights of nature helps us understand how those rights are circumvented or ignored when applied to Indigenous groups or people of color in the US as discussed in environmental justice (Chapter 7).

RECOMMENDED READING

Global Exchange. 2014. "The Stillheart Declaration." In *Rights of Nature and the Economics of the Biosphere*. Retrieved from: https://www.movementrights.org/resources/RONStillheart.pdf, with the full report here: https://the-rightsofnature.org/wp-content/uploads/pdfs/Biggs_et_al_Economics_Biosphere_2013.pdf.

Myers, N., Mittermeier, R. A., Mittermeier, C. G., Da Fonseca, G. A., and Kent, J. 2000. "Biodiversity hotspots for conservation priorities." *Nature*, 403(6772): 853.

Secretariat of the Convention on Biological Diversity. (2010) "Executive Summary." In *Global Biodiversity Outlook 3*. Montréal, Quebec.

READING AND DISCUSSION PROMPTS

1. What is your best definition of an ecosystem how does this compare to the idea of natural capital?

2. According to your reading, why are there always more prey animals than predators in an ecosystem? (Hint: it's an energy issue!)
3. What is the original source of the energy in fossil fuels?
4. The article "Ecosystem Properties as a Basis for Sustainability" discusses resiliency and stability. How does biological diversity affect those? What do you think that means for conservation of biological resources?

READING 4.1

Ecosystem Properties as a Basis for Sustainability

By AnnMari Jansson and Bengt-Owe Jansson

INTRODUCTION

For a long time now ecologists have tried to explain how natural systems work and why it is necessary to preserve their species, structure, and functions for the benefit of mankind. Economists in general, on the other hand, tend to regard the services from functioning ecosystems—like producing food, fresh air, clean water—as self-evident, seemingly free, unlimited, and lasting forever. Evolution during millions of years has developed systems with those properties, still evolving but susceptible to "new" disturbances like man's fossil fuel-based activities. It is imperative for the human society to develop behavior patterns in tune with the properties of ecosystems and the carrying capacity of the earth's ecosystems to support economic growth.

In a natural ecosystem, each species performs work like fixing solar energy, filtering water for food particles, or decomposing fallen leaves to get fuel for its own metabolism. But each species is also dependent on the rest of the ecosystem for its maintenance. It has a life-support system, which must be kept intact. The actual base of a species is thus not the mere pool of its potential food, but the amount of solar energy fixed by its ecosystem. The human species is not exempt from this general rule even if an abundant supply of fossil energy has made it believe so for some time.

Knowledge of the natural systems and how they work is required for an ecological-economic governance of our natural resources. There is a great need for fundamental research and critical examination of principles for ecological-economic interactions. In that work we need to use the same language. Calibrating the terminology may sound trivial, but as some conceptual names have deteriorated in the everyday vocabulary, it is crucial for avoiding serious misunderstandings. In this chapter we present and discuss some fundamental notions in their proper ecological context. The cited publications have been selected more for their basic treatment of the respective concepts than in an attempt to review the most recent literature.

SUSTAINABILITY REQUIREMENTS

As one of today's buzzwords, "sustainability," means for most people sustainability of the economic activities regardless of how large they may grow. However, what only a few decades ago was taken for granted—an infinite and stable environment for man to use without restrictions, inexhaustible both as a resource producer and a waste dump—has shown to change at an increasing rate, and has reached the limits for providing society with fresh air, clean water, and fertile soils. The growth of the human population and resulting environmental impacts have become so extensive that they are threatening to lead to significant global changes inimical to human survival. In its basic ecological sense, sustainability is actually the main property of the ecosystem, long known under other names such as *persistence,* which is attained through the complex structures and functions of natural systems, some of which will be addressed here.

Before turning to the separate properties, let us look at one example of an ecosystem (see Figure 4.1.1) and its contributions to the human society to stress that the separate properties and services are working in concert and not individually. The illustration shows a forest ecosystem, using solar energy, rain, soil, water, and minerals to produce trees, a diverse bird life, mushrooms, berries, and other products for the pleasure and use of the human community. The forest ecosystem also maintains a stable groundwater reservoir of low mineral content. Man transfers the trees to timber and the groundwater to drinking water. Through overexploitation like clearcutting, however, the groundwater table is lowered, the soil is eroded, and the essential minerals are leached from the soils. The spreading of toxic substances for controlling outbreaks of noxious insects poisons birds and other wildlife species. The atmospheric deposition of pollutants from the burning of fossil fuels acidifies the soil water and wipes out the fish populations of the lakes in areas lacking sufficient lime.

Obviously several of the essential properties of ecosystems have been violated in this single example. Figure 4.1.2 shows these major properties and how they relate to each

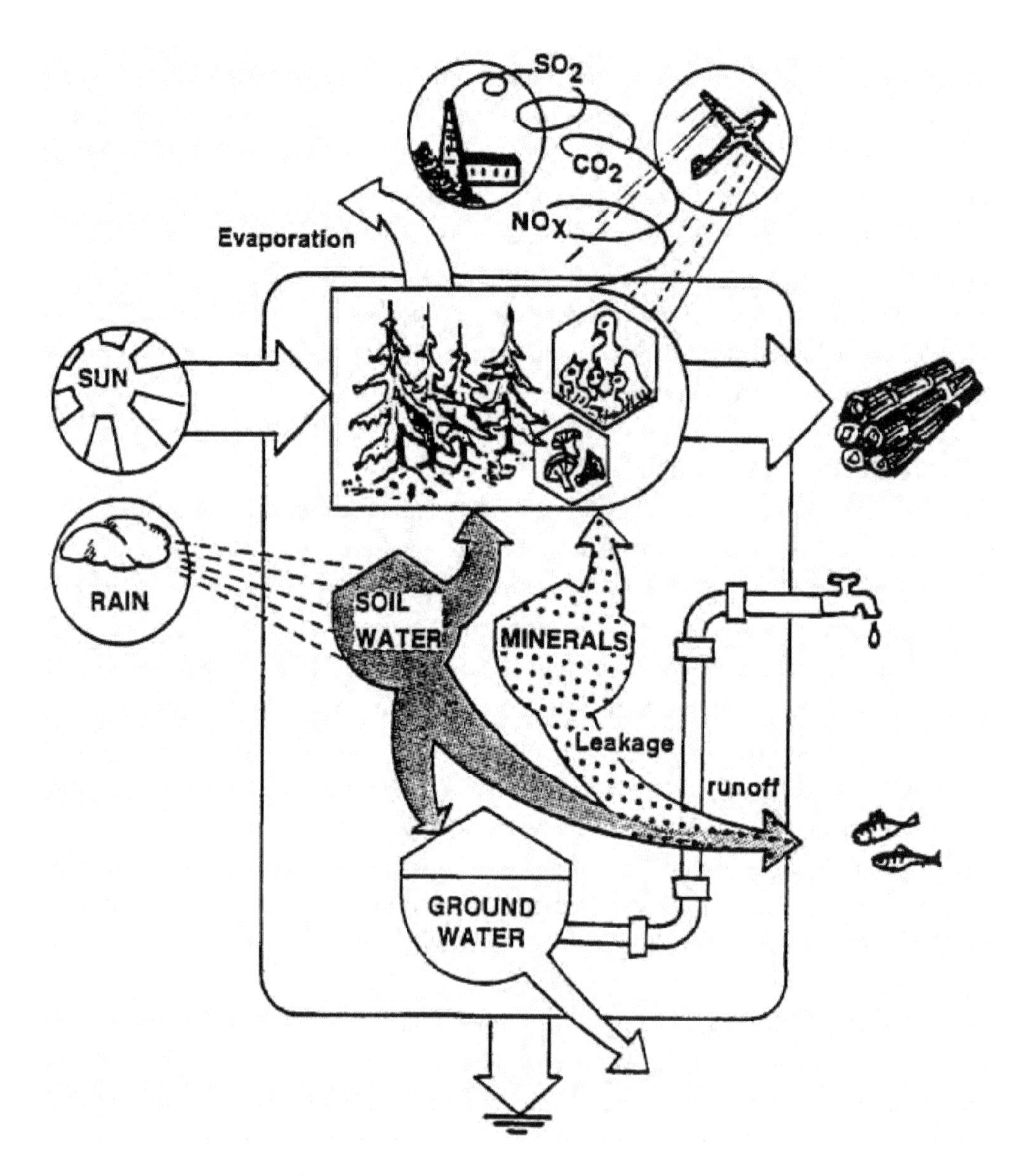

Figure 4.1.1 A forest ecosystem acting as a source and sink for human society. Based on solar energy, soil water, minerals, and carbon dioxide, the forest produces timber, wildlife, mushrooms, and berries, and provides various environmental services including the production of clean groundwater.

other. Greatly simplified, an ecosystem consists of a *production base* of green plants, constituting the resource base for a complex *network of consumers*—animals arranged in *trophic levels* according to their diet. Each level displays different degrees of *species diversity*, and the number of levels corresponds to the *functional diversity*. The total *community metabolism* of this assembly of organisms is maintained through a *recycling* of critical elements via dead *organic matter*, which is broken down by *decomposers* where bacteria and fungi play an important role. As ecosystems are very complex, the theoretical meaning of many

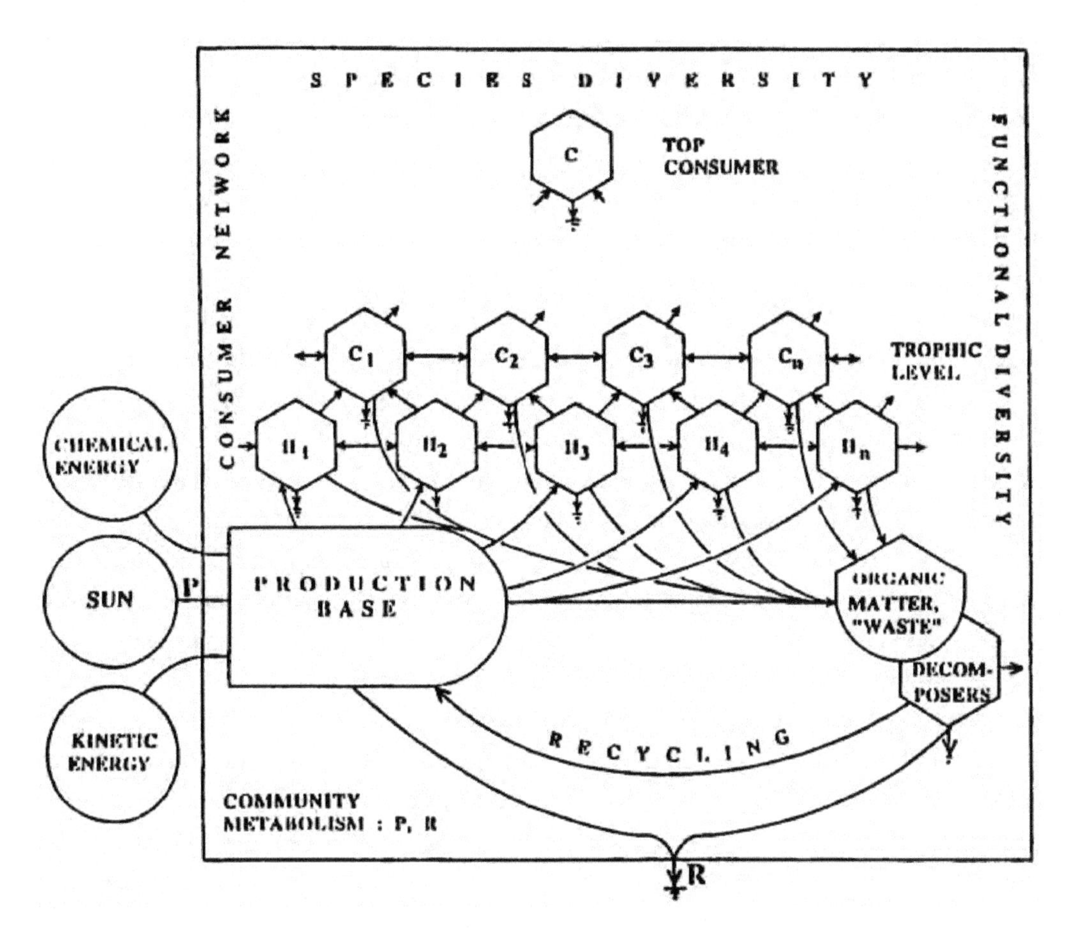

Figure 4.1.2 The main structure of an ecosystem. The green plants of the production base create living organic material by fixing solar energy (P) and using carbon dioxide and nutrients. The consumer network starts with many species of plant-eating animals (H), sources for different levels of carnivore species (C). The waste from the plants and animals, including the dead organisms, is broken down by decomposers, especially bacteria and fungi. Resulting inorganic matter like phosphorus and nitrogen compounds are recycled to the plants and the biogeochemical cycle starts again. The community metabolism incorporates the total production of the system (one measure is the total amount of fixed solar energy, P) and the total energy loss from all the processes, mainly as heat (R; for organisms this is the respiration). R is a crude measure of the total costs of running the system.

concepts are still subject to scientific debate. The view presented here is personal, based on long experience from work in the field.

Production Base

The establishment of an energy base is a first precondition for sustainability (see Figure 4.1.2). in a virgin area this base is established by the invasion of plants, fixing solar energy by the cell's cycling receptor of chlorophyll. This synthesis is the only real production of organic matter that, constituting food for a consumer network of animals, forms the ultimate base for all living organisms on earth, including humans. The term has been misinterpreted, however, through the use of the concepts "secondary and tertiary" production, when describing the energy flow in a food chain. These processes should rather be termed *transformations* as no "new" organic matter is produced—only the already synthesized organic matter is involved. In a pure ecological context most "industrial production" is therefore a form of consumption, because the manufacturing of goods implies the transformation of given natural resources, requires large inputs of extra energy, and produces large amounts of wastes capital to the environment.

It is important to discriminate between two measures of production: *gross production* and *net production*. This is seldom done, however. The difference can be explained by studying a plant enclosed in a jar during a day and night cycle. During the day plants synthesize organic matter from carbon dioxide, nutrients and water. Oxygen is produced in equivalent amounts in this process. By measuring the oxygen concentration in the jar for 24 hours, we can observe how the plant produces oxygen during the day, but consumes oxygen during night. The night consumption constitutes the *respiration* of the plant and is a measure of the metabolic work, the "cost" necessary for maintaining the life processes of the organism. The respiration process also takes place during the day, in fact even more intensively, but it is masked in the measurements by the much larger production at the presence of light. The production value during the day corresponds to the net production and adding the respiration gives a value of gross production. Figure 4.1.3 shows real values from measurements of community metabolism of a seaweed community during two diurnal cycles. A similar dynamic pattern is exhibited during the year with a productive pulse during the summer and a respiration phase during the dark winter period.

Compared to the annual economy of a tourist industry, which in temperate latitudes also has its main activity during the light part of year, the respiration costs would be analogous to the cost of maintaining the business: keeping the stock, human labor, advertising (in terrestrial systems comparable to exhibiting the bright color of flowers to attract insects for the necessary pollination). The net income during summer would have to pay for the costs during the rest of the year. When the term *production* is used in everyday conversation, it usually means net production, probably because the physical result we see

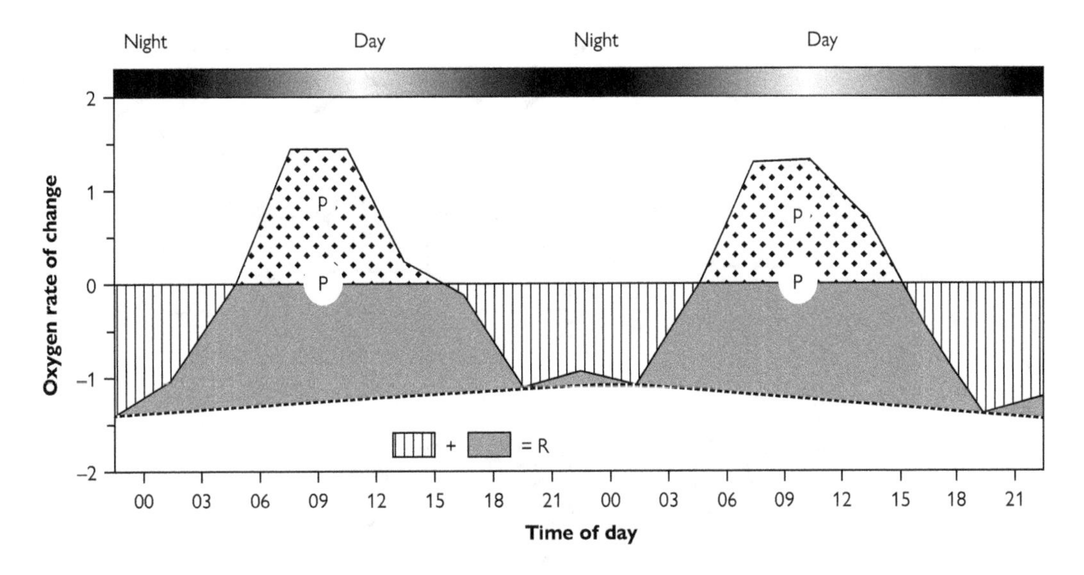

Figure 4.1.3 Production and consumption (respiration) of a marine seaweed system, enclosed in a transparent plastic bag and measured as diurnal oxygen changes. The whole area below the 0-base line to the horizontal dashed line is the respiration or maintenance costs (R) during the two diurnal cycles. The lightly stippled area above the 0-base is the net production (p), which together with the dark stippled area constitutes the gross production (P).

in the form of, for example, the green grass of the lawn or the manufactured cars in the factory are the mere products. But they do not show all the energy-consuming processes that made their production possible. The careless use of the word production actually has far-reaching consequences. It makes us forget that persistence requires much potential energy for pure maintenance. This is probably easier to recognize when it involves personal labor like the necessary watering of potted plants or the cleaning of the personal car. When we admire the effectiveness of genetically improved organisms or technically sophisticated racing cars, we tend to disregard that these technical wonders actually need a more expensive maintenance than their original prototypes.

Because the *energy efficiency* of green plants (i.e., the gross production as percentage of incoming solar insolation), is only a few per cent, it has often been wrongfully compared with the much greater efficiencies of man-made machines. The comparison is invalid because the green plant through respiration pays not only for running its metabolism but also for repair and propagation. To be fully comparable, a car, for example, would not only repair itself but also generate new specimens. When comparing energy efficiencies, it is important to consider both solar and fossil energy inputs during the whole life of a given product. Industrial agriculture may, for example, seem highly productive but compared

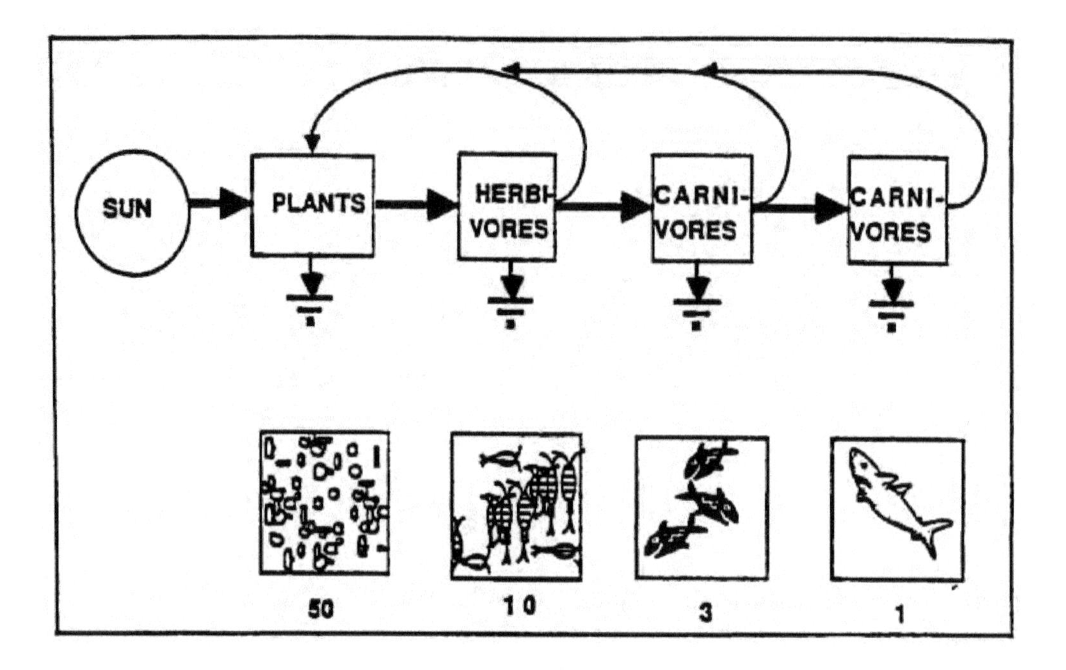

Figure 4.1.4 This simplified foodchain shows increasing life support areas and thus decreasing number of organisms per unit area higher up in the food chain. The control functions of the higher trophic levels on the lower ones are indicated by feedback loops (upper diagram).

to natural ecosystems that are not fossil fuel-subsidized, it actually consumes more energy than it delivers and should therefore be regarded as a consumer system.

Consumer Network

In the real world no organism, whether plant, animal, or bacterium can carry out its life processes in isolation. The producers are the base in a *foodweb* containing consumers of various kinds, linked in *foodchains,* and aggregated into *trophic levels* (Figure 4.1.4). There are seldom any straight foodchains in nature since most animals eat from more than one trophic level. But for the sake of clarity, we can depict an unramified flow of energy and matter from the producer level through the successive consumer levels. Summarizing several empirical attempts to quantify *the food transformation efficiency* showing variable but generally low efficiencies, we find an average of 90% reduction at each step in the foodchain. This is due not only to the basic respiration of the consumers and the varying quality of their food items but also to the costs for obtaining the food by running, swimming, and digging. Theoretically, therefore, the producers may put a limit to the number of possible trophic levels in the foodchain, which seldom exceed five, In most instances, however, disturbances rather than the basic energy flow seem to determine food chain length (Pimm 1988).

According to the "Emergy" concept developed by H. T. Odum (1988), there is an increase of the *energy quality* with each step of the food chain, which means that more solar energy is needed to generate and maintain one gram of fish than one gram of its food items like the water fleas. Also, the number of individuals usually decreases at higher trophic position. In an aquatic system the number of microscopic algae per unit area is much higher than the number of individual water fleas that feed on them and in turn are food for a much smaller number of fish. This means that the size of territory per individual is larger the higher the trophic position. Food has to be collected over a much larger space—*the life-support area* is large (Odum 1988). As this area has to comprise the entire lifespan of an organism, it can be quite large and difficult to estimate for migrating species like a salmon, an Arctic tern, or a reindeer.

The life-support area concept is also valid for the human species. Some 40% of the net terrestrial productivity on earth is presently channeled to human usage (Vitousek et al. 1989). In addition, about 8% of the productivity of the sea surface area is exploited by world fisheries. These studies imply that even if the built up area of a world population of 5.3 billion people occupies only 2 million km^2, the human support area is in the order of 100 million km^2. Like an ecosystem, the economic system consists of a network of sectors, each sector requiring inputs of energy, goods, and services from other sectors. The total energy costs (*embodied energy*) of the final products from a sector that is further removed from the initial energy sources (solar as well as fossil) are usually very high, but this fact is seldom reflected in their market value.

Another important aspect of Odum's emergy theory is that the *control functions* exerted by the species are stronger the higher up they are in the food chain. There are numerous examples of such "invisible control wires" between species, (e.g., pollination of flowers by insects, birds eating fruits and dispersing their seeds, and humans performing work that stimulates the development of a diverse landscape pattern).

As top consumer, man has really shown the power of affecting the whole biosphere. For example, the greatly increased exploitation of intermediate trophic levels by world fisheries since World War II has been made possible through increased inputs of technology and energy in harvesting and by near extinction of the competing top consumers of marine mammals. This may lead to large indirect effects in lower trophic levels, such as increased algal blooms and changes in the biogeochemical cycling (Folke et al. 1989; Hammer et al. 1993).

Community Metabolism

The community metabolism of whole systems is the summed production and respiration of all the participating organisms during their work (see Figure 4.1.2), and tells us if the system is self-supported by its producers or if it needs import of already synthesized organic material. Coral reefs and tropical rainforests show very low net production. Respiration (maintenance) costs are almost equal to the rate of primary production. Apparently much potential energy has been invested in adaptations during the evolution of these self-organizing systems. Other ecosystems, especially those in temperate climates like saltmarshes and hardwood forests, are highly productive during summer but are "dormant" during winter. Man is changing these large-scale patterns. The coastal areas may be driven heterotrophic through the increased inputs of organic matter and nutrients from various human activities. Instead of serving as carbon sinks taking up carbon dioxide from the atmosphere, they are now switching to become sources of carbon dioxide and other gases speeding up the global warming process (Smith and Mackenzie 1987).

Recycling

Recycling is necessary for ensuring the continuous flow of critical elements like nutrients and trace metals to the producers. In a balanced ecosystem a large part of the material flows is recycled. In the upper layers of the open sea carbon and nutrients in the organic matter are recycled many times through microbial activity, and only low calorific fecal pellets from the animals are sinking out of the pelagic system to settle on the bottoms. The coral reef and the tropical rain forest are systems with a very efficient recycling. The seawater flushing the reef and the soil supporting the rainforest contain only small amounts of nutrients—they are all in circulation in the organisms. The organic material produced in the reef is consumed there by the myriads of organisms. Similarly, the nutrients in the old leaves continuously shed in the tropical rainforests are resorbed before they fall to the ground, But these are rather rare examples. Usually ecosystems accumulate materials in storages of long duration, (e.g., tree trunks or peat layers). Fossil fuels, coal, oil, and gas, are the transformed products of organic matter deposited outside the active flows in ancient ecological systems and stored in the ground or at the bottom of the sea for millions of years.

Lately, recycling has become a goal of the industrial society for managing the impending problem of waste generation. In these efforts it should be remembered that speeding up recycling requires inputs of extra energy. An alternative strategy to decrease the use of materials would probably afford a better solution. In any case the flows should be compatible with the biogeochemical cycles of the biosphere and to the capacity of natural ecosystems to store and process wastes.

Self-organization

Although industrial man is the most powerful species in reorganizing natural structures and redirecting flows of energy and matter to his own advantage, other organisms do not just passively adjust to their environment either. In their instinctive struggle to sustain and disperse their species, they change and control the energy flow through what might be described as numerous feedback loops. Each species has been forced by natural selection to "pay" for its existence in the system by feeding back potential energy that amplifies the network it uses at least as much as it drains (Odum 1971, 1983). This interchange between the living and nonliving compartments gives the ecosystem its *self-organizing* ability. For example, by modifying the waterflow, wetland plants cause the sedimentation to increase giving their roots better attachment. Tree crowns create aerodynamic conditions that make pollen, seeds, and other airborne particles accumulate at the fringe of the wood. Predators control the grazing of primary production through eating the grazers, and grazers stimulate the plant production by the fertilizing effect of their excretion. There is much to learn from studying such self-organizing mechanisms in nature about how to develop better feedbacks between human societies and the life-supporting ecosystem.

The self-organizing ability makes it possible for devastated areas to redevelop persistent ecosystems given a set of climatic and edaphic variables. Stripped of its organisms by some disturbance of the environmental conditions—such as a forest fire or an oil spill—the system is open for colonization by invading organisms, starting a *succession* process. Given enough time for exploitation of the released resources, a conservation or climax phase will be reached of largely the same structure as the one that existed before. The climax phase will last until the next "creative destruction" starts a renewal process again (Holling 1986). The strength of this process is very strong. If we for example want to exchange the native grass of our lawn for some foreign, greener species, we have to work against the natural succession by watering, fertilizing, and cutting the lawn. Left unattended, the foreign species will otherwise be outcompeted by native ones because it has other requirements. Falk (1976) estimated that the energy costs for keeping a suburban lawn free from being overgrown with weeds corresponded to more than half the net primary production of that system. In the same way the maintenance of our agrarian monocultures have to be paid for by large inputs of human labor and fossil energy.

Diversity

Conserving biodiversity is regarded as one of the major issues for maintaining the natural capital of the life-supporting ecosystems. At least 5 million species (Wilson 1988), in size classes from microns up to tens of meters and lifetimes from hours to hundreds of years, are involved in the living machinery that is driven by solar insolation and helps turn the biogeochemical cycles. The accelerating loss of species and populations of animals and plants has created an increased interest in the concept of biodiversity and what it means for sustainability. *Biodiversity* (Rosen, in Wilson 1988) is a well-known term that has not been clearly defined, but seems in most cases to refer to species diversity. However, biodiversity rightly encompasses many different levels in time and space that are all important to consider.

Species diversity is a property of the population level dealing with the numbers and distribution of species and populations. Because it is relatively easy to get data on species diversity by merely counting the different animals (and plants, which is seldom done, however) in an area, it has often been improperly used as an indicator of ecosystem complexity and organization.

Functional diversity is focused on what the different species do (their "jobs") and is a property of the ecosystem level (O'Neill et al, 1986). It is strongly related to ecosystem stability. In an ecosystem with a high diversity of species, there are many different species performing the same life-support functions like solar energy fixation, nitrogen fixation, filterfeeding, or decomposition (see Figure 4.1.2). Through the elasticity of the total gene pool in each functional group or *guild*, the persistence of the system is secured even during adverse conditions.

With a low species diversity the buffering capacity of an ecosystem decreases even if the species involved are rather tolerant, A comparison between the North Sea and the Baltic Sea is a good example. The former high-salinity system has at least 1000 macroanimal species, while the brackish Baltic has fewer than one tenth of that number to perform the same ecosystem functions. The northernmost part of the Baltic lacks macroscopic filterfeeders—clams and mussels—resulting in a less effective processing of organic material (Elmgren et al. 1984). This might be one of the reasons for the very low primary productivity of that area.

Spatial diversity or spatial heterogeneitys is of basic importance for both the structure and performance of an ecosystem. This can be exemplified in the vertical distribution of production and respiration (decomposition) of different systems due to the gradual extinction of sunlight (see Figure 4.1.5). In the open sea the main production takes place in the surface layer, while the primary and long-term decomposition goes on several thousand meters down. The settling of organic material and the up-transport of inorganic nutrients occur over long distances. The recycling of nutrients necessary for the primary production therefore takes place mostly within the water column through the bacteria and microscopic animals and through transport by vertically migrating crustaceans and fish. In a forest the distance between the primary production of the green leaves in the tree crown and the respiration that goes on in the root zone is much less, and the transports

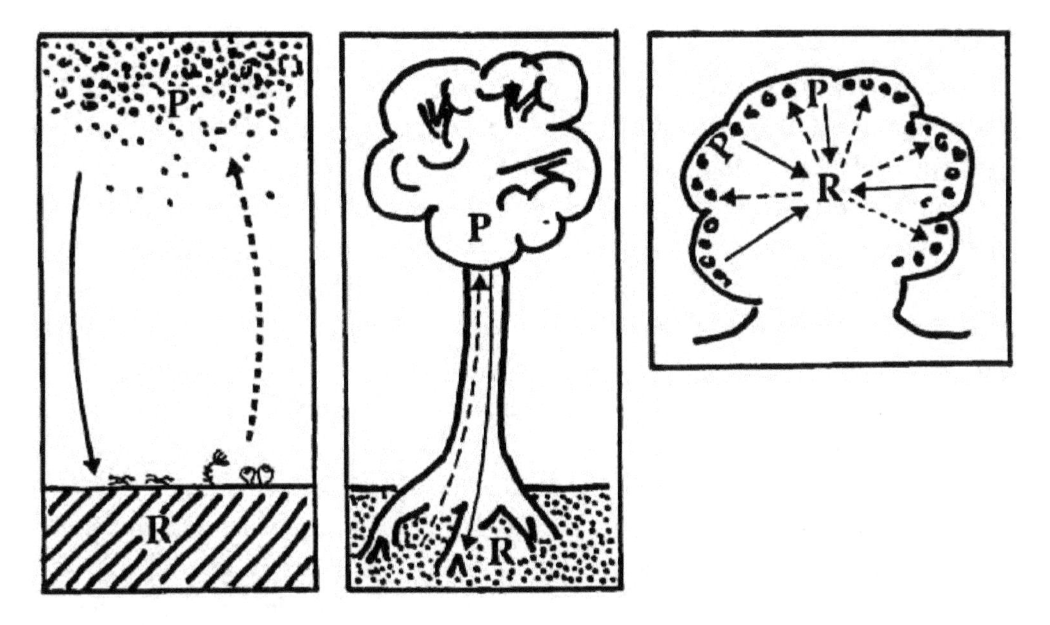

Figure 4.1.5 The distribution of main centers of production (P) and respiration-decomposition (R) in three different ecosystems: the open ocean (A), a tree (B) and a coral head (C), small circles indicate symbiotic green algae. The solid arrows indicate transport of synthesized organic material, the dashed ones indicate recycling of regenerated inorganic nutrients (adapted from Odum 1971).

take place in the circulatory canals in the tree trunk. In the coral reef the two processes are intimately connected thanks to the small distance between the producing, microscopic green algae and the embedding, consuming coral animals. This might be one of the explanations for the extremely efficient recycling in a coral reef. If a similar principle for spatial organization were applied to human societies, there should be a much closer association between the producers and the consumers than in a typical industrial society. Decreasing the distance between the production in agricultural areas and the consumption in urban centers by developing more diverse settlement patterns is probably a feasible policy for improving recycling and energy efficiency.

The diversity in space is supplemented by a *temporal diversity.* Pulses of energy and matter, like the daily and seasonal variations in sunlight are, important "clocks" for the ecosystem and its individual organisms. The temporal diversity of species at the producer and consumer levels provide a solid energy basis for top consumers like the human species. In economics, however, one seeks to level out as much as possible the natural fluctuations to secure a steady delivery of certain goods or functions preferred by the consumers.

Stability

This is a property of ecological systems that is a rather vague concept in spite of efforts to amalgamate its ecological meaning with terms from physics (Orians 1975). Still, accurately defined in space and time, the stability concept gives valuable information on ecosystem dynamics. We prefer here a broad definition: the ability of a system to stay in a steady-state condition or oscillating equilibrium, rapidly recovering its balance after perturbation with an intact structure. "Diversity begets stability," meaning species diversity, is a statement that has occupied theoretical ecologists for several decades since coined by MacArthur (1955). The reverse has also been found—"stability begets diversity"—(May 1973) and probably has higher relevance, provided energy flow has a reasonable magnitude.

The main reason for the confusion about the stability concept in ecology seems to be that some scientists are focusing on the stability of the separate populations, and others on the stability of whole ecosystems. In environmentally stable habitats like the coral reef, the tropical rainforest, the deep sea, the species diversity attains high numbers, whereas in stochastically fluctuating environments, like estuaries and rockpools, the number of species remains low. In such environments, species must expend more energy to cope with survival, while less excess energy remains for diversification. Odum (1983) has provided a convincing explanation that there is competition for potential energy between creating physiological structures to meet the changes in the external medium and evolving high species diversity to fulfill the main functions of the ecosystem. A parallel in economics would be the choice that has to be made between investing in new infrastructure to be able to produce more of one particular good or to start diversifying the business.

Nonlinear systems may have several stability domains, and there are common examples of large-scale systems switching to a new steady state when forced beyond a certain threshold level. Overgrazing of the African savannah has turned grasslands to deserts. Overfishing in the Great Lakes has turned the former community, dominated by large species into a community characterized by small species. Such *surprises* (Holling 1986) create a feeling of great uncertainty about the future development of the global ecosystems, considering the ongoing large-scale changes occurring in the terrestrial, aquatic, and atmospheric environments.

A fruitful way of looking at ecosystems from a stability point of view is the *mosaic-cycle concept* (Aubreville 1938; Remmert 1991). It mainly stresses the spatial heterogeneity of the ecosystem, where the different patches undergo a similar succession but in a desynchronized fashion (see Figure 4.1.6). In a tropical rainforest, the dense cover of vegetation is occasionally broken up by a falling tree, letting in sunlight and starting a succession, ultimately leading to the regrowth of another large tree. Because of the desynchronized pulsing of patches or subsystems, the separate minima and maxima even out, giving stability to the total system. The cycles are clearly coupled to the species diversity, which shows a maximum in areas undergoing a fast succession, but a minimum in the mature stages. This stresses both the importance of stochastic events like storms and proper recognition of the time and space scales. A deeper insight into this problem area seems decisive for achieving a sustainable relationship between ecological and economic systems.

Resilience

The ability of a system to keep structure and function after disturbance has been labeled *resilience* (Holling 1973). Contrary to stability, which emphasizes equilibrium, low variability, and resistance to and absorption of change, *resilience* is characterized by events far from equilibrium. It therefore stresses the boundaries of the stability domain, high adaptation, and high variability. Temperate systems exposed to changes in climate usually have high resilience and low stability. Systems evolved during stable conditions like coral reefs and tropical rainforests show high stability and low resilience probably because in the stable environment there has been no need for establishing structures to meet perturbations. Consequently, these systems, as well as the deep sea, are easily disturbed by man's activities like eutrophication, overfishing, forestry, or exploitation of manganese nodules.

Figure 4.1.6 Basic ecological concepts demonstrated for a woodland. Two previous treefalls or clearcuttings of recent (A) and older date (B) have created clearings where herbs and shrubs invade, constituting *successions* of different stages. The hierarchial structure of the system comprises a *horizontal division* in structures of similar quality and time characteristics—holons—and a *vertical division,* which is based on the frequency of the behavior of the structures. The interactions between the holons are usually stronger than between the vertical levels.

Hierarchy

The large span of both space and time scales in natural systems offers numerous examples of hierarchical organizations that can be subject to successful analysis using hierarchy theory (Webster 1979). A horizontal organization is seen in the patchy distribution of structures in the space dimension. Structures of similar quality and time characteristics have been called "*holons*" (Koestler 1967), and can be exemplified by the different species within the vertical levels of a wood—herbs, shrubs, and trees (see Figure 4.1.6). A patchiness may start with a small nucleus resulting from some heterogeneity in the substrate or from an uneven dispersal of propagules and successively grow to larger areas. The larger the patch, the stronger its influence on the local environment. A patch also needs to attain a critical size to persist using the normal resource flows of the surrounding environment. Single trees, groves, and forests may have the same species assembly of inhabiting species but as entities at different time scales. This *vertical hierarchial structure* (see Figure 4.1.6) is created by the difference in metabolic rates. Small scale structures like individual cells show higher turnover rates than populations, that in turn have faster dynamics than ecosystems. From the point of a view of an observer at a lower level, the dynamics at the upper level seem nearly constant. Seen from an upper level, the high process frequencies of the lower levels appear as a sampled statistical behavior. What looks like an unexpected catastrophic event from a lower level may just be a normal pulse in the larger time scale of the higher level. Disturbances at the lower levels of a multilevel system might be easily incorporated and repaired like a forest, which continues its normal behavior in spite of the cutting of individual trees.

The growth of the human society with increasing cultivation and urbanization of land has led to a successive *fragmentation* of the landscape with great implications for the dynamics of the natural systems. The plant and animal populations have been cut up into *metapopulations,* small "satellites" that are totally dependent on immigration from large "cores" (Hanski 1982). This increasing reduction of patches to undercritical sizes is a large threat for the proper functioning of our life support system. In many regions of the world the fast expansion of the traffic system is one of the major factors disintegrating the terrestrial landscape, which at the same time impairs the capacity of the ecosystems to assimilate and process the exhausts from the car traffic.

TOWARDS A SUCCESSFUL MAINTENANCE OF OUR LIFE-SUPPORT SYSTEM

In the course of evolution the size of flows and storages of the systems were strongly related to the influx of solar energy, and the speed of the biogeochemical cycles was set by the naturally aging systems. When man learned to use fossil fuels, additional, auxiliary, and high quality energy was put into processes that could replace, outcompete, or amplify the natural flows of energy and matter (Odum 1971). For example, the use of artificial fertilizers has increased the primary production both on land and in the sea. But the decomposition rate of dead organic matter from the increased biomasses of plants and animals has not increased by any comparable stimulation. Well known results of this mismatch are the eutrophication problems with inland and coastal waters, and the garbage problems in densely populated areas. Aware of the demand for recycling, how do we cope with the waste problems? Does efficient sorting and reuse of glass, plastics, paper, and metals really solve the problem? Eugene Odum (1989) argues for *input management,* that is, to reduce the use of fossil energy and raw materials instead of focusing primarily on the polluting outputs, as a major strategy for minimizing waste. The only way to ecological sustainability is to keep our natural life-support systems working. We cannot withdraw from maintaining the structures we want to use. For a successful herring fishery, the spawning grounds, although far from the fishing areas, have to be kept intact. There is no sense in spraying with pesticides to get a higher production of fruits when the bees performing the pollination are killed off at the same time.

The dynamic behavior of the ecosystems has to be respected as a basic rule in human affairs. While other species are exposed to and regulated by nature's pulsing patterns at many levels, humans, due to the extensive use of fossil energy, not only show an exponential population growth but also a steady increase in the per capita use of natural resources. If we are not able to change this trend, we will soon exceed the carrying capacity of our natural resource base with accompanying social disruptions and economic crises. Equally important is an increased attention to the life-support areas required for various human activities. Just as an oyster reef with a restricted substrate area can have many individuals sitting in several stories on top of one another when the waterflow is good, so can humans build skyscrapers as the space in a city grows scarce if there is enough energy to support these structures. The life-support area does not decrease because people live on top of each other. Instead, the maintenance costs often rise rapidly as car parks and maintenance areas have to be added proportionally to maintain the flow of workers and materials. Conversely, if we restrict the waterflow for the oyster reef by constructing embankments, we kill off most of the oysters as their life-support area becomes subcritical.

Extensive natural areas have to be saved around human settlements to perform the necessary life-support functions (Odum and Odum 1972). A virgin archipelago may be a tempting subject for a developer, who sees it as still unused. But it is actually continuously working producing oxygen, taking up carbon dioxide, filtering the water, recycling nutrients. The exploited areas further away would be worse off without the life-support from fully functioning coastal systems that generate clean air, process wastes, help reduce erosion, and act as barriers against the oceans. To replace these functions by technical substitutes would be very expensive, if at all possible. Instead we should try to maximize the services from natural ecosystems by investing in technologies that take advantage of their capabilities for self-organization, productivity, and recycling. The global ecosystems have done well without human beings, especially without their overuse of fossil fuels. In order to survive in the post-fossil era, humans have to learn how exponential growth can be switched into a pulsing stability without destroying human cultural achievements. This is perhaps the most urgent and difficult challenge of ecological economics.

REFERENCES

Aubieville, A. 1936. La foret coloniale: les forets de l'Afrique occidentale francaise. *Annales de L'Academie des Sciences Coloniales* 9: 1–245.

Elmgrcn, R., R. Rosenberg, A-B. Andersin, S. Evans, P. Kangas, J. Lässig, E. Leppäkoski, and R. Varmo. 1984. Benthic macro- and meiofauna in the Gulf of Bothnia (Northern Baltic). *Finnish Marine Resources* 250: 3–18.

Falk, J. H. 1976. Energetics of a suburban lawn ecosystem. *Ecology* 57: 141–50.

Folke, C., M. Hammer, and AM. Jansson. 1991. Life-support value of ecosystems: a case study of the Baltic Sea Region. *Ecological Economics* 3: 123–37.

Hammer, M., AM. Jansson, and B-O. Jansson. 1993. Diversity, change, and sustainability: implications for Fisheries. *Ambio* 22: 97–105.

Hanski, 1. 1982. Dynamics of regional distribution: the core and satellite species hypothesis. *Oikos* 38: 210–21.

Holling, C. S. 1973. Resilience and stability of ecological systems. *Annual Revue of Ecological Systems* 4: 1–23.

———. 1986. Resilience of terrestrial ecosystems: local surprise and global change. In Sustainable Development of the Biosphere, eds. W. C. Clark and R. E. Munn. Cambridge: Cambridge Univ. Press.

Koestler, A. 1967. The Ghost in the Machine. New York: Macmillan.

May, R. M. 1973, Stability in randomly fluctuating versus deterministic environments. *American Naturalist* 107: 621–50.

McArthur, R. H. 1955. Fluctuations of animal populations, and a measure of community stability. *Ecology* 36: 533–6.

Odum, E. P. 1989. Global Stress on Life-Support Ecosystems Mandates Input Management of Production Systems. Crafoord Lectures. Stockholm: The Royal Swedish Academy of Sciences.

Odum, E. P., and H. T. Odum. 1972. Natural Areas as Necessary Components of Man's Total Environment. Proceeding 37, North American Wildlife and Natural Resources Conference. Washington: Wildlife Management Institute.

Odum, H. T. 1971. Environment, Power and Society. New York: Wiley.

———. 1988. Self-organization, transformity, and information. *Science* 242: 1132–9.

O'Neill, R. V., D. L. DeAngelis, J. B. Waide, and T. F. H. Allen. 1989. A Hierarchial Concept of Ecosystems. Princeton: Princeton Univ. Press.

Orians, G. H. 1975. Diversity, stability and maturity in natural ecosystems. In Unifying Concepts in Ecology, eds. W. H. van Dobben and R. H. Lowe McConnell. The Hague: Dr. W. Junk B. V. Publishers.

Pimm, S. L. 1988. Energy flow and trophic structure. In Concepts of Ecosystem Ecology, eds, L. R. Pomeroy and J. J. Alberts. Berlin: Springer-Verlag.

Remmert, H. 1991. The Mosiac-Cycle Concept of Ecosystems. Berlin: Springer-Verlag.

Smith, S. V., and F. C. McKenzie. 1987. The ocean as a net heterotrophic system: implications from the carbon biogeochemical cycle. *Global Biogeochemical Cycles* 1: 187–98.

Vitousek, P., P. R. Ehrlich, A. H. Ehrlich, and P. M. Matson, 1986. Human appropriation of the products of photosynthesis. *BioScience* 36: 368–73.

Webster, J. R. 1979. Hierarchial organization of ecosystems. In Theoretical Systems Ecology, ed. E. Halfon. New York: Academic Press.

Wilson, E. O. 1988. The current state of biological diversity. In Biodiversity, ed. E. O. Wilson. Washington: National Academy Press.

CHAPTER FIVE

Climate Change, Climate Crisis

Perhaps more than any other issue, climate change illustrates the importance of interdisciplinary fields like environmental studies. It has become increasingly clear over the past 20 years that climate change currently impacts or will soon influence every economic, social, and ecological system on the planet. The path to sustainable solutions that mitigate and adapt to the consequences of climate change begins with recognizing and addressing the links between the impacts on multiple systems. In this chapter, we reaffirm the basic science supporting anthropogenic climate change, explore current and predicted impacts of climate change, and learn how climate change disproportionately affects poor people globally and people of color in the US.

Recent US polls show that 80% of adults aged 18–29 believe that the planet is getting warmer because of human activity.[1] Statistically speaking, most of us already understand that current climate change is real and is caused by humans. However, you may not be familiar with the data behind climate scientists' confidence that current climate change is anthropogenic, meaning "caused by humans." In the selected reading by John Perkins, "Climate Change" from *Changing Energy: The Transition to a Sustainable Future* (2017), we learn that although the planet's climate has varied immensely over the past 4.5 billion years, current concentrations of carbon dioxide in the atmosphere are higher than they have ever been since Homo sapiens evolved. Most of this increase in carbon dioxide is a direct result of burning fossil fuels, a topic which we explore at length in Chapters 8 and 9. Perkins outlines major economic impacts of climate change, including the devastating costs of crop failures, forest fires, floods, and other natural disasters.

1 Jon A Krosnick and Bo MacInnis, (2020), "Climate Insights 2020: Overall Trends," *Resources for the Future*, Washington, DC.

Most people can connect intuitively to why they should worry about the economic impacts of climate change. However, how should we care about the impacts on biodiversity? The recommended reading from Elizabeth Kolbert's book *The Sixth Extinction* (2016) explains the magnitude of biodiversity loss we will face due to climate change. Besides a "moral mandate" to protect other species, why should we be concerned that by the end of this century climate change will likely be the main driver of species extinctions on our planet? In the recommended article, "Biodiversity, Climate Change and Poverty: Exploring the Links" (2008), authors Hannah Reid and Krystyna Swiderska address this question. They lead us through the process by which biodiversity loss contributes to poverty and disproportionate exposure to climate change impacts, and they provide compelling evidence for how protecting biodiversity can lead to more human resilience in the face of climate change. For example, greater genetic diversity in food crops helps ensure that when the climate changes, farmers have access to new types of seed that can thrive in drier, wetter, or hotter environments.

The heaviest burdens of climate change are not borne equally by all people. In the US, people of color are more likely than their white counterparts to experience bodily injury, property loss, and dislocation as a result of extreme weather events caused by climate change. When these communities attempt to rebuild, they face additional barriers put in place by institutionalized racism, including difficulty obtaining loans and inadequate access to health services and medical insurance. The recommended reading by Richard Allen Williams and Elena Rios, "Climate Change Raises the Stakes for Affordable Health Care Coverage" in *The Hill* (2017), is a case study. The authors explain how changes in federal policy can either help or hurt communities of color as they work to address the health impacts of climate change. This article addresses a critical theme in environmental studies which will reoccur throughout this text: environmental justice is a prerequisite to solving the environmental challenges we are all facing.

RECOMMENDED READING

Kolbert, E. 2016. "Prologue." In *The Sixth Extinction: An Unnatural History*, 1–3. New York: Macmillan.

Reid, H. and Swiderska, K. 2008. *Biodiversity, Climate Change and Poverty: Exploring the Links*. International Institute for Environmental and Development. Retrieved from: https://pubs.iied.org/17034IIED/?a=K+Swiderska&p=6.

Williams, R. and Rios, E. 2017. "Climate Change Raises the Stakes for Affordable Health Care Coverage." In *The Hill*, 1521–1568. Retrieved from: https://thehill.com/blogs/congress-blog/healthcare/316471-climate-change-raises-the-stakes-for-affordable-health-care.

RECOMMENDED VIEWING

Murray, L. 2008. "Wake Up, Freak Out" (11:34).
WATCH AT https://tinyurl.com

READING AND DISCUSSION PROMPTS

1. What is the difference between weather and climate?
2. The atmosphere allows visible light to pass through it and reach the surface of the earth. So why can infrared radiation (heat) not escape back through the atmosphere into space? How does this "one-way trip" lead to global warming?
3. Look at Figure 5.1.2 in the Perkins reading. What do you think is the significance of Keeling's research in terms of how it affected our understanding of climate change at that time?
4. This chapter discusses several impacts of climate change. Which of these were you not aware of or were a surprise to you?

READING 5.1

Climate Change

By John H. Perkins

If only benefits flowed from the massive heat supplied by the big-four fuels (coal, oil, gas, uranium), the rest of this book would be unnecessary. Unfortunately, science has steadily uncovered dark effects of the Third Energy Transition. These consequences suggest the possibility of truly cataclysmic impacts globally, even in areas in which people did not enjoy the benefits of the Third Transition.

This chapter turns to climate change, the best known and most discussed challenge posed by the backbone of the Third Energy Transition, the fossil fuels (coal, oil, and gas). The risks of climate change alone require phasing out fossil fuels over time. Unfortunately, much needless misinformation and confused information surrounds the scientific evidence about climate change. This chapter summarizes the evidence and logic of climate science and suggests the likely impacts of climate change.

EMERGENCE OF A SCIENTIFIC CONSENSUS

Carbon dioxide and methane emissions associated with the energy economy are the biggest contributors to climate change. The association of carbon emissions with the energy economy shows clearly in a Sankey diagram of the United States in 2014 (Figure 5.1.1).[2]

Burning fossil fuels (coal, oil, and gas) releases carbon dioxide (CO_2) into the atmosphere, as do deforestation and other land use changes. Once there, this gas traps heat and thus alters climate. In addition, methane (CH_4, natural gas) traps heat and alters climate if released to the atmosphere. Other gases—collectively called greenhouse gases—also trap heat, but I focus on the problems associated with the fossil fuels.

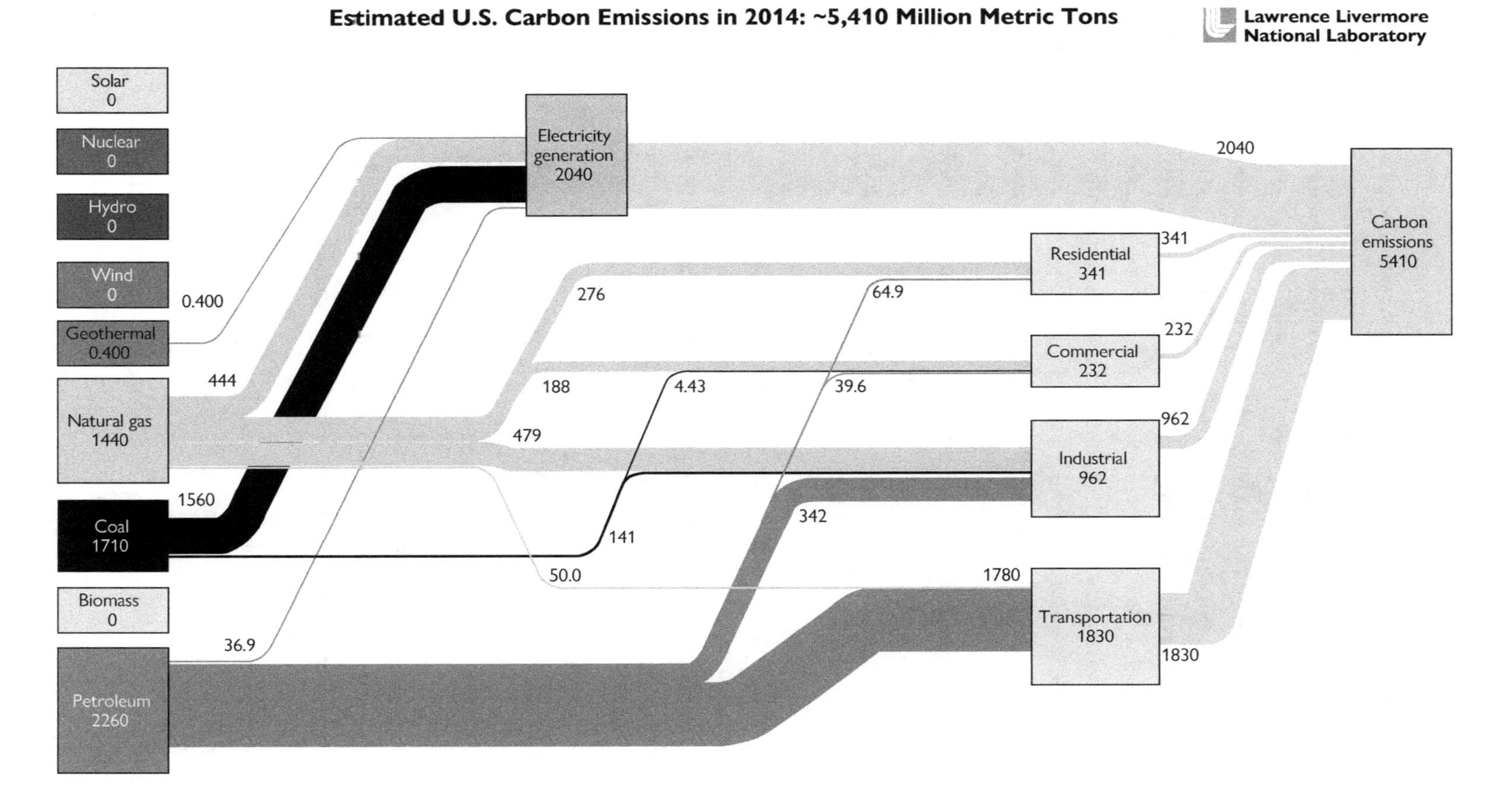

Figure 5.1.1 Carbon emissions of the United States from the energy economy, 2014. source: Lawrence Livermore National Laboratory, courtesy of Anne Stark.

Questions about energy and climate change became increasingly important beginning in the 1970s and have grown more serious and urgent over the past four decades. Since the 1800s, scientific studies had recognized the potential for increasing concentrations of carbon dioxide from fossil fuels to warm the global climate, but during the 1900s, increasing industrialization and widespread agriculture, plus occasional volcanic eruptions, threw various pollutants into the air that might cause cooling. What was the balance between these two opposing effects, more warming or more cooling?

Conclusions shifted toward more warming in the late 1970s. Since then, continuing research has convinced close to 100 percent of the scientific community that earth's surface temperatures have warmed as a result of human influences, especially the use of fossil fuels. Most scientists also agree that without reductions in emissions of CO_2 and CH_4 from fossil fuels warming will continue and that projected climate changes could drastically, perhaps catastrophically, alter climate. The exact timing and amount of warming and other attendant changes remain under research and debate, but the overwhelming scientific consensus predicts dangers ahead.

The Intergovernmental Panel on Climate Change (IPCC), organized under the auspices of the United Nations, stated the following in 2013:

> Warming of the climate system is unequivocal, and since the 1950s, many of the observed changes are unprecedented over decades to millennia. The atmosphere and ocean have warmed, the amounts of snow and ice have diminished, sea level has risen, and the concentrations of greenhouse gases have increased....
>
> The atmospheric concentrations of carbon dioxide (CO_2), methane, and nitrous oxide have increased to levels unprecedented in at least the last 800,000 years. CO_2 concentrations have increased by 40% since pre-industrial times, primarily from fossil fuel emissions and secondarily from net land use change emissions....
>
> The total radiative forcing is positive, and has led to an uptake of energy by the climate system. The largest contribution to total radiative forcing is caused by the increase in the atmospheric concentration of CO_2 since 1750....
>
> It is extremely likely that human influence has been the dominant cause of the observed warming since the mid-20th century.[3]

IPCC's statement outlines the theory of human-caused climate change, or *anthropogenic climate change* (ACC), but its implications for public policy require addressing two further points: What is the evidence for ACC, and what likely consequences will follow it?

EVIDENCE FOR ACC

The idea that humans can alter the climate of earth rests on scientific conclusions reached between the 1820s and today. They compel attention and argue for changes in the energy economy.

ACC, however, resists an easy, intuitive understanding. It asserts that slight changes in the amount of carbon dioxide and methane in the atmosphere can unleash all sorts of unanticipated and unpleasant consequences. How could that be? Can a person who is not a scientist grasp why the vast majority of scientists believe the theory is true?

Consider the following fictional statement, which some intelligent, skeptical, and slightly irascible citizen might make.

> OK, so I burn gasoline in my automobile and I use electricity made from burning coal. I heat my house with gas, and I buy lots of stuff, which I know took energy to make. I also know a lot of this stuff was made in China, and some ship burning diesel fuel brought it to me. I also know that my great-great-grandparents homesteaded in Ohio and cleared the forest to plant corn. And OK, I'll accept that because of all these things, done by people over the whole world, the amount of carbon dioxide in the air changed.
>
> But is this really a big deal? Since 1700, the change has been almost nothing. It used to be about three molecules of carbon dioxide for every 10,000 molecules of the other things in air, and now it's about four, and OK maybe it's headed to five or six. Out of 10,000! What's the big deal? You want me to believe that small changes in amounts of carbon dioxide have warmed the air and oceans, diminished snow and ice, and raised sea levels? And even if it has, is this bad? Come on, how can such a little bit of carbon dioxide do all these things?
>
> And isn't carbon dioxide something that occurs naturally? Don't we exhale it? Don't green plants use it to grow? Don't we put it in our soda pop to make it fizzy? How can a teeny-tiny increase of this stuff possibly cause real trouble?
>
> Why should I believe such a story that sounds so cockamamie?[4]

The doubts raised by our fictional, skeptical citizen resonate with the fact that the theory of human-induced climate change rests on the importance of a seemingly small change in the composition of the atmosphere. Scientists participating in the IPCC understood the wonderment that such small changes could be important, and the theory became convincing only because of multiple conclusions about the earth's climate system, developed over the course of two hundred years and summarized below.

1. Radiation and heat balance of the earth. The sun warms the earth, and in the ensuing night the area in darkness cools. During the year, the sun's warmth waxes and wanes through the seasons. Early in the early nineteenth century, Joseph Fourier of France calculated that even though the sun was the prime source of the warmth, the atmosphere affected the earth's average temperature. Something in the atmosphere kept earth warmer than it otherwise would be.[5]

Fourier based his ideas on the notion that all bodies, including the earth, emit heat. In other words, heat from the sun during the day dissipates during the night. This emitted radiation is now called infrared radiation, which most people know from things such as infrared heat lamps. It is invisible to the eye, but some molecules absorb infrared radiation. When they do, they move faster and we perceive heat or warmth (see chapter 2).

Stable climate depends on the balance between the incoming and outgoing heat. Over each day and each year, the earth has a steady average temperature, or equilibrium temperature: warmer in the day and in the summer, cooler at night and in the winter. Only scientists tend to think of earth as an "infrared radiator," but the validity of this concept—that all things with a temperature above absolute 0° (0 K) emit heat as infrared radiation—meshes with all of modern physics.

Climate change theory begins with the notion that some molecules in the atmosphere reduce the amount of infrared radiation lost from the earth, which in turn changes the heat balance and increases the earth's temperature. Much of climate science, therefore, focused on the question, What happens as the atmosphere changes? That was an easy question to ask, but finding good answers took a great deal of hard work and considerable debate.

2. Carbon dioxide and several other gases absorb infrared radiation. Why did the earth not shed all of its warmth and cool to the frigid temperatures as Fourier had calculated? In 1859, John Tyndall in England found an answer. He knew that most of the atmosphere was nitrogen and oxygen, and he found that visible light from the sun passed right through them; they were colorless and invisible. Water vapor and carbon dioxide also allowed visible light from the sun to reach the surface of the earth, and they, too, were colorless and invisible. When light reaches earth, much of it is absorbed and the energy of the absorbed light warms the earth. The warmer earth emits more infrared radiation.

Water vapor and carbon dioxide, however, absorb infrared radiation. These gases present at low levels in the air block the passage of infrared and in so doing become agitated, vibrate, and move faster. The air "warms up," as detected by thermometers and our bodies. Tyndall thus answered Fourier's question: the warmth kept in the atmosphere by water vapor and carbon dioxide makes the earth warmer than it otherwise would have been.[6] As long as the amounts of water vapor and carbon dioxide don't change, heat coming in and heat leaving will equal each other, temperature will go up and down each day and over the seasons, but the equilibrium temperature will remain steady, and climate will be stable. Fourier's and Tyndall's work underpins all of modern climate science.

3. *Earth's climate varies immensely over long periods.* Most people, from everyday experiences, think of climate as stable. Some years have more cold, snow, and ice, and others have more heat, but overall not much changes. New England is cold compared to Florida, and Sweden is cold compared to Kenya; these observations are stable.

In 1837, Louis Agassiz, a Swiss naturalist, boldly upset this common perception by proposing that glaciers from the north had once spread over much of Europe, Asia, and North America. Despite skepticism from many, Agassiz and others pieced together the evidence that ultimately made the theory of repeating ice ages common knowledge.[7]

Agassiz opened entirely new questions: What caused normal weather patterns to go so off kilter that glaciers covered much of the earth? When? Why? Would a new ice age come? Many theories emerged as geologists, oceanographers, biologists, and astronomers each contributed ideas about what might govern earth's climate. Changes in water vapor in the atmosphere? New mountains or volcanic eruptions? Changes in ocean currents like the Gulf Stream? Variations in the sun's output? Variations in the earth's orbit?[8]

The Swedish physicist Svante Arrhenius advanced a new theory in 1896. He concluded that changes in carbon dioxide concentrations in the atmosphere can stop and start ice ages. Arrhenius juxtaposed his conclusions to findings from geology that carbon dioxide levels in the atmosphere can change enough to affect climate.[9]

Arrhenius focused on triggers for ice ages, and he thought countries like Sweden might benefit if carbon dioxide from fossil fuels warmed things up. His work did not gain rapid acceptance, because many considered his calculations wrong. Others thought increases in carbon dioxide would be locked up in rocks and the ocean, and new additions from fossil fuels would leave the atmosphere and not trap heat on earth.

Not until the 1930s did new work resurrect Arrhenius's findings and direct questions away from ice ages toward the idea that burning fossil fuels might warm the climate. Gilbert Plass in the 1950s in the United States noted that studies since Arrhenius clarified the infrared absorption patterns of carbon dioxide and concluded that increasing levels of carbon dioxide could absorb increasing amounts of infrared radiation and thus increase the temperature of the earth.[10]

4. *Human actions can alter the earth in major ways.* Agassiz, Arrhenius, and Plass had

opened the door for ideas about long-term changes in climate, but another barrier still hindered ready acceptance of ACC. For most of human history, human beings considered themselves subject to major natural events over which they had no control. Cold, heat, droughts, floods, plagues, earthquakes, and volcanoes happened, often producing great destruction and hardship. Natural disasters came from angry spirits or an angry god, possibly in retribution for human evil. People identified, named, and feared natural calamities, but people could not change climate, especially over short periods of time.

George Perkins Marsh's book, *Man and Nature* (1864), had argued that humans could significantly affect the earth, but such ideas gained little traction until after 1945, when two books reflected the change in perspective. Fairfield Osborn's *Our Plundered Planet* (1948) and William Vogt's *Road to Survival* (1948) both saw expanding human populations with new technologies that could bring both benefits and massive, unwanted, destructive change.[11] For example, testing nuclear weapons led to the far-flung distribution of strontium-90, and DDT insecticide showed up everywhere, even in penguins in Antarctica, a place where no one used the chemical. Rachel Carson's widely acclaimed book, *Silent Spring* (1962), saw the parallels between weapons testing and pesticides and left the indelible conclusion that human activities really could rapidly alter the entire earth in ways never before imagined.[12]

5. Climate change may not be slow. Theories about ice ages envisioned temperature and climate changes in cycles of thousands of years. Findings of human impacts on a global scale could clearly occur within a time of a few years, but what about climate? Could climate changes also occur within a small time period? Did it matter if the changes were natural or anthropogenic?

By the 1960s and early 1970s, scientists such as Reid Bryson of the United States raised questions about impacts on climate of dust and aerosols as well as carbon dioxide. Bryson, a climatologist, also worked with anthropologists, archaeologists, and botanists, and they found that Native American groups had suffered from rapid shifts in climate before European contact. Not only was climate changeable in either direction; its changes could be rapid, perhaps within one human life span.[13]

These new perspectives on long-term changes, short-term human-caused global changes, and short-term shifts in climate all shaped research in the late 1960s and after. A power plant or factory burning coal and releasing carbon dioxide, and dusts, previously seen as a benefit of modern engineering and inconsequential on a global scale, became an agent of potentially earth-altering importance.

But was carbon dioxide the driving force? And what about the dust? Where did the balance lie between factors favoring cooling compared to heating? Scientists with different opinions about these matters raised concerns about warming and cooling, but scientific uncertainty ruled. In 1975, the U.S. National Academy of Sciences could not resolve competing claims and urged more research.[14]

6. *Carbon dioxide and temperatures increased in the past two centuries.* In the mid-1950s, no scientific research could say what was happening to levels of carbon dioxide and temperature. The fact that fossil fuels released carbon dioxide meant only that levels of carbon dioxide in the atmosphere *might* be increasing. But were they really increasing, or was the gas going into vegetation, the oceans, or mineral deposits? If so, then it wouldn't block infrared radiation from leaving the earth. And if the levels of the gas were changing, was it really due to burning fossil fuels? And what about temperature? Did temperature track levels of carbon dioxide? Between the 1950s and now, new studies answered these questions: carbon dioxide and temperatures have increased, and increased temperature can be traced to increased carbon dioxide.

David Keeling of the United States found direct evidence of changes in carbon dioxide levels in the atmosphere starting in 1958 with new instruments on top of Mauna Loa in Hawaii, a spot in the Pacific Ocean very far from the industrial centers of the world that burned most of the fossil fuels. Keeling believed that maybe here he could measure carbon dioxide after the gas had been uniformly mixed and thus would represent "average"

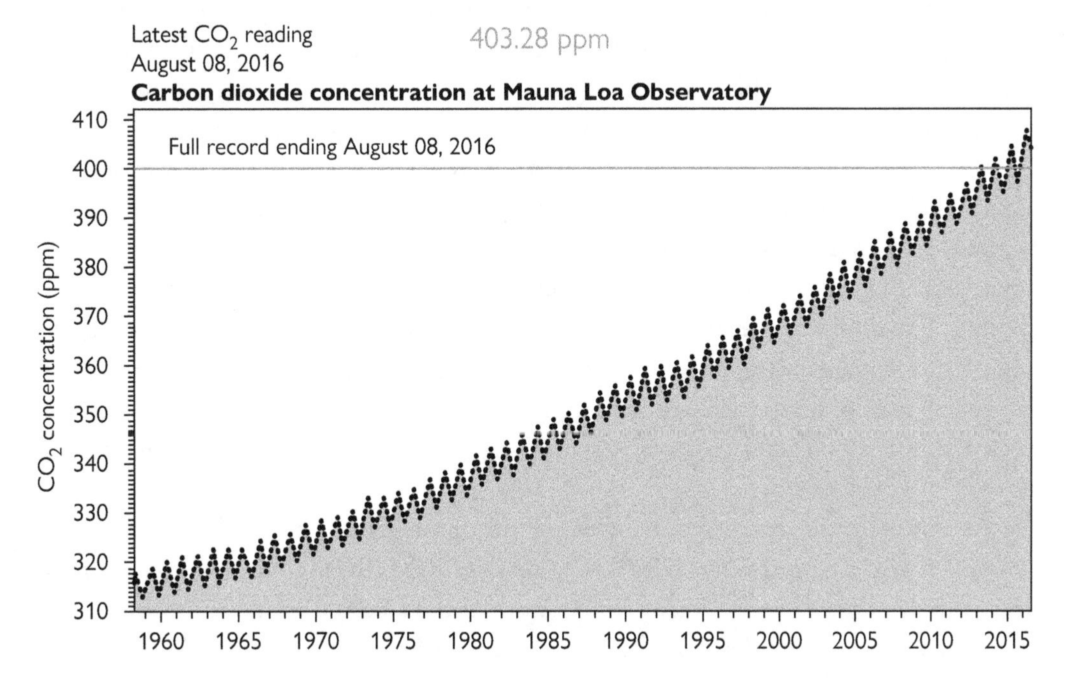

Figure 5.1.2 Keeling curve showing increase of carbon dioxide in the atmosphere since the late 1950s.

Source: Scripps Institute of Oceanography, https://scripps.ucsd.edu/programs/keelingcurve/wp-content/plugins/sio-bluemoon/graphs/mlo_full_record.pdf, April 27, 2016.

levels.[15] Since the late 1950s, the concentration of carbon dioxide in the atmosphere rose steadily, a pattern not yet changed (Figure 5.1.2).[16]

During each year, carbon dioxide levels rose in the northern hemisphere's winter and dropped the following summer. Despite the annual drop, the average levels climbed steadily through the years, and now the minimum is about 400 parts per million (ppm). Keeling explained the summer drop as the absorption of carbon dioxide by green plants in the northern hemisphere.

In the 1980s, Swiss scientists analyzed the carbon dioxide found in air bubbles in ice cores taken in Antarctica. They found that the concentration of carbon dioxide in 1750 was about 280 parts per million and that the concentration increased steadily after that time. Moreover, the composition of the carbon dioxide found in the ice indicated the increase came from burning fossil fuel and deforestation.[17]

What was happening to temperatures while carbon dioxide was increasing? Significant numbers of direct readings of temperature at the earth's surface, that is, with a thermometer, exist only since about the mid-nineteenth century. Temperatures rose from this time until about 1940, then fell slightly until the mid-1960s, and then began to rise steadily again after that.[18]

Carbon dioxide levels rose steadily during this time period. But was the concomitant rise of both just an association or was it a cause-and-effect relationship? If the latter, did the increase in carbon dioxide cause temperature to rise, or was it the other way around? Then there was the dip between about 1940 and the mid-1960s: if carbon dioxide was rising steadily and trapped heat, why was there a downturn in temperatures?

This tangle of questions stimulated intensive research that pointed to water vapor, carbon dioxide, methane, nitrous oxide, ozone, chlorofluorocarbons, and other gases as heat trappers (greenhouse gases) that would increase temperatures. Clouds, soot particles, volcanoes, and sulfate aerosols could reflect solar radiation away from earth and cause cooling. The dip in temperatures from 1940 to 1965 may have represented a period in which the cooling constituents of the atmosphere dominated heat trapping. After 1965, increasing uses of fossil fuels and fertilizers, deforestation, and increasingly intensive livestock and rice farming, plus other factors, steadily pushed the heat trapping into first place.[19]

As temperatures rose, positive feedback loops exerted a magnifying effect. For example, warmer temperatures put more water vapor into the air, and water vapor is an important heat-trapping gas. Rising temperatures melted ice and snow, which caused less reflection of incoming radiation, and thus the earth warmed more.

7. Reconstructions of paleoclimates added perspective and confidence. Paleoclimates are climates that existed before there were direct human records of climatic patterns, that is, before a few centuries ago. Scientists reconstruct paleoclimates with proxy measurements of temperature, carbon dioxide levels in the air, ice volumes, and other factors that affect climate or reflect climatic conditions.

Proxy measurements rely on numerous physical markers known to depend on temperature and/or carbon dioxide levels in the atmosphere, such as the width of tree rings, growth rings in coral reefs, the composition of shells of microscopic marine organisms in ocean floor sediments, the composition of water in ice cores from polar regions, and the concentration of carbon dioxide in tiny bubbles trapped in different layers of these ice cores.[20] Proxy measurements based on multiple methods done by multiple groups in many countries showed substantial agreement and allowed reconstruction of climate and carbon dioxide concentrations for periods extending to 800,000 years before the present (Figure 5.1.3).[21]

An important point is clearly shown in Figure 5.1.3: the level of carbon dioxide in the atmosphere now stands at about 400 parts per million, a level unprecedented for 800,000 years. *Homo sapiens* had not even evolved 800,000 years ago. In other words, modern humans have increased carbon dioxide levels to amounts never seen since before they appeared on earth.

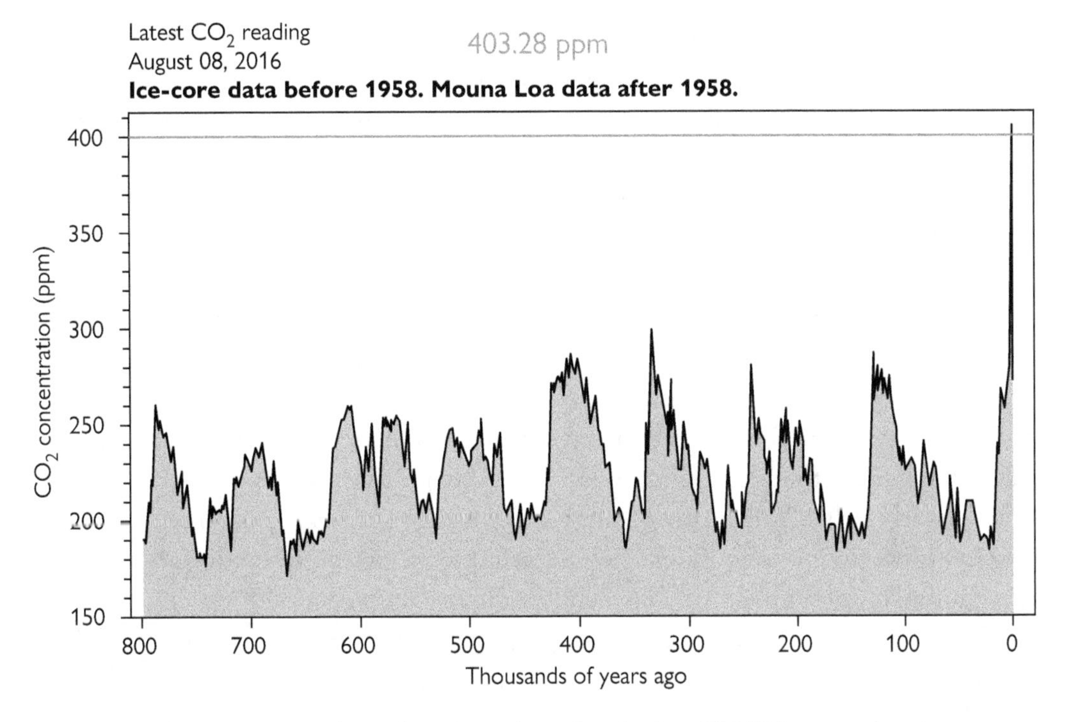

Figure 5.1.3 Carbon dioxide in the atmosphere for the last 800,000 years, showing current levels unprecedented in that time.

Source: Scripps Institute of Oceanography, https://scripps.ucsd.edu/programs/keelingcurve/wp-content/plugins/sio-bluemoon/graphs/co2_800k.pdf, March 25, 2016.

Ice cores suggested a resolution of the nineteenth century debate about the causes of waves of ice ages. The physical composition of water in the ice cores indicated a regular pattern of warmer and cooler temperatures, and the low temperatures caused the ice to expand from the polar regions. These patterns matched the changing distances between earth and the sun predicted by slight irregularities in earth's orbit around the sun. These changing distances occur regularly in cycles—the Milankovitch cycles—calculated by the Serbian astronomer Milutin Milankovitch in the early 1900s. Ice ages began and ended based on the very slight cooling and warming caused by earth moving farther from or closer to the sun.[22]

Ice cores also yielded samples of ancient air in bubbles trapped in the ice. From these bubbles, scientists learned the concentration of carbon dioxide in the air at the time the air bubbles froze in solid ice. Thus ice cores yielded both temperature and carbon dioxide data, which revealed that temperatures and carbon dioxide rose and sank approximately in synchrony.

Did an increase in temperatures before carbon dioxide was a factor mean that something else caused the warming? Was increased carbon dioxide simply a result of warmer temperatures, not a cause? If ends of ice ages really didn't depend on increased carbon dioxide, did that mean that evidence suggesting carbon dioxide caused temperature increases in the past two centuries might be wrong? The fact that carbon dioxide absorbs the energy in infrared radiation meant that the absorbed energy no longer radiated from the earth and thus warmed the atmosphere. This trapping of energy gave a powerful reason to suspect that increased temperatures stemmed at least in part from increased carbon dioxide.

Research on the triggers that started and stopped ice ages is still under way. For example, an important reconstruction of the end of the last ice age, about 11,500 years ago, indicated that first the northern hemisphere warmed and melted ice, which caused sea levels to rise. Freshwater from ice melt interrupted ocean currents that carried cool water to the southern hemisphere, which caused warming in Antarctica. Various processes, still not entirely understood, led to increased carbon dioxide levels. One possible mechanism is loss of carbon dioxide from the oceans by "degassing," like a carbonated soft drink will lose its fizziness as it warms. Researchers argued that increased carbon dioxide was a key mechanism in warming the earth and ending the last glacial period.[23]

Reconstruction of paleoclimates based on proxy measurements added the perspective of long periods and cycles through many climatic changes. Knowledge of past climates also showed that the warming observed in the twentieth century had no counterparts in the historical past. For example, claims of a "medieval warm period" (1000–1400) in England did not represent global conditions, nor were these claims derived from replicable proxy data. Most important, data suggesting a warm period in the Middle Ages, followed by cooling and then warming again in the late nineteenth century, did not capture the highly significant increases in average global temperatures after 1950.[24] Early Holocene (10,000–5,000 years before present) global average temperatures, however, exceeded today's. Nevertheless, temperatures predicted by climate models will soon exceed the early Holocene temperatures substantially.[25]

8. *Climate models can reproduce past events with increasing accuracy.* First, a word about distinctions between *weather* and *climate*. A scientist who can accurately tell a person whether or not to take an umbrella tomorrow is a weather forecaster using weather models. Weather focuses on exactly what temperature, rainfall, and wind patterns will prevail at a specific place, generally the size of a city, at a specific time, generally for one to ten days in the future.

Climate forecasts, in contrast, focus on average and extreme temperatures, average and extreme rainfall and droughts, and average and extreme winds over large areas (from region or state to world) and over longer periods (years to centuries). A climate forecaster tells farmers, for example, that reliable rains received almost every year will start to fail half of the time starting about fifty years from now.

Scientists began more intensive efforts to model weather after World War II, and an offshoot of these efforts turned to building climate models. The two types of models share some characteristics, the most important being that both types use equations to predict movements of air and moisture at specific places and times caused by heat inputs from the sun. Climate models, especially general circulation models, require an enormous number of calculations, and parallel development of rapid computers provided the only possible way to use the more complex climate models.[26]

Weather forecasting and climate predictions, however, differ in important ways. Weather forecasters receive rapid feedbacks about the accuracy of their predictions, often from wet citizens who received a forecast indicating no need for an umbrella. Long-term climate forecasting receives no immediate feedback on accuracy, and the definitive test of accuracy may not occur until the climate scientist is dead.

As a result, climate scientists check the likely accuracy of their models by reconstructing past, known conditions. If, for example, in 2010 they took the conditions of the atmosphere in 1900 as "given," could they accurately re-create the climatic patterns that actually occurred between 1900 and 2010? If yes, then they gained confidence that they could take the conditions of 2010 as given, make assumptions about the future inputs of carbon dioxide and other materials into the atmosphere, and with their model predict what the climate conditions would be in 2050 or 2100.

Not surprisingly, the first climate models could match past conditions only approximately, and climate modelers believed therefore that they could make only approximate predictions for the future. Nevertheless, climate models of the late 1970s were sufficiently good to cause a committee of the National Academy of Sciences to conclude that if concentrations of carbon dioxide doubled from preindustrial times, the average global surface temperature would increase from 2° to 3.5°C. Higher latitude regions near the poles would warm even more. Significant socioeconomic results would follow, but the committee could not predict them.[27]

This brief report in 1979 began to settle the uncertainty among scientists about whether the cooling effects of aerosol pollutants would outweigh the warming effects of carbon dioxide. In the following years, 1980 to the present, the consensus in the scientific community on warming steadily increased to near-unanimity.[28]

By 2013, models replicated the previous century's changes in surface temperatures over land and ocean, ocean heat content, and sea ice at the poles if and only if the simulations included human factors, especially increases in CO_2. Simulations with natural factors alone, such as volcanos and changes in solar radiation, did not replicate the observed changes (Figure 5.1.4).[29] Reproduction of already known changes increased confidence in the accuracy of future predictions.[30]

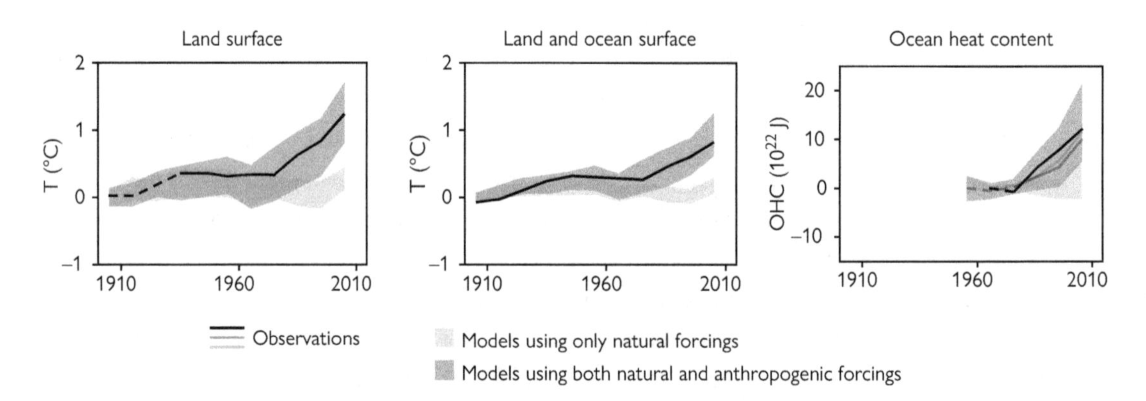

Figure 5.1.4 Models of past changes reproduce observed changes only if model includes CO_2 in atmosphere.

Source: Figure SPM.6 (bottom panels) from IPCC, 2013: Summary for Policymakers. In *Climate Change 2013: The Physical Science Basis. Working Group I Contribution to the Fifth Assessment Report of the Intergovernmental Panel on Climate Change* [Stocker, T. F., D. Qin, G.-K. Plattner, M. Tignor, S. K. Allen, J. Boschung, A Nauels, Y. Xia, V. Bex, and P. M. Midgley (eds.)]. Cambridge University Press, Cambridge, UK, and New York, USA. Used by permission.

LIKELY IMPACTS OF CLIMATE CHANGE

Points 1 through 8 above identified and explained climate events that have already happened: (a) the atmosphere has always kept earth at a warmer temperature than it would be without it, the "greenhouse effect"; (b) temperatures on earth have risen since the mid-1800s, sea levels have risen since 1900, the heat contained in the upper 700 meters of ocean has risen since 1950, and Arctic summer sea ice has decreased since 1900; (c) CO_2 and CH_4 increased in the atmosphere after the eighteenth century, mostly from uses of fossil fuels; (d) the levels of CO_2 in the atmosphere have reached levels unprecedented since before modern *Homo sapiens* evolved; and (e) CO_2 and CH_4 have contributed most of the additional warming of the earth. In addition, CO_2 dissolved in the ocean has made seawater more acidic; that is, it has lowered its pH.[31]

Delving deeply into the methods and conclusions of the IPCC goes far afield from the study of energy.[32] Suffice it to say that projections of the new global average temperatures likely to be reached by 2100 will be higher by 1.5°C, compared to temperatures in the period 1850–1900. If humanity does not curtail emissions of greenhouse gases, temperature increases will likely be greater than 2°C, with a fifty-fifty chance of exceeding 4°C (7.2°F).[33]

These changes may seem small, especially because from day to night and from summer to winter people and ecosystems already experience changes each day and each year far larger than these predictions. It's easy to imagine our intelligent, skeptical, and somewhat irascible citizen asking, "OK, maybe it's going to be a bit warmer, but do you really want me to get excited by a temperature rise of just a few degrees? That doesn't look like anything to worry about based on normal changes already taking place all the time."

Unfortunately, the scientific projections of global *average* temperatures hide a great deal. First, the projections generally mentioned in the media generally go no further than the year 2100, at most. Suppose, however, people continue using fossil fuels in the future at the same rates they do today. With this assumption, the IPCC projected that after 2100, global average temperatures would rise more than 4°C (7.2°F) and perhaps up to 7.8°C (14°F), with a small chance of rising 12.6°C (22.7°F).[34] Thus the rises projected today are *minimums*, not what temperatures might eventually reach if societies make no changes in energy systems.

Second, even the seemingly small changes in temperature projected by 2100 will adversely affect people in three major ways: more heatwaves will occur, precipitation patterns will alter, and sea levels will continue rising. More heatwaves will bring discomfort and probably lower agricultural production. Altered precipitation patterns will lower agricultural yields by either too much or too little rain. Rising sea levels will inundate coastal areas and many of the world's biggest cities. Some of the increased CO_2 in the atmosphere will dissolve in the oceans, make it more acidic, and adversely affect many ocean species.[35]

Changes that have already occurred, consistent with projections, raise anxiety rather than reassure. For example, in 2012, James Hansen, an American climate scientist, and his colleagues compared seasonal (three-month) temperatures during 1980–2010 with those during 1951–1980. The global average temperature went up about 0.5° to 0.6°C (about 1°F). Not very much, at least on the surface! Unfortunately, even these small global averages had apparently increased the areas with hot summers. In 1951–1980, hot summers covered about 33 percent of the area. In 1980–2010, these hot summers covered about 75 percent. At the same time, areas having a "cold" summer decreased from 33 to 10 percent.

More important, "extremely hot" summers emerged as a new category. They covered at most a few tenths of 1 percent of the land in the early period, but now they occupy about 10 percent of the land area each summer. The extent of land area now covered by very warm summers also surpasses the very hot years of the 1930s, a period of severe heat and drought in the United States. Some of those years had temperature extremes as high as those observed recently, but the maximum area covered by an "extremely hot" summer never exceeded 2.7 percent, compared to the recent average of about 10 percent and some years as much as 20 percent.[36]

These extremely hot summers already show evidence of clobbering agricultural yields over large areas, enough to seriously impair food reserves of entire nations, even if to date they have not induced actual famines. Heat waves in Western Europe in 2003 and in central Russia in 2010 were extraordinary by any standard, and Hansen's group argues that such events almost surely derived from human-induced climate change.

In 2003, Western Europe experienced a pronounced heat wave. Temperatures soared far higher than normal in June, July, and August. Highest temperatures arrived in the first two weeks of August and ranged from 35°C to over 40°C (95°–104° F). Drought also affected the area as 300 mm (about 12 inches) of "normal" rain failed to fall.[37] Scientific analysis of this heat wave demonstrated that the average temperatures observed for the three months were exceptionally unusual. The summer of 2003 was probably the hottest in Europe since, at latest, 1500.[38] The unusualness of this summer was so extreme that it was virtually impossible in the climate of pre-1980.[39]

High heat caused excess mortality of perhaps 35,000 people. Extensive wildfires roared through the dry, hot landscape, particularly in southern Europe. In Portugal over 5 percent of the forested land burned. The Danube, Po, Rhine, and Loire Rivers ran low, which interfered with navigation, irrigation, and the operation of electric generating plants.[40]

Mortality, fires, and impaired river services stretched the abilities of governments to respond, but in a subtler way the heatwave's impact on agriculture posed the largest long-term risks. Wheat and maize, two major European crops, both suffered significant yield losses. Overall national yields of wheat in France and maize in Italy both dropped by about 21 percent compared to 2002.[41]

Wheat suffered somewhat less, because at the time the heatwave began winter wheat had mostly finished it growth and flowering. Maize was in the middle of growth and flowering, so its productivity suffered more from the excessive temperatures. In the areas most affected by the heat, productivity of maize dropped 36 percent, for example, in the Po Valley of northern Italy. Yields in Western Europe declined mostly due to the excessive heat, while in Eastern Europe (Ukraine and Romania) they declined mostly due to drought.[42]

The summer of 2010 also proved to be exceptionally warm in Europe, but in that year the center of the excessive heat lay over central Russia. Temperatures in Moscow in July broke the previous record by 2.5°C.[43] They reached 38.2°C (100.8°F), and nighttime lows in the region were also high (25°C, or 77°F, in Kiev, Ukraine). A close examination of exceptionally high daily maximum temperatures over all of Europe during the entire summer indicated that for one-week and two-week periods, the average maximum temperatures in central Russia exceeded the average for 1970–99 by 13.3°C (23.9°F) and 12.3°C (22.1°F), respectively. For the statistically minded, these average maxima were 4.4 and 5.2 standard deviations, respectively, above the long-term average.[44] In simple English, this means that these temperatures were extremely unlikely to occur by chance alone, unless the climate had changed.

Climate scientists believed that the 2003 and 2010 events in Europe presaged the weather patterns that would become more common in the years ahead, based on the warming trends already visible from increasing levels of greenhouse gases.[45] A group of scientists at the National Oceanographic and Atmospheric Administration argued that the 2010 heatwave in Russia was not entirely unprecedented and that this episode was not necessarily by itself a signal of climate change. Nevertheless, their model projections indicated that 2010 was the type of event that would move from very rare to quite common in the years ahead.[46]

Physically, therefore, the summer of 2010 displayed highly unusual features. Did it affect Russia? Without a doubt, it did. The heat caused an estimated 55,000 excess deaths, caused crop failures of 25 percent, aggravated fires over one million hectares, and led to economic losses of $15 billion, one percent of Russia's GDP.[47]

Both yield and total production of grains took serious hits. Yields of wheat, the most important grain, for example, dropped to 78 percent of yields in 2008. Barley, the second most important grain, yielded only 69 percent in 2010 compared to 2008. Rye, a minor grain, yielded only 57 percent of what it had in 2008. Total grain production dropped from 99.8 million tons in 2008 to 56 million tons in 2010. The land harvested was only 73 percent of the harvested area in 2008.[48]

Loss of yield, based on the raw numbers, looks serious. Compared to 2008, the grain harvest in 2010 lost about 44 million tons. To put this large number in perspective, Russia consumes about 77 million tons per year of grain for people and livestock, so the losses from the heatwave represented three-fifths of the country's normal consumption. Russia did not suffer a famine due to the heatwave, but the losses surprised and significantly disrupted the government's economic planning. Since the dissolution of the USSR in 1991, Russia has revamped its agriculture to increase production, decrease imports, and increase exports of grain, plus increase livestock production. At the time of the heatwave, the country had good reserves of grain. Thus the losses, viewed at the national level, appeared largely as a 30 percent drop in exports and a 65 percent drop in reserves from 2008–9 to 2010–11.[49]

These examples, however worrisome they may be, may or may not indicate the ultimate global impacts of climate change. Moreover, physical events, the easiest to predict, will in turn have economic and cultural consequences, which are more difficult to predict and subject to mitigation by adaptation. The exceptionally thorough studies of the International Panel on Climate Change and these detailed case studies of Europe, however, suggest potentially serious, adverse effects on human societies and economies.

In other words, climate science predicts *risk*, the probability—but not 100 percent certainty—of harm. Humanity thus faces the task—now—of deciding whether the predictions and their consequences look acceptable, tolerable but not ideal, or unacceptably damaging. The inevitable followup task is deciding what is to be done. Something? A little? A great deal? Nothing? Does the best course of action lie in accepting the most thorough scientific studies? Or should we bet that things won't really turn out too bad, a bet that has no significant support from the scientific community?

The urgency of decision making about climate change leaps from some simple numbers in the latest report of the IPCC. By 2011, humanity had already released about 515 GtC (gigatons of carbon; giga = billion, or 10^9) and was adding about 10.4 GtC per year in 2011,[50] over 90 percent of which (9.5 GtC per year) from burning fossil fuels. In order to have a good chance (greater than 2 out of 3), of keeping global average temperature rise less than 2°C, the total amount of carbon released into the atmosphere cannot exceed 1,000 GtC.[51]

Put simply, humanity has already emitted over 50 percent of the "carbon budget" required to have a good chance of minimizing rising temperatures. After 2011, humanity could emit an additional 485 GtC (1,000 – 515 = 485), and human activities were doing so at about 10.4 GtC per year, a rate that, if held steady, would total 485 GtC in forty-seven years. It is projected that 2058 will be the year that the amount of carbon released into the atmosphere will exceed the budget intended to have a good chance of keeping temperature increases below 2°C.

It's important to note that keeping the global average temperature increase below 2°C is not a guarantee of safety. This target figure was merely a rough estimate that increases beyond 2°C were likely to create climate effects increasingly detrimental to human welfare. The increase of average global temperatures had reached 0.85°C by 2012,[52] but the discussion above indicated that societies have already been affected adversely by this rise, which is less than 2°C.

Despite strong scientific consensus about the seriousness of climate change and the urgency for reducing carbon emissions, the United States has since the 1980s experienced an ongoing argument between (a) the majority of scientists and their professional associations and (b) a small minority of scientists plus a host of political, business, and media leaders. The latter group has questioned the existence of climate change; the role of natural climate variability compared to human-caused variations; the rate, magnitude, and seriousness of change; and the feasibility of successful mitigation actions.

This skepticism in its various forms has little relationship to an understanding of climate science; instead it rests on a political ideology that is opposed to regulations limiting the uses of fossil fuels. This climate change countermovement has resisted and blocked essentially all proposals to regulate these energy sources or reduce their uses in the United States.[53] The disputes have acquired a distinctly partisan flavor, with Republicans generally opposed to the conclusions of scientists and Democrats generally supportive and a few from each party breaking ranks with their respective majorities. As a result, an alleged controversy about the science, a controversy that has not existed in the scientific community for nearly a generation, has crowded public debate with political disagreements masquerading as scientific ones.[54] Resolutions of these debates could be assisted by better and more comprehensive risk analyses, better systematic decision making, and improved models for educating the public about the risks of climate change.[55]

NOTES

1 Lydia Saad and Jeffrey M. Jones, "U.S. Concern about Global Warming at Eight-Year High," March 16, 2016, www.gallup.com/poll/190010/concern-global-warming-eight-year-high.aspx, July 29, 2016.

2 Lawrence Livermore National Laboratory, carbon flowcharts, https://flowcharts.llnl.gov/commodities/carbon, April 27, 2016.

3 Intergovernmental Panel on Climate Change (IPCC), *Summary for Policy Makers, Working Group I Contribution to the IPCC Fifth Assessment Report Climate Change 2013: The Physical Science Basis* (Cambridge: Cambridge University Press, 2013), 4, 11, 13, 17.

4 This statement is not an actual quote from any known living person. It is easy to find media sources, however, that make claims and raise questions very much like those presented here. See, e.g., Rush Limbaugh, on September 27, 2013, www.rushlimbaugh.com/daily/2013/09/27/last_gasp_of_the_climate_change_cult.

5 Spencer R. Weart, *The Discovery of Global Warming* (Cambridge, MA: Harvard University Press, 2003), 2–3.

6 Weart, *Discovery of Global Warming*, 2–3; John Tyndall, "On Radiation through the Earth's Atmosphere," *Philosophical Magazine* 25, ser. 4 (March 1863): 200–206; John Tyndall, *On Radiation: The "Rede" Lecture* (New York: D. Appleton & Co., 1863), 14–16.

7 G. Frederick Wright, "Agassiz and the Ice Age," *American Naturalist* 32 (March 1898): 165–71.

8 Weart, *Discovery of Global Warming*, 11–19.

9 Weart, *Discovery of Global Warming*, 7–8; Svante Arrhenius, "On the Influence of Carbonic Acid in the Air upon the Temperature of the Ground," *Philosophical Magazine and Journal of Science* 41, ser. 5 (April 1896): 239–76.

10 Weart, *Discovery of Global Warming*, 1, 7–8, 24; Gilbert N. Plass, "Carbon Dioxide and the Climate," *American Scientist* 44 (July 1956): 302–16.

11 Fairfield Osborn, *Our Plundered Planet* (Boston: Little, Brown, 1948); William Vogt, *Road to Survival* (New York: W. Sloane Assoc., 1948).

12 Michael Egan, *Barry Commoner and the Science of Survival: The Remaking of American Environmentalism* (Cambridge, MA: MIT Press, 2007), 47–78; Rachel Carson, *Silent Spring* (Boston: Houghton Mifflin, 1962).

13 Reid A. Bryson, "A Perspective on Climatic Change," *Science* 184 (1974): 753–60; Weart, *Discovery of Global Warming*, 71–72.

14 S. I. Rasool and S. H. Schneider, "Atmospheric Carbon Dioxide and Aerosols: Effects of Large Increases on Global Climate," *Science* 173 (July 9, 1971): 138–41; R. J. Charlson, Halstead Harrison, Georg Witt, S. I. Rasool, and S. H. Schneider, "Aerosol Concentrations: Effects on Planetary Temperatures," *Science* 175 (January 7, 1972): 95–96; National Research Council, *Understanding Climatic Change: A Program for Action* (Washington, DC: National Academy of Sciences, 1975).

15 Weart, *Discovery of Global Warming*, 35–38.

16 Scripps Institution of Oceanography, "The Keeling Curve," https://scripps.ucsd.edu/programs/keelingcurve/wp-content/plugins/sio-bluemoon/graphs/mlo_full_record.pdf, April 27, 2016.

17 A. Neftel, E. Moor, H. Oeshger, and B. Stauffer, "Evidence from Polar Ice Cores for the Increase in Atmospheric CO_2 in the Past Two Centuries," *Nature* 315 (May 2, 1985): 45–47; H. Friedli, H. Lötscher, H. Oeschger, U. Sidlerstrasse, and B. Stauffer, "Ice Core Record of the $^{13}C/^{12}C$ Ratio of Atmospheric CO_2 in the Past Two Centuries," *Nature* 324 (November 20, 1986): 237–38.

18 James Hansen and Sergej Lebedeff, "Global Trends of Measured Surface Air Temperature," *Journal of Geophysical Research* 92 (1987): 13,345–72; P. D. Jones, S. C. B. Raper, R. S. Bradley, H. F. Diaz, P. M. Kelly, and T. M. L. Wigley, "Northern Hemisphere Surface Air Temperature Variations: 1851–1984," *Journal of Climate and Applied Meteorology* 25 (1986): 161–79.

19 Bryson, "A Perspective"; Stephen H. Schneider and Clifford Mass, "Volcanic Dust, Sunspots, and Temperature Trends," *Science* 190 (November 21, 1975): 741–46.

20 Weart, *Discovery of Global Warming,* 71–75.

21 Dieter Lüthi et al., "High-Resolution Carbon Dioxide Concentration Record 650,000–800,000 Years before Present," *Nature* 453 (May 15, 2008): 379–82.

22 J. Jouzel et al., "Vostok Ice Core: A Continuous Isotope Temperature Record over The Last Climatic Cycle (160,000 Years)," *Nature* 329 (October 1, 1987): 403–8; J. M. Barnola et al., "Vostok Ice Core Provides 160,000-Year Record of Atmospheric CO_2," *Nature* 329 (October 1, 1987): 408–14; C. Genthon et al., "Vostok Ice Core: Climatic Response to CO_2 and Orbital Forcing Changes over the Last Climatic Cycle," *Nature* 329 (October 1, 1987): 414–18; Urs Siegenthaler et al., "Stable Carbon Cycle–Climate Relationship during the Late Pleistocene," *Science* 310 (November 25, 2005): 1313–17; Maureen E. Raymo and Peter Huybers, "Unlocking the Mysteries of the Ice Ages," *Nature* 451 (January 17, 2008): 284–85.

23 Jeremy D. Shakun, Peter U. Clark, and Feng He et al., "Global Warming Preceded by Increasing Carbon Dioxide Concentrations during the Last Deglaciation," *Nature* 484 (April 5, 2012): 49–54.

24 P. D. Jones et al., "High-Resolution Palaeoclimatology of the Last Millennium: A Review of Current Status and Future Prospects," *Holocene* 19, no. 1(2009): 3–49; Michael E. Mann, *The Hockey Stick and the Climate Wars: Dispatches from the Front Lines* (New York: Columbia University Press, 2012), 34–36.

25 Shaun A. Marcott et al., "A Reconstruction of Regional and Global Temperature for the Past 11, 300 Years," *Science* 339 (March 8, 2013): 1198–1201.

26 Weart, *Discovery of Global Warming,* 57–59.

27 National Research Council, *Carbon Dioxide and Climate: A Scientific Assessment* (Washington, DC: National Academy of Sciences, 1979), 1–22.

28 Naomi Oreskes, "The Scientific Consensus on Climate Change," *Science* 306 (3 December 3, 2004, corrected January 21, 2005): 1686; William R. L. Anderegg et al., "Expert Credibility in Climate Change," *Proceedings of the National Academy of Sciences,* www.pnas.org/cgi/doi/10.1073/pnas.1003187107, 2010.

29 IPCC, *Summary for Policymakers,* 18.

30 Richard B. Alley, *The Two-Mile Time Machine: Ice Cores, Abrupt Climate Change, and Our Future* (Princeton, NJ: Princeton University Press, 2000), 8.

31 IPCC, *Summary for Policymakers,* 5–12.

32 Detlef P. van Vuuren, Jae Edmonds, and Mikiko Kainuma et al., "The Representative Concentration Pathways: An Overview," *Climatic Change* 109 (2011): 5–31; IPCC, *Summary for Policymakers,* 14.

33 IPCC, *Summary for Policymakers,* 20.

34 IPCC, *Climate Change 2013: The Physical Science Basis. Contribution of Working Group I to the Fifth Assessment Report of the Intergovernmental Panel on Climate Change* (Cambridge: Cambridge University Press, 2013), 1054–55, figure 12.5, table 12.2.

35 IPCC, *Summary for Policymakers,* 19–29.

36 James Hansen, Makiko Sato, and Reto Ruedy, "Perception of Climate Change," *Proceedings of the National Academy of Sciences*, published online, August 6, 2012, E2415–E2423. doi10.1073/pnas.1205276109.

37 IPCC, *Climate Change 2007: Impacts, Adaptation and Vulnerability, Contribution of Working Group II to the Fourth Assessment Report of the Intergovernmental Panel on Climate Change* (Cambridge: Cambridge University Press, 2007), 845–46.

38 P. A. Stott, D. A. Stone, and M. R. Allen, "Human Contribution to the European Heatwave of 2003," *Nature* 432 (December 2, 2004): 610–14.

39 C. Schär, P. L. Vidale, D. Lüthi, C. Frei, C. Häberli, M. A. Liniger, and C. Appenzeller, "The Role of Increasing Temperature Variability in European Summer Heatwaves," *Nature* 427 (January 22, 2004): 332–36.

40 IPCC, *Climate Change 2007*, 845–46.

41 Food and Agriculture Organization of the United Nations, *FAOSTAT*, http://faostat3.fao.org/faostat-gateway/go/to/download/Q/QC/E, January 10, 2014; percent calculated by author.

42 P. Ciais et al., "Europe-Wide Reduction in Primary Productivity Caused by the Heat and Drought in 2003," *Nature* 437 (September 22, 2005): 529–33.

43 Dim Coumou and Stefan Rahmstorf, "A Decade of Weather Extremes," *Nature Climate Change* 2 (July 2012): 491–96.

44 David Barriopedro et al., "The Hot Summer of 2010: Redrawing the Temperature Record Map of Europe," *Science* 332 (April 8, 2011): 220–24, figure 1, 221.

45 Coumou and Rahmstorf, "A Decade of Weather Extremes,"; Barriopedro et al., "The Hot Summer of 2010"; Randall Dole et al., "Was There a Basis for Anticipating the 2010 Russian Heat Wave?," *Geophysical Research Letters* 38 (2011): doi:10.1029/2010GL046582.

46 Dole et al., "Was There a Basis?"

47 Barriopedro et al., "The Hot Summer of 2010."

48 Statistics from http://faostat.fao.org/; percent calculations by author.

49 Stephen K. Wegren, "Food Security and Russia's 2010 Drought," *Eurasian Geography and Economics* 52, no. 1 (2011): 140–56, table 1, 147; percent calculations by author.

50 IPCC, *Summary for Policymakers*, 12.

51 IPCC, *Summary for Policymakers*, 27.

52 IPCC, *Summary for Policymakers*, 5.

53 Naomi Oreskes and Erik M. Conway, *Merchants of Doubt* (New York: Bloomsbury Press, 2010), 169–215.

54 Robert J. Brulle, "Institutionalizing Delay: Foundation Funding and the Creation of U.S. Climate Change Counter-Movement Organizations," *Climatic Change*, December 21, 2013, doi 10.1007/s10584–013–1018–7; Oreskes and Conway, *Merchants of Doubt*.

55 Paul C. Stern, John H. Perkins, Richard E. Sparks, and Robert A. Knox, "The Challenge of Climate-Change Neoskepticism," *Science* 353 (August 12, 2016): 653–54.

CHAPTER SIX

Agriculture and Food Systems

As of 2020, almost 40% of the Earth's land area has been converted to crop and livestock production, yet approximately 1 in 9 people in the world is undernourished,[1] and farmers worldwide struggle with novel pest infestations, crop failures, and soil death. So, what is going wrong? What is the solution?

Agriculture developed in multiple human societies around the world about 12,000 years ago, and for most of the time since then, our agricultural production methods provided sufficient food for continued human population growth while not destroying the fertile soil, clean water, natural pest control, and pollinator communities that agriculture depends on. This all changed approximately 70 years ago when World War II ended, and the US found itself with a surplus of ammunitions factories and a new trove of bioweaponry knowledge with no immediate use. These considerable resources began to be used instead to produce "weapons" in the battle to increase food production: synthetic fertilizers, pesticides, herbicides, and fungicides. As these products were rolled out to farmers, agriculture began to look less like part of a healthy ecosystem and more like a war against nature. Farmers globally were now applying synthetic pesticides and herbicides, irrigating dry land, planting in extensive monocultures, adopting tilling practices which led to erosion, and transitioning to farm machinery that ran almost exclusively on unsustainable fossil fuels. The selected reading by Harvey Blatt, "Soil, Crops and Food" from *America's Environmental Report Card: Are we making the grade* (2006), explores the effects of these agricultural practices in detail.

This time period is known as "The Green Revolution" because these new practices led to a dramatic increase in agricultural yields. However, it did not take long for

1 Sustainable Development Knowledge Platform, 2019, *Sustainable Development Goal 2*, United Nations. Retrieved from: https://sustainabledevelopment.un.org/sdg2.

some agriculturalists, farmers, and activists to notice the destructive effects of these practices on the environment and to sound the alarm. One well-known example of this is Rachel Carson's *Silent Spring*, which you will learn more about in Chapter 10. Opponents of the unsustainable industrial agricultural methods began to promote a return to more traditional, sustainable practices, and the field of sustainable agriculture was born. Blatt (2006) describes many of the alternative practices promoted by sustainable agriculture, including conservation tilling, integrated pest management, agroforestry, and soil restoration. A wide range of studies has shown that farmers using these practices can achieve yields equal to or higher than those achieved in industrial agriculture with the significant benefit of not destroying the natural resources that sustain their farms.

The next selected reading in this chapter, "Food—Systems—Racism: From Mistreatment to Transformation" from *Food First* by Eric Holt-Giménez and Breeze Harper, as well as the recommended reading, Margaret Gray's "Sustainable Jobs? Ethnic Succession and the New Latinos" from *Labor and the Locovore: The Making of a Comprehensive Food Ethic*, focus on the often-neglected issue of how "racism and our food system have co-evolved" (Holt-Gimenez and Harper [2016]) and how racism continues to shape who grows our food, who owns our farms, and who does and does not have reliable access to affordable, nutritious food. For example, according to the USDA's 2017 agricultural census, 95% of farm owners in the US identify as white while 57% of hired farm laborers identify as people of color. Structural driving patterns like this are explored in the reading by Gray (2013), who tracks the history of agricultural laborers in New York State to illustrate how systemic racism and the vulnerability of undocumented farm laborers have created an unsustainable agricultural work force with no clear path to becoming farm owners.

RECOMMENDED READING

Gray, M. 2013. "Sustainable Jobs? Ethnic Succession and the New Latinos." *Labor and the Locavore: The Making of a Comprehensive Food Ethic*. Berkley and Los Angeles: University of California Press.

READING AND DISCUSSION PROMPTS

1. The Blatt article tries to summarize all of the issues with modern industrial agriculture in one article—and there are a lot! Name one of the issues Blatt discusses, and explain why it threatens our future food supply.
2. Blatt notes that the average age of the US farmer is older each year and that there are fewer people reporting on the census that their occupation is farming.

Why do you think this happens? What are some of the reasons that Americans are no longer choosing farming as a livelihood?

3. According to this article, why does organic food cost more than conventional food in the store? Is it because it is more expensive to grow? Explain what the author is saying.
4. Holt-Giménez and Harper describe many ways that our food system disproportionately affects people of color. Describe one instance of institutional racism as it shows up in our food or agricultural systems.

READING 6.1

Soil, Crops, and Food

By Harvey Blatt

> Whoever could make two ears of corn to grow upon a spot of ground where only one grew before, would deserve better of mankind than the whole race of politicians put together.
>
> —Jonathan Swift, *Gulliver's Travels*

Food ranks with clean water as essential for human existence, and for most Americans the concept of food scarcity is hard to imagine. Most of us are burdened by surpluses rather than shortages and our health problems have more to do with being overweight (61 percent, of whom 20 percent are obese) than with being hungry. Specialty manufacturer Goliath Casket Company now produces a triple-wide coffin, 44 inches across rather than the 24-inch standard, and their business is expanding (ouch!) by 20 percent annually.

We are the world's major breadbasket. We produce 25 percent of the world's food, and our waistlines show it. The National Center for Health Statistics says 15 percent of children between ages 6 and 18 were obese in 2000, compared with 6 percent in 1980, and experts believe the numbers are still increasing. Surgery to shrink the stomachs of obese Americans (bariatric surgery) increased 40 percent between 2001 and 2002 to 80,000, and the number is expected to climb to 120,000 in 2003.[1]

Compared to costs in the rest of the world, our food is almost free. Americans spend only 12 percent of their disposable income on food, a percentage that would be even less if we ate more meals at home rather than in expensive restaurants. Can America's agricultural abundance be maintained indefinitely? There are signs that even breadbasket

America may be facing its productivity limit. The major reason for this looming catastrophe is our neglect of the soil in which our crops grow.

THE NATURE OF SOIL

> This nation and civilization is founded upon nine inches of topsoil. And when that is gone there will no longer be any nation or any civilization.
>
> —Hugh Bennett

What is soil and where does it come from? Soil is born as rocks decay under the onslaught of rain and sun. The decay process produces the sediment we call soil, a mixture of clay and other minerals from the rotted rock. In addition to these grains, soils also generally contain a small percentage of black organic matter formed by organisms in the soil and the dead plants they feed on. One heaping tablespoon of soil may contain up to 9 billion microorganisms, 50 percent more than the human population on earth. So soil is a mixture of clay, other minerals, and organic matter. The organic matter is the stuff that makes the upper part of the soil dark and rich and good for growing vegetables, flowers, lawns, and crops. This black stuff also is responsible for holding most of the water in the topsoil. In an ideal agricultural soil the amount of organic matter is about 5 percent, composed of both living and dead plants and animals (bacteria, fungi, worms, and other small creatures).

Soils have a layered structure (Figure 6.1.1). The layers or horizons are termed O, A, B, and C, from top to bottom. The A-horizon is also known as topsoil and this is the horizon in which our crops are rooted and live. It is the horizon we plow and fertilize and is usually only a few inches thick. It is hard to believe that so few inches of dirt nourish us as well as a large part of the world. Imagine 6 billion people dependent for their existence on an accumulation of a few inches of dirt. Clearly, such a thin earthskin is fragile and needs to be protected at all cost. How have we been doing at this job? By any reasonable standard, not well. As an academic, I would award America's effort no more than a C-, even with grade inflation. What are we doing wrong and how can we do better?

FARMLAND: WHERE IS IT AND WHY?

> A place for everything, and everything in its place.
>
> —Samuel Smiles, *Thrift*

About 29 percent of America's land area is devoted to agriculture.[2] Where is America's farmland located and why there? There are three major requirements for a prime agri-

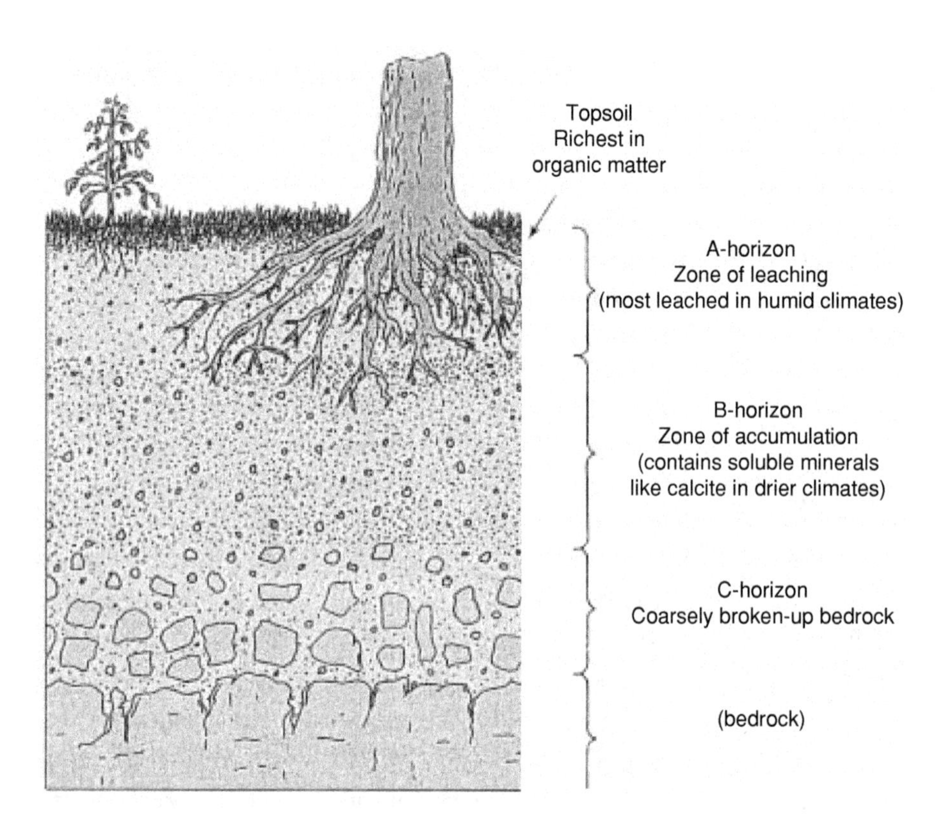

Figure 6.1.1 A generalized soil profile. Individual horizons vary in thickness and some may be locally absent. The A-horizon is dominated by mineral grains in various stages of decay, releasing plant nutrients in the process. Water and air are present between the mineral grains. The B-horizon is enriched in either red hematite (iron oxide) in humid climates or calcite (calcium carbonate) in dry climates.

cultural region: an extensive area of flat ground, a moderate to warm climate, and an adequate water supply. Where in the United States are such areas located? The regions that come to mind for extensive flatness and moderate to warm climate are the vast midcontinent of our country between the Appalachians and the Rocky Mountains, Florida, and the inland valley of central California (the San Joaquin Valley). So at first glance America is indeed blessed with agricultural land. The flat midcontinent alone covers about half the 48 contiguous states.

But there are problems with using some of this flat land, the major one being not enough precipitation. The best farmland needs 30–40 inches of rainfall each year to reach its maximum potential, and both the midcontinent and the San Joaquin Valley fall considerably short of this goal. The annual precipitation averages 15–30 inches in the midcontinent (Figure 6.1.1); in the San Joaquin Valley, it averages only 8–12 inches. Our largest flat area is thus marginal in terms of precipitation, and central California would seem an unlikely place to locate agricultural abundance. After all, 8–12 inches of rain is typical of southern Arizona and not many people think of that area as an agricultural breadbasket. But extensive crops are grown in both the midcontinent and southern Arizona because of underground aquifers, aquifers that are fast becoming depleted, as we saw in chapter 1. Insufficient aquifer water is rapidly becoming a major problem for America's agricultural community.

URBAN GROWTH AND FARMLAND LOSS

> The enormous superstructure of American society rests on the tiny point where fewer and fewer farmers with larger and larger machines mine as much food as they can from fields that are less and less what they once were.
>
> —Jane Smiley

> They paved paradise and put up a parking lot.
>
> —Joni Mitchell, "Big Yellow Taxi"

Impending water shortages are only one of the problems facing America's farmland. Another is urban sprawl, which is moving ever faster with each passing year. From 1982 to 1992, an average of 2.5 million acres of farmland was lost each year to urban development. From 1992 to 1997, the rate was 3.2 million acres per year. The number of people living in our cities rose 80 percent between 1950 and 1990, while the land covered by those areas expanded 305 percent. These lost farm acres stopped sprouting grain and instead sprouted housing developments, shopping malls, and other construction. In California, where half of the nation's fruits and vegetables are grown, 16 percent of the best soils now underlie urban areas, as do 9 percent of the next-best soils.[3] There is 20 percent less farmland in the United States today than in the 1960s because of commercial development. Commercial developments not only absorb farmland but also drive up land prices. This provides a large financial incentive for financially stressed farmers living nearby to "take the money and run," further decreasing the amount of farmland. The development process feeds on itself to eliminate farmland.

The decrease in farmland caused by people moving to cities for increased opportunities is made even more serious by the increasing average age of America's farmers, up from 51 in 1970 to 57 in 1998. The average age of all U.S. workers is 38. Thirty-five percent of farmers are now 65 or older, compared to 13 percent of all Americans.[4] Nationwide, there are 300,000 fewer farmers than there were 20 years ago. The financial hardships of running a farm (predicted to get worse with global warming), a decline in the size of the average farm family, and increasing opportunities in other fields mean that many farmers will not be replaced when they retire. The farmland will then probably be purchased by commercial developers for more suburban housing. Developers prefer land with deep, well-drained, and nearly level soils, areas best suited for agricultural production. Thus, the retirement of farmers not only leaves fewer people producing food, but also less farmland.

Urban sprawl has another bad effect on farming, but a more subtle one than the obvious loss of farmland. When people concentrate in cities air pollution from cars and factories increases significantly, which causes a significant decrease in crop yields (Table 6.1.1). The smoggy haze decreases the amount of sunlight available for photosynthesis, and the chemical soup in the haze reduces a plant's growth and fruit yield and increases its susceptibility to disease and insect attack.[5]

Table 6.1.1 Estimated crop losses in southern California, determined by growing crops in filtered, unpolluted air and in smoggy air.

CROP	PERCENT
Alfalfa	8.6
Beans	10.3
Cotton	18.6
Grapes	28.1
Oranges	26.2
Potatoes	14.9
Rice	5.3
Tomatoes (processing)	3.8

Source: California Air Resources Board, 1991.

As a result of both the decreasing amount of farmland and increased mechanization, only 2.6 percent of Americans work on farms nowadays; the number of farms has decreased by 50 percent but average size has doubled in the last 50 years.[6] The 8 percent of farms with sales above $250,000 occupy about 27 percent of farmland but generate 68 percent of total farm output.[7] They also get the lion's share of the $19 billion in annual farm subsidies from Washington. There are still a large number of "mom and pop" farms but most are not profitable and their numbers are decreasing. They are becoming a nostalgic and romanticized vestige of America's past.

SOIL EROSION

> Man has always found it difficult to appreciate the delicacy of quality and texture of soil, and to realize that it is not inexhaustible, and that some processes are virtually irreversible.
>
> —Anthony Huxley

The "muddy Mississippi" is a stereotype in the American consciousness but few of us think about where the mud comes from. It takes but a moment to realize that it must be dirt sloughed off from the land bordering the river—mostly farmland. And a lot of it is the precious topsoil in which we base our agricultural abundance. Some of American agricultural land may be losing topsoil faster than nature can reform it, but it is not clear whether the average rate of topsoil loss is too great to be sustainable. The average rate of soil erosion in American agricultural areas is hotly debated among the experts, but all agree it is a problem that needs to be addressed. Available data are not good enough to determine whether the loss of topsoil is increasing, decreasing, or remaining constant. Similarly, the relationship between the rate of loss of topsoil and its formation by natural processes is also uncertain. In the climate of the American midcontinent it takes many decades or perhaps hundreds of years to form 1 inch of agricultural soil.

WHY DOES IT HAPPEN?

> The leveled lances of the rain at earth's half-shielded breast take glittering aim.
>
> —Paul Hamilton Hayne, *A Storm in the Distance*

The major culprit is raindrops smashing into loose dirt. A large raindrop falling in still air can reach a speed of 20 miles per hour, and when the rain is wind-blown the speed is even greater. Every drop of water is a hammer dislodging and moving soil particles down even the gentlest slope. When we take into account that millions of raindrops fall in a typical rainstorm the potential for soil movement downslope toward the nearest stream is easy to see.

About one-third of soil movement results from wind blowing across the land surface. In some areas of America's breadbasket the wind is a more potent soil-moving force than water, sometimes four to five times more potent. The midcontinent is America's windiest flatland. This was disastrously brought home to farmers during the infamous dust-bowl years of the 1930s. The combination of soil loosening by the plow and lack of rainfall during an extended drought left the soil surface exceptionally vulnerable to movement by the wind, a circumstance that continued for several years. As we noted in chapter 1, annual precipitation in our largest farming area is far below the 30–40 inches that is optimum for agriculture, averaging perhaps 20 inches over the region. In about one year in five the annual precipitation drops to 15 inches, virtually a recipe for crop failure unless the rainfall is supplemented by irrigation water from underground aquifers. There was not nearly the amount of irrigation in the 1930s that there is today, so the farmland was drier. A dust-bowl phenomenon is much less likely today than it was 70 years ago.

HOW CAN SOIL EROSION BE STOPPED?

> The worst farming practices use up eight inches of topsoil (which took 7,000 years to create) in 36 years. The best practices would make that eight inches last 2,224 years.
>
> —Iowa Department of Soil Conservation

When new crops are ready to be planted using conventional agriculture, the remains of last year's crop are plowed into the soil, exposing a bare soil surface. Then the bare soil surface is broken up to make a smooth bed for seeds. Finally, after the seeds are planted the soil between the rows is stirred to rip out weeds. Thus, the topsoil is repeatedly worked over, granulated into tiny fragments, and any existing soil-holding roots from the previous crop are destroyed. The soil is left unprotected until the new seeds germinate and develop roots, which takes several months. The soil is not protected from being carried away by rainwater during the spring rains. Standard cultivation practices increase soil erosion by a staggering 10 to100-fold.

CONSERVATION FARMING

A better planting method now used by most farmers is called conservation farming. Two principles are central to this farming method: (1) reduce the amount of soil disturbance—that is, plowing; (2) do not leave the soil bare and exposed to wind and rain. The amount of plowing and disturbance of the soil is kept to a minimum. There may be no plowing of the soil at all. Seeds are planted directly over the residue of last year's crop, regardless of whether the new crop is the same or different from the previous one. This way nearly all the soil remains protected during spring rains. In addition, moisture is retained in the soil by living plant roots, holding the soil together and reducing runoff of water and topsoil from the field. Soil loss is reduced by more than 90 percent. Another benefit of conservation farming is that valuable soil organisms such as earthworms are not turned into wormburger meat by the plow. Experience has shown that no-till farming results in higher crop yields, with lowered use of water, pesticides (weed seeds are not brought to the surface), and tractor fuel.

CONTOUR PLOWING

When the ground has a significant slope a technique called contour plowing should be used. Ridges and furrows are constructed following the contours of the ground slope so that the downhill flow of water is reduced. Even a small decrease in flow velocity produces a large decrease in erosion. Contour plowing is effective on slopes of less than 8°. On steeper slopes terracing is effective, but America's extensive open spaces for agriculture make this farming method unnecessary.

THE NEED FOR TREES AND FORESTS

Trees serve two functions for farmers. In windy country such as the American Midwest, lines of trees act as a windbreak to reduce wind erosion. Perhaps more importantly, trees and their root systems on slopes hold water and are essential to prevent flooding of nearby agricultural fields during heavy rains. Forested areas also prevent slope erosion and smothering of cropland margins by sediment moving rapidly downslope.

SOIL POLLUTION

> All this is not to say there is no insect problem and no need of control. I am saying, rather, that … the methods employed must be such that they do not destroy us along with the insects.
>
> —Rachel Carson, *Silent Spring*

> A caterpillar on your cauliflower is a sign that both are safe to eat.
>
> —Peter Thomson

Fertilizers of some sort are always applied to crop-growing land to increase plant health and productivity. Perhaps most common are the commercial NPK (nitrogen, phosphorous, potassium) products, the elements needed in greatest quantity by most plants. These are universally agreed to be good for crops. However, an analysis of 29 commercial fertilizers by the U.S. Public Interest Research Group revealed that each of them contained 22 toxic heavy metals. In 20 of the products, levels exceeded the limits set for waste sent to public landfills.[8]

More contentious is the use of sewage sludge, about whose health risks there is "persistent uncertainty," according to the National Academy of Sciences. Before passage of the Clean Water Act in 1970, most raw sewage was dumped into oceans or rivers. Now almost everything flushed down toilets and poured into drains by industrial plants, hospitals, gas stations, and householders eventually finds its way to a wastewater-treatment plant. The water, with toxins removed, is treated and returned to waterways. The rest, sewage sludge, may be treated to a greater (more expensive) or lesser (less expensive) degree. The more expensive treatment produces sludge with the least health risk but is not as rich in plant nutrients as the less expensive treatment. But the less expensive treatment leaves more pathogens in the sludge. Farmers get sludge free, and in some cases may even be paid to take it.

About 5.6 million tons of sewage sludge, commonly called biosolids in environmental literature, is generated each year in the United States. More than half of it is recycled into our soil, and the rest is buried in landfills or burned.[9] According to the National Sludge Alliance, sewage sludge contains 60,000 toxic chemicals, a mix of residential, industrial, and commercial discharge that includes hospital wastes, street runoff, heavy metals, PCBs, dioxin, solvents, asbestos, and radioactive wastes.[10] The EPA published purity standards for sludge in 1993 that many scientists now consider inadequate, but there have been no scientific investigations or documentation of health impacts by the EPA. Numerous lawsuits have been filed by people who believe their health has been compromised by toxins in sludge.

Nearly all of America's 2.2 million farms today use herbicides and insecticides to control unwanted insects and plants ("weeds"). Most farmers consider these products essential to maintain productivity and apply 1 million tons of them to their fields each year. But less than 1 percent of applied pesticide reaches the target pests.[11] The FDA has determined that at least 53 carcinogenic pesticides are presently applied in massive amounts to our major food crops. And in 1998 they found that 35 percent of U.S. food samples contained pesticide residues. Also, because the chemicals applied to the crops dissolve in water they cannot be contained within the boundaries of the farm. They drain outward into adjacent waterways as well as downward into groundwaters. Pesticides have become 10 to 100 times more toxic than they were 30 years ago, and their use results in between 3.5 million and 5 million acute poisonings each year. Farms produce 70 percent of the stream pollution in the United States.

There are no health data for many of these chemicals, although the EPA in cooperation with the chemical industry is now testing large numbers of previously untested chemicals for general toxicity and for evidence of endocrine disruption. However, many chemicals have not been tested on humans to determine possible long-term effects and, because many new chemicals are devised each year, such testing can never be completed. Thorough testing takes a great deal of time, but it takes little time for chemists to concoct new poisons.

Perhaps even more frightening is the realization that chemicals ingested in combination can be many times more harmful than the chemicals are individually.[12] Yet chemicals are still only tested by the EPA for their carcinogenic or mutagenic potential in isolation from each other. But we face an unsolvable testing problem. To test just the commonest 1,000 toxic chemicals in combinations of 3 at a standardized dosage would require at least 166 million different experiments. And what about different dosages?

Even ingredients listed on pesticide labels as "inert," commonly more than 90 percent of a pesticide product, may not be safe for humans. According to a survey by the Northwest Coalition for Alternatives to Pesticides, about a quarter of inert substances are classified as hazardous under the Clean Air Act, the Safe Drinking Water Act, and other federal statutes.[13]

In May 2001, the United States signed the Convention on Persistent Organic Pollutants (POPs), committing us to reduce and/or eliminate the production, use, and/or release of the 12 POPs of greatest concern to the global community. The treaty also established a mechanism by which additional chemicals can be added to the list in the future as new dangers are recognized. Most herbicides are not harmful to humans but can be toxic to fish and other wildlife. Many types of insecticides, however, harm not only birds and fish but humans as well. Studies show that farmers who work with pesticides get Parkinson's disease and several kinds of cancer more often than the general public does. Each year thousands of people, most of them not farmers, are admitted to hospitals in the United States for pesticide poisoning. Because of increasing fear of pesticides, the use of these chemicals has declined somewhat over the past 20 years but they are still considered staples in most American farming. Because of pesticide pollution, loss of soil fertility caused by conventional plowing practices, soil erosion, and the increased incidence of pesticide-resistant crop diseases, it is unclear whether farming as now practiced in the United States can be sustained indefinitely.

It is worth noting that insect pests seem able to develop resistance to new pesticides as fast as the pesticides are developed by agricultural chemists. In 1950 there were about 10 species of insects and mites resistant to pesticides; today the number approaches 600. The number of weeds and plant diseases with this resistance has increased from near 0 in 1950 to more than 400 today.[14] Nevertheless we hear from Monsanto and the other pesticide manufacturers that newer pesticides are more potent than older ones.

Even though the amount of insecticides used in the United States increased tenfold between 1945 and 2000,[15] 37 percent of preharvest crops were lost to insects in the 1990s, compared to 30 percent in the early 1940s. The percentage of the crop harvest destroyed by pests in medieval Europe was 30 percent.[16] Today the world average loss is 35–42 percent, despite the increasing use of pesticides in recent decades. Are pesticides making our pest problem worse? If they are, not everyone will be saddened. In Japan, a memorial service has been held by the Society of Agricultural Chemicals Industry annually for the past 40 years to honor the memory of insect "victims" of agrochemicals.[17]

INTEGRATED PEST MANAGEMENT

A minority of farmers, wary of pesticides, have sharply reduced their use, preferring a system of pest control called *integrated pest management.* Crops are rotated yearly from field to field to disrupt pest infestations. Conservation farming is practiced to build fertility and reduce the need for expensive fertilizers, most of which contain toxic levels of heavy metals. Predatory organisms are released into the fields to control harmful insects. Pesticide use is not entirely abandoned but used only if pests reach a threshold level. Studies of integrated pest management in Britain showed increased harvests, and farmers' profits increased by 20 percent.

ORGANIC FARMING

> What is a weed? A plant whose virtues have not yet been discovered.
>
> —Ralph Waldo Emerson

Some farmers have eliminated all use of synthetic pesticides and fertilizers, a process known as *organic farming.* While the total number of farmers has been falling, the number of organic farmers, now at 12,000, has been rising steadily in response to increasing public concern about pesticides in food. Younger farmers are more likely to farm organically. The average age of organic farmers is 10 years less than that of other farmers. There was a 15–20 percent increase in organic acreage each year during the 1990s. About one-third of Americans buy some organic products. Between 1980 and 2001, organic farming revenues climbed from $78 million annually to $9–9.5 billion of a $500 billion grocery market.[18]

Only 0.3 percent of crop acreage in the United States is farmed organically.[19] On these farms, the use of synthetic fertilizers has been abandoned in favor of animal manure and crop residues. As in integrated pest management, crops are rotated and predatory insects such as ladybugs (are any of them males?) are introduced to control harmful pests. Soap may be sprayed on plants to protect them rather than insecticides.

In the European Union a certain species of naturally occurring bacteria is sprayed onto wheat, barley, and oat seeds to combat fungal diseases. It is nontoxic and has proven 98–100 percent effective.

Organic fields that have been under a sustainable, fertility-building agricultural regime for many years—or whose fertility has never been "drawn down" by chemical applications and repeated monocultures—can outperform industrially farmed ones.

They use much less commercial fertilizer, half the energy per unit yield, and increase the number of nutrient-cycling microbes, worms, and helpful fungi. In the U.S. Midwest, farmers who produce grain and soybeans organically are finding that their net profits equal or surpass those from conventional production, even when they do not charge the premium prices that organic crops generally command.

However, it takes 5–10 years of sustained organic farming to eliminate the pollution caused by decades of pesticide applications and, until these poisons are washed from the soil, crop yields from organic farming are lower than those obtained using chemical sprays. An added benefit of eliminating the use of pesticides is that organic systems are more resilient in maintaining productivity in drought years that lead to disastrous failure in conventional agriculture.

In response to growing public interest in organic food, the U.S. Department of Agriculture earmarked $5 million in the 2001 budget for research on organic food production. In October 2002, the USDA implemented a voluntary labeling program for organic food sold in stores. The label "100 percent organic" certifies that the food was grown without pesticides, hormones, antibiotics, irradiation, or genetic modification. "Organic" means at least 95 percent and "made with organic ingredients" means at least 70 percent. Products containing less than 70 percent organic ingredients can identify organic ingredients on their ingredient list.

Food grown without pesticides contains substantially higher concentrations of 21 nutrients[20] as well as increased amounts of antioxidants and other health-promoting compounds compared to crops produced with pesticides.[21] Heavy use of pesticides and chemical fertilizers seems to disrupt the ability of crops to synthesize certain chemicals that are associated with reduced risk of cancer, stroke, heart disease, and other illnesses. This discovery is another piece of evidence demonstrating that messing with the environment in which we evolved is a bad idea and should be avoided whenever possible, which is most of the time.

About a third of medium-priced restaurants now offer items they term organic on their menus. The nation's largest organic grocery chain has a growth rate of 30 percent, about double that of the supermarket industry in general. One out of every four Americans buys organic products. Gerber, Heinz, General Mills, Nestlé, and Unilever have now entered the organic produce market with baby food, flour, and other products. Almost half of American consumers say they are interested in purchasing organically grown products, now available at 73 percent of grocery stores. A newly founded city in Iowa has banned the sale of nonorganic food within the city limits.

Organic farming is promoted by governments outside the United States. The Israeli government gives subsidies to organic farmers. At present only 1–2 percent of their population buys organic food. Sales of organic food items in Britain rose 50 percent in 1999 compared to 1998, and rose another 50 percent in 2000. In Western Europe the amount of land under organic production is now more than 3 percent of total EU agricultural area. In several European nations 5–10 percent of total agricultural area is organic. The current record holder is Austria with 10.4 percent.[22] In 2003, ministers from the European Union countries published an action plan to promote organic farming. In 2003, the Ethical Exchange Management Company, based in London, opened the first international commodities exchange devoted entirely to organic products. Cuba has adopted organic farming as the official government strategy for all new agriculture in Cuba, after its highly successful introduction in 1990.

THE COST OF PURITY

An important question for American consumers is price. Organic food costs more in the stores, 57 percent more on average than nonorganic food. Why is this? There are several reasons, not necessarily related to the cost of growing the crops. Conventional farms are generally larger than organic farms and are heavily subsidized by the federal government—that is, nonorganic produce does not carry its full cost. American taxes subsidize it. However, this inequitable financial burden on organic farming may be changing. The U.S. Department of Agriculture budget has included an organic crop insurance program since 2001.

Another reason organic foods cost more in stores is that the organic produce infrastructure has been too small to benefit from economies of scale. However, the organic products food sector is now growing at a rate of 25 percent a year, which has resulted in the emergence of large organic food supermarket chains such as Whole Foods, Trader Joe's, and Wild Oats. Whole Foods has 143 stores in the United States and Canada and offers more than 1,200 items. Wild Oats competes with 102 stores.[23] Most or all of the difference in cost between conventional and organic food products would disappear if organic farming were a larger-scale operation and were able to reap the financial benefits that accrue to large farms under existing federal agricultural policies.

GENETICALLY MODIFIED FOODS

> The control of nature is a phrase conceived in arrogance, born of the Neanderthal age of biology and philosophy, when it was supposed that nature exists for the convenience of man.
>
> —Rachel Carson, *Silent Spring*

A revolution in commercial agriculture began in 1994 with the introduction of the Flavr-Savr tomato, engineered for delayed ripening. Two years later genetic engineering took off and now is spreading like wildfire. Large areas of genetically modified (GM) or transgenic crops seem to be taking over America's farmland. Extensive fields of GM soybeans, corn, cotton, and canola are now being grown in the United States. In 2002, 80 percent of America's soybean acreage was planted with GM herbicide-resistant seeds. This compares to 75 percent in 2001, 54 percent in 2000, 47 percent in 1999, 12 percent in 1997, and only 2 percent in 1996. In fields planted with the genetically modified soybeans weeds were more easily controlled, less plowing was needed, and soil erosion was minimized. GM corn is now 38 percent of all corn being grown; it produces its own insecticide. GM cotton in 2002 was 70 percent of cotton grown, up from 61 percent in 2000 and 48 percent in 1999; it is engineered to tolerate herbicides. Transgenic potatoes, tomatoes, melons, beets, and other crops have been approved for production by the U.S. Department of Agriculture. The operative phrase seems to be "full speed ahead."

Rice, the world's number one food staple, has been turned into yellow-colored "golden rice" in greenhouse experiments (gene from a daffodil). This GM rice yields a crop 35 percent larger than normal rice, has built-in resistance to pests, and contains vitamin A and iron, substances lacking in normal rice. Yellow rice is touted as a way to end the loss of vision that results from lack of vitamin A as well as a way to end most iron-deficiency anemia among rice-loving Asians. However, the average person would have to eat 20 pounds of cooked rice every day to get the necessary vitamins.[24] Yellow rice will soon be available for planting; seeds will be distributed free of charge to farmers in poor countries such as Vietnam, Thailand, and Bangladesh. Proponents of GM crops see the rice as the solution to feeding the coming world population of 8 or 10 billion people without destroying additional land, forests, and water.

The latest twist in genetically modified crops is called "biopharming," the production of "edible vaccines." In biopharming, crops and animals (e. g., milk from cows) are turned into factories to make drugs. Building vaccines into cornflakes or other foods could be especially helpful for developing countries, where syringes, refrigeration, and trained medical personnel often are scarce. One company has added a virus gene to corn to create corn that protects the consumer from hepatitis B.

GM crops are produced by transferring a few selected genes from one organism to another to produce a specific useful effect. Hundreds of variously modified foods are now in the supermarket pipeline, with genes borrowed from every form of life—bacterial, viral, insect, even animal. Bacterial genes can be put in corn; fish genes can be inserted into tomatoes. A gigantic game of "mix and match" is in progress. As of 2002, more than 50 different "designer" crops have received federal approval, and about 100 more are undergoing field trials.

The U.S. produces more than 70 percent of the world's genetically engineered crops. Two-thirds of the products on supermarket shelves contain genetically modified ingredients such as soy or corn.[25] We have all been eating genetically modified food products despite the fact that only 25 percent of American consumers believe GM plants are safe and more than half of Americans say they do not want to eat GM food. The U.S. Congress has yet to pass a law requiring labeling of foods that contain genetically modified ingredients, despite a recent poll showing that nearly 92 percent of the public wants such labeling.[26]

OBJECTIONS AND FEARS CONCERNING GM CROPS

Tampering with nature always involves risks. A growing number of studies have suggested that GM crops could lead to rapid evolution of pesticide-resistant insects, creation of new plant diseases, weeds that can no longer be controlled, and harm to insects that benefit humankind. Controversial laboratory investigations suggest that physiological changes in humans may result from seemingly innocuous gene manipulations in the food we eat. We may be creating Frankenfoods. A national poll by the Pew Research Center in 2002 revealed that 55 percent of Americans (47 percent of the men, 62 percent of the women) believed that genetic engineering will upset the balance of nature and damage the environment; 37 percent believed this was not likely. Democrats are more concerned than Republicans, 58 percent to 51 percent.

What is particularly worrisome is that because biological systems reproduce, genetic "pollution" cannot be cleaned up like a chemical spill or recalled like a defective automobile. Once the gene, or genie, is out of the bottle, so to speak, it cannot be put back in. And the genie is out.

Europeans have been particularly anxious about eating GM foods; 94 percent want them labeled (they were in 2003) and 70 percent object to eating them.[27] They were outraged by the announcement in May 2000 that genetically modified seed was accidentally planted on several farms in Europe. A company in the United States says the inadvertent planting of GM seeds is probably commonplace. The company, Genetic ID, screens agricultural products for GM material. They found that 12 of 20 random samples of conventional seed taken from American distributors contained some GM seed. Surveys in 2000 of grain handlers found that 80–90 percent intended to purchase biotech crops, but only 10 to 25 percent will segregate crops.

In 1999, Canadian farmers reported weeds that had acquired herbicide tolerance from neighboring transgenic crops just 2 years after the crops had been planted. Stray pollen and seed from GM oilseed rape, or canola, is now so widespread in Canada that it is difficult to grow conventional or organic strains without them being contaminated. In 2001 pollen from genetically modified maize was found in remote mountainsides of Mexico, having been blown there from plots of GM maize 60 miles away. In Hawaii in 2003 genes from an experimental crop of bioengineered corn spread to other corn growing nearby.[28] Common sense suggests that it is not possible to build a wall high enough to keep genetically modified organisms out of the environment, because pollen often drifts for miles on the wind, potentially contaminating everything in its path. Farmers are being sued by Monsanto for inadvertently growing GM products without permission. The farmers are, reasonably enough, outraged that they are being held responsible for blowing wind.

In rebuttal, supporters of GM crops say the critics ask the impossible: technology without risks and a promise of unconditional safety. They point out that there can never be a guarantee that anything is harmless. But unless there is evidence of harm, we shouldn't worry. Without risk taking there can be no experimentation, and therefore no progress. There is no such thing as total proof, no such thing as zero risk.

The supporters of transgenic crops say there is no difference between genetic modifications of plants by classical breeding methods to produce, for example, hybrid corn and using gene transfer to accomplish a similar result. If anything, they say, genetic engineering is more precise because it introduces just one or two genes into a plant. With conventional breeding, thousands of unknown genes are transferred in order to get the one with the desired trait. If altering genetic makeup is "unnatural," they say, humans have been performing unnatural acts for thousands of years. You don't find poodles or seedless grapes in nature. With the assortment of genes now known, crop designers can simply choose the traits they want and impart them in one step instead of by trial and error. Simply replace a gene believed to be neutral for humans with one that is beneficial.

The contamination problem may be particularly worrying in regard to pharmaceuticals produced from GM crops. Although some drugs you might ingest without realizing it would be digested before entering your bloodstream, others would not. Some oral drugs, such as plant-derived birth-control hormones, would not be digested and could cause havoc if they found their way into food. As one health expert has put it, "Just one mistake by a biotech company and we'll be eating other people's prescription drugs in our cornflakes."

The most extreme skeptics fear we may lose ourselves in the rush to play God. They point out that biotechnology deals with information coded chemically in living cells.

Tools are being developed that enable us not only to decode this information that's encoded in DNA, but also to change it. This has never before been possible. We may be charging into a dark room that has no exit after we enter. Are GM crops another example of technological abilities outstripping wisdom?

As I write this late in 2003, there seems to be a growing resistance in some parts of the American business community to genetically modified foods. Several major companies—including Frito-Lay, McDonalds, Gerber, and IAMS pet foods—have said they will no longer use genetically modified ingredients in their products. Major producers of baby food, in response to consumer preference, have stated they will not use them either. Pets and babies are sensitive issues in the American marketplace. And some major grain handlers have announced they want genetically engineered corn and soybeans kept separate from unmodified varieties, although this is probably impossible to achieve with 100 percent accuracy. Genetically modified food is the most contentious issue in American agriculture today.

It is too late to debate whether genetically modified food is a gift from God or a spawn of the Devil. It is here to stay and will likely be more widely accepted as the years pass. After years of investigation, there is no convincing evidence that GM crops pose risks to human health or that they will lead to an ecological breakdown. However, it is a good idea to be vigilant about GM experimentation, so that excesses in its use do not occur. In 2001, lawmakers in 36 states introduced 130 pieces of legislation dealing with agricultural biotechnology. Twenty-two state legislatures passed bills dealing with GM crops.[29]

SALT ACCUMULATION IN THE SOIL

> And the whole land thereof is brimstone, and salt, and a burning, that it is not sown, nor beareth, nor any grass groweth therein.
>
> —Deuteronomy 29:22

All natural waters contain dissolved salts obtained from rocks at the earth's surface. When the water evaporates, these salts precipitate and form mineral accumulations at and immediately below the soil surface, a process called salinization that affects 6 percent of America's farmland. It is a problem mostly in heavily irrigated areas such as the Western United States, where low annual precipitation necessitates extensive irrigation. In the San Joaquin Valley of California, for example, reports from more than a century ago tell of farmland abandoned because it became too salty for crops. Today, in California's Imperial Valley, more land is being taken out of production than is entering because of salinization. In Utah, a highway outside Salt Lake City offers a view of barren former croplands now crusted with poisonous white salts. Salinization is affecting more and more of America's cropland.

There is no easy or perfect solution for soil salinization. Flushing the soil with large amounts of low-salt water is very expensive and only slows the salinization process. And the flushed salty water simply migrates downstream to plague another farmer. Further, the flushing must be done slowly, for if the soil is flushed more rapidly than the salty water can drain away, the soil becomes waterlogged and unsuitable for planting.

Perhaps the best hope for taking the salt out of salinized soils is genetic modification of plants. A gene has recently been discovered that not only enables plants to withstand extreme salinity, but also helps them draw salt from the soil. Crops with a more active version of the gene could rehabilitate land lost to salinization.

CLEANING POLLUTED SOIL

> What we need is more people who specialize in the impossible.
>
> —Theodore Roethke

Cleaning organically polluted soil is expensive, takes much time, and is difficult under the best of circumstances. As we have already noted, it may take a decade to restore the vitality of insecticide-damaged soil. Other pollutants can last almost indefinitely—for example, spilled hydrocarbons (petroleum products such as gasoline). Perhaps the most promising method at present for cleaning polluted soil is the injection of contaminant-eating bacteria. Some exist naturally in soil and are quite specific in their tastes. Different organisms attack oil, raw sewage, treated sewage sludge, and other wastes. Within a year or two the amount of contaminant can be reduced to safe levels. Biologists are now creating genetically modified soil organisms that find particular contaminants particularly tasty. There is a glimmer of hope for restoring organically polluted soil.

AGRICULTURE AND CLIMATE CHANGE

> Climate is what you expect. Weather is what you get.
>
> —Robert A. Heinlein

There is more carbon dioxide in the air now than at any time in the past few thousand years. Rainfall in the United States has increased significantly during the past hundred years. And the climate is getting warmer. What do these changes mean for American agriculture? The answer at present is uncertain. On the plus side, more carbon dioxide means more photosynthesis. Rainfall also stimulates plant growth. Warmth is likewise good for plants. And the effects of these climatic changes are already visible. Satellite data from 1980 to 2000 reveal that plant density has increased significantly. Data from northern latitudes between 42° latitude (where Boston and Chicago are) and 70° latitude (northern Canada) indicate that the growing season in Alaska has lengthened by 17 days since 1950. Spring is arriving earlier and summer is ending later. At lower latitudes (most of the midcontinent grain belt) the lengthening is only 12 days[30] because the temperature change has been less. But the trend seems clear—more plant growth.

Unfortunately, some of the negative factors that influence plant growth and crop production are also increasing. Weeds (plants you don't want) also benefit from increased carbon dioxide, rainfall, and temperature. So do insect populations and plant fungal diseases. As a result there may be an intensified cry for more herbicides and insecticides or more crops genetically modified to resist insects and fungi by farmers and perhaps a resulting decrease in the growth rate of organic farming. An added negative factor for crop production is an observed increase in extreme precipitation events and resulting flooding and crop damage. Exactly how the pluses and minuses for agriculture associated with climate change will balance out is not yet clear. Data are still too few for firm conclusions to be drawn.

CONCLUSION

A few inches of dirt is all that separates us from mass starvation. We need to protect and preserve this layered surficial resource we call soil at all costs, but many or most farming practices concentrate on short-term profit rather than long-term survival. Unnecessary erosion, deliberate pollution by artificial chemicals, and salinization have been going on for many decades and now threaten the productivity of breadbasket America. Unless these trends are reversed we, as well as the many nations that depend on us for food, are in deep trouble.

The amount of land being farmed in the United States has been continually decreasing since 1950. Part of this decrease has resulted from increasing urbanization and suburban sprawl, phenomena that show no signs of stopping. As they say, money talks, and when a commercial developer offers big bucks for farm property, farmers are no different from the rest of us. They are likely to sell. Another factor in the decrease of farmland is the trend of young people leaving the farm for the lure of the big city. Farming as a "calling" is not as strong a factor as it once was for the children of farmers. The average age of farmers is increasing.

The effects of genetically modified crops on the future of farming are not clear. There are recognized benefits but also some reasons for concern. But the genie is out of the bottle. Experiments with transgenic crops are certain to continue, and we can only hope that the light of better crops to come is not the light beam of an oncoming train.

Most of the changes associated with our increasingly warm climate probably will be beneficial for American agriculture. But it will not be all sunshine and roses. Some plant pests and diseases are likely to become more bothersome and may spur a call for more herbicides and insecticides. Or perhaps for more crop varieties genetically modified to resist these invasions. American agriculture has entered an era of rapid and perhaps fundamental change. It cannot be stopped. We hope it can be controlled.

NOTES

1 M. Freudenheim, "A Boom in Surgery to Shrink the Stomach," *International Herald Tribune*, August 30–31, 2003, p. 9; R. Winslow, "Obese American Teens Seek Stomach Surgery," *Wall Street Journal*, October 9, 2003, p. 20.

2 A. Ananthaswamy, "Cities Eat Away at Earth's Best Land," *New Scientist*, December 21/28, 2002, p. 9.

3 J. R. "Sprawling Over Croplands," *Science News*, March 4, 2000, p. 155.

4 M. Yudelman and J. M. Kealy, "The Graying Farmers," *Population Today*, May-June 2000, p. 6.

5 California Air Resources Board, "Smog and California Crops," 1991, pp. 2–3.

6 *Agriculture Fact Book 2001–2002*, U.S. Department of Agriculture, 2003, p. 24, http://www.usda.gov/factbook/2002factbook.pdf.

7 *Agriculture Fact Book 2001–2002*, U.S. Department of Agriculture, 2003, p. 30, http://www.usda.gov/nass/pubs/trends/farmnumbers.htm.

8 "Organic Agriculture: Implementing Ecology-Based Practices," *Organic Trade Association Newsletter*, No. 19, October-November 2001, p. 3.

9 Reuters, July 4, 2002. http://www.planetark.org/dailynewsstory.cfm.newsid/ 16699/story.

10 T. C. Rembert, "Food Porn," *E Magazine*, May-June, 1998, p. 19.

11 E. Dooley, "Protected Harvest," *Environmental Health Perspectives*, May 2002, p. A237.

12 H. I. Zeliger, "Toxic Effects of Chemical Mixtures," *Archives of Environmental Health*, January 2003, pp. 23–29.

13 D. J. Epstein, "Secret Ingredients," *Scientific American*, August 2003, p. 12.

14 B. Halweil, "Pesticide-Resistant Species Flourish," *Vital Signs*, ed. L. Starke (New York: Norton, 1999), 124.

15 "In Brief," *Environment*, September 2001, p. 8.

16 C. Bright, "Bioinvasions," *World-Watch*, July-August, 1998, p. 39.

17 Japan Chemical Week, December 21–28, 1995.

18 C. Green and A. Kremen, "U.S. Organic Farming in 2000–2001," *USDA Economic Research Service, Agriculture Information Bulletin no. 780*, 2003.

19 C. Green and A. Kremen, "U.S. Organic Farming in 2000–2001," *USDA Economic Research Service, Agriculture Information Bulletin* No. 780, 2003.
20 S. Deneen, "Food Fight," *E Magazine,* July-August 2003, p. 28.
21 B. Halweil, "Organic Food Found to be Higher in Heath-Promoting Compounds," *World-Watch,* July-August 2003, p. 9.
22 B. Halweil, "Organic Gold Rush," *World-Watch,* May-June 2001, p. 24.
23 R. Sheer, "Organic Profits," *E Magazine,* July-August 2003, p. 44, 46.
24 B. Halweil, "Farming in the Public Interest," *State of the World 2002,* ed. L. Starke (New York: Norton, 2002) p. 58.
25 K. Brown, "Seeds of Concern," *Scientific American,* April 2001, pp. 39–45.
26 "GM Food and Safety," *The Ecologist,* April 2003, p. 11.
27 J. Geary, "Risky Business," *Time,* July 28, 2003, p. 42.
28 "World Updates," *World-Watch,* July-August 2003, p. 11.
29 B. H. "Biotech Crop Laws Were Big in 2001," *Science News,* February 2, 2002, p. 77.
30 "Increased Plant Density in Northern Latitudes," *Environmental Science & Technology,* November 1, 2001, p. 443A.

READING 6.2

Food–Systems–Racism

FROM MISTREATMENT TO TRANSFORMATION

By Eric Holt-Giménez and Breeze Harper

Racism—the systemic mistreatment of people based on their ethnicity or skin color—affects all aspects of our society, including our food system. While racism has no biological foundation, the socio-economic and political structures that dispossess and exploit people of color, coupled with widespread misinformation about race, cultures and ethnic groups, make racism one of the more intractable injustices causing poverty, hunger and malnutrition. Racism is not simply attitudinal prejudice or individual acts, but an historical legacy that privileges one group of people over others. Racism—individual, institutional and structural (see Box 6.2.3)—also impedes good faith efforts to build a fair, sustainable food system.

Despite its pervasiveness, racism is almost never mentioned in international programs for food aid and agricultural development. While anti-hunger and food security programs frequently cite the shocking statistics, racism is rarely identified as the cause of inordinately high rates of hunger, food insecurity, pesticide poisoning and diet-related disease among people of color. Even the widely-hailed "good food" movement—with

This article benefited from the helpful comments of Alison Alkon, Ph.D. of University of the Pacific, Hank Herrera of the Center for Popular Education, Research and Policy, Inc., J. Miakoda Taylor of Fierce Allies, and Ana C. Galvis Martinez from Food First.

Source: Creative Commons

its plethora of projects for organic agriculture, permaculture, healthy food, community supported agriculture, farmers markets and corner store conversions—tends to address the issue of racism unevenly.[1] Some organizations *are* committed to dismantling racism in the food system and center this work in their activities. Others are sympathetic but are not active on the issue. Many organizations, however, see racism as too difficult, tangential to their work, or a divisive issue to be avoided. The hurt, anger, fear, guilt, grief and hopelessness of racism are uneasily addressed in the food movement—if they are addressed at all.

This Backgrounder is first in a series about how racism and our food system have co-evolved, how present-day racism operates within the food system, and what we can do to dismantle racism and build a fair, just and sustainable food system that works for everyone.

CASTE, FOOD AND CAPITALISM

The term *racial caste* describes a "stigmatized racial group locked into an inferior position by law and custom."[2] Racial caste is one consequence of a hierarchical imbalance in economic, political and social power (sexism and classism are others). In North America and much of Europe, this racial caste system privileges light-complexioned people of Northern European ancestry.

Any country that has been subjected to Northern colonialism has been structured by a racial caste system in which 'whiteness' concedes social privileges. This system was originally developed to justify European colonialism and enable the economic exploitation of vast lands in the Americas, Africa, and Asia. Outright dispossession through genocidal military conquest and government treaties affected 15 million indigenous people—most of whom were farmers and lived in towns—throughout the period of US "westward expansion." Colonization was largely carried out by white planters and aspiring white smallholder-settlers.[3]

In the Americas, Europeans and people of European descent murdered and dispossessed indigenous populations for their natural resources, sometimes enslaving them (e.g., the Spanish Catholic missions and *encomiendas*). People from West African regions were enslaved, forcibly shipped across the Atlantic Ocean and sold as chattel to do backbreaking labor, primarily on sugar, tobacco and cotton plantations. While slaves acquired through war and trade had been part of many societies for thousands of years, widespread commerce in human beings did not appear until the advent of capitalism and the European conquest.

The super-exploitation of enslaved human beings on plantations allowed slave systems to out-compete agrarian wage labor for over two hundred years. Under slavery, human beings were bought, sold and mortgaged as property. The tremendous wealth generated from slavery was sent to northern banks where it was used to finance military conquest, more plantations and ultimately, the industrial revolution.[4] The centrality of slavery and dispossession in the emergence of 19th century capitalism flies in the face of many myths about our food system (and capitalism). As Bekert [5] points out,

> "[It] was not the small farmers of the rough New England countryside who established the United States' economic position. It was the backbreaking labor of unremunerated American slaves in places like South Carolina, Mississippi, and Alabama ... After the Civil War [and Abolition], a new kind of capitalism arose, in the United States and elsewhere. Yet that new capitalism—characterized first and foremost by states with unprecedented bureaucratic, infrastructural, and military capacities, and by wage labor—had been enabled by the profits, institutions, networks, technologies, and innovations that emerged from slavery, colonialism, and land expropriation."

The social justification for the commoditization of human beings was the alleged biological inferiority of the people who were used as property, and the divinely-determined superiority of their owners. This division of power, ownership, and labor was held in place through violence and terrorism. It also required constant religious and scientific justification constructed on the relatively new concept of "race." Although enslaved peoples came from ethnically and culturally different regions of West Africa, they were classified as *Black*. Though slave owners came from different areas of Europe where they had been known by vague tribal names like Scythians, Celts, Gauls and Germani, they were classified as *White*.

Slavery and colonization produced over a century of "scientific" misinformation that attempted to classify human beings on the basis of their physical traits. Eventually, people were racialized into three major categories: Mongoloid, Negroid, and Caucasoid, with Caucasians awarded superior intelligence, physical beauty and moral character. Scientists argued over how to classify the many peoples that didn't fit into these categories (such as the Finns, Malays and most of the indigenous people in the Americas). The messiness of the categories was unimportant to the political and economic objectives of racism.

Systematically erasing the unique ethnic, tribal, and cultural backgrounds of the world's people while elevating a mythical Caucasian race was a shameful exercise in egregiously bad science, but it endured because it supported the control of the world's land, labor and capital by a powerful elite.[6]

BOX 6.2.1: THE BIRTH AND MUTATIONS OF WHITENESS

From the beginning, the concept of race has been fluid, constantly accommodating to the changing needs of capital and the ruling class while undermining struggles for equality and liberation. For example, in the colonial Americas, there was little social difference between African slaves and European indentured servants. But when they began organizing together against their colonial rulers, the Virginia House of Burgesses introduced the Virginia Slave Codes of 1705. These laws established new property rights for slave owners; allowed for the legal, free trade of slaves; established separate trial courts for whites and Blacks; prohibited Black people from owning weapons and from striking a white person; prohibited free Black people from employing whites and allowed for the apprehension of suspected runaways. Much later, during the early 20th century, poor, light-skinned Irish Catholic immigrants living in the US were initially treated as an inferior race and experienced discrimination as non-white. As the Irish began to organize for their rights—often across racial barriers—they were steadily categorized as white, setting them apart politically—if not economically—from Black and indigenous people.[7] Mediterranean people, some eastern Europeans and light-complexioned Latin Americans have had similar experiences.

Slavery had a tremendous influence on food and labor systems around the world and was the central pillar of capitalism's racial caste system until it was widely abolished in the late 19th century. In the US, after nearly three years of bloody civil war, the Emancipation Proclamation of 1863 released African-Americans living in Confederate states from slavery (though it took nearly two more years of war before ex-slaves could freely leave their plantations).[8] The Thirteenth Amendment to the US Constitution finally put a legal end to slavery in the US in 1865. But after a "moment in the sun" African Americans living in the former Confederacy were quickly segregated and disenfranchised through "Jim Crow" laws designed to maintain the racial caste system in the absence of slavery.

Racial caste has systematically shaped the food system, particularly during periods of labor shortage. During WWII for example, when much of the US's labor force was fighting in Europe and the Pacific, the *Mexican Farm Labor Program Agreement* of 1942 imported Mexican peasants to keep the US food system running. Without them, the US could not have fought the war. After the war, the *Bracero Program* brought in over 4 million Mexican farmworkers. Mexican labor was cheap and legally exploitable. The "immigrant labor subsidy" transferred billions of dollars in value to the sector, turned WWII into a decades-long agricultural boon and transformed labor relations in agriculture.[9]

But just as African-Americans are not recognized for their role in establishing the US as a nation (or capitalism as its economic system), racial caste invisiblizes the contribution of Mexican farmworkers to the US's survival during WWII and stigmatizes Mexican-Americans as citizens. Similar scenarios have played out with Asian, Filipino and Caribbean immigrants. To this day, important sectors of the food systems in the US and Europe continue to be defined by dispossessed and exploited immigrant labor from the Global South. Their systematic mistreatment is justified by the centuries-old racial caste system.

RACISM IN THE FOOD SYSTEM

Calls to "fix a broken food system" assume that the capitalist food system used to work well. This assumption ignores the food system's long, racialized history of mistreatment of people of color. The food system is unjust and unsustainable but it is not broken—it functions precisely as the capitalist food system has always worked; concentrating power in the hands of a privileged minority and passing off the social and environmental "externalities" disproportionately on to racially stigmatized groups.

Statistics from the US confirm the persistence of racial caste in the food system:

African-Americans once owned 16 million acres of farmland. But by 1997, after many decades of Jim Crow, several national farm busts and a generally inattentive (or obstructionist) Department of Agriculture (USDA), less than 20,000 Black farmers owned just 2 million acres of land.[10] The rate of Black land loss has been twice that of white land loss and today less than 1 million acres are farmed.[11, 12] According to the USDA 2012 Census of Agriculture, of the country's 2.1 million farmers, only 8 % are farmers of color and only half of those are owners of land. Though their farm share is growing (particularly among Latinos, who now number over 67,000 farmers), people of color tend to earn less than $10,000 in annual sales, produce only 3% of agricultural value, and farm just 2.8% of farm acreage.[13]

While white farmers dominate as operator-owners, farmworkers and food workers—from field to fork—are overwhelmingly people of color. Most are paid poverty wages, have inordinately high levels of food insecurity and experience nearly twice the level of wage theft than white workers. While white food workers' average incomes are $25,024 a year, workers of color make only $19,349 a year. White workers hold nearly 75% of the managerial positions in the food system. Latinos hold 13% and Black and Asian workers 6.5%.[14]

The resulting poverty from poorly paid jobs is racialized: Of the 47 million people living below the poverty line in the United States, less than 10% are white. African-Americans make up 27% of the poor, Native Americans 26%, Latinos 25.6% and Asian-Americans 11.7%.[15]

Poverty results in high levels of food insecurity for people of color. Of the 50 million food insecure people in the US 10.6% are white, 26.1% are Black, 23.7% are Latino and 23% are Native American.[16] Even restaurant workers—an occupation dominated by people of color (who should have access to all the food they need)—are twice as food insecure as the national average.

Race, poverty and food insecurity correlate closely with obesity and diet-related disease; nearly half of African-Americans and over 42% of Latinos suffer from obesity. While less than 8% of non-Hispanic whites suffer from diabetes, 9% of Asian-Americans, 12.8% of Hispanics, 13.2 % of non-Hispanic African-Americans and 15.9 % of Indigenous people have diabetes. At $245 billion a year, the national expense in medical costs and reduced productivity resulting from diabetes are staggering.[17] The human and economic burdens of diabetes and diet-related disease on low-income families of color are devastating.

TRAUMA, RESISTANCE AND TRANSFORMATION: AN EQUITABLE FOOD SYSTEM IS POSSIBLE

Recognizing racism as foundational in today's capitalist food system helps explain why people of color suffer disproportionately from its environmental externalities, labor abuses, resource inequities and diet related diseases. It also helps explain why many of the promising alternatives such as land trusts, farmers' markets, and community supported agriculture tend to be dominated by people who are privileged by whiteness.[18] Making these alternatives readily accessible to people of color requires a social commitment to racial equity and a fearless commitment to social justice. Ensuring equity of access to healthy food, resources and dignified, living wage jobs, would go a long way towards "fixing" the food system.

BOX 6.2.2: PEDAGOGY OF THE OPPRESSED

"[The] great humanistic and historical task of the oppressed [is] to liberate themselves and their oppressors as well. The oppressors, who oppress, exploit, and rape by virtue of their power, cannot find in this power the strength to liberate either the oppressed or themselves. Only power that springs from the weakness of the oppressed will be sufficiently strong to free both. Any attempt to "soften" the power of the oppressor in deference to the weakness of the oppressed almost always manifests itself in the form of false generosity; indeed, the attempt never goes beyond this. In order to have the continued opportunity to express their "generosity," the oppressors must perpetuate injustice as well. An unjust social order is the permanent fount of this "generosity," which is nourished by death, despair, and poverty. That is why the dispensers of false generosity become desperate at the slightest threat to its source."[19]

The trauma of racism is inescapable. In addition to the pain and indignity of racialized mistreatment, people of color can internalize racial misinformation, reinforcing racial stereotypes. While white privilege benefits white communities, it can also immobilize them with guilt, fear and hopelessness. Both internalized racism and white guilt are socially and emotionally paralyzing, and make racism difficult to confront and interrupt.

Difficult, but not impossible.

Since before the Abolition movement and the Underground Railroad of the mid-1800s, people have found ways to build alliances across racial divides. The history of the US food system is replete with examples of resistance and liberation: from the early struggles of the Southern Tenant Farmers Union to the Black Panther's food programs and the boycotts and strikes by the United Farm Workers. More recently, the Food Chain Workers Alliance have fought for better wages and decent working conditions. The increase of local food policy councils run by people of color and the spread of Growing Power's urban farming groups reflect a rise in leadership by those communities with the most at stake in changing a system that some have referred to as "food apartheid." Oppressed communities have developed ways of healing historical trauma and there are peer counseling groups with skills for working through the immobilizing feelings of internalized oppression, fear, hopelessness and guilt. All of these resources and historical lessons can be brought into the food movement.

Racism still stands in the way of a "good food revolution." If the food movement can begin dismantling racism in the food system—and within the food movement itself—it will have opened a path not only for food system transformation, but for ending the system of racial caste.

BOX 6.2.3: DEFINITIONS

- Interpersonal Racism: This refers to prejudices and discriminatory behaviors where one group makes assumptions about the abilities, motives, and intents of other groups based on race. This set of prejudices leads to cruel intentional or unintentional actions towards other groups.
- Internalized Racism: In a society where one group is politically, socially and economically dominant, members of stigmatized groups, who are bombarded with negative messages about their own abilities and intrinsic worth,

may internalize those negative messages. It holds people back from achieving their fullest potential and reinforces the negative messages which, in turn, reinforces the oppressive systems.

- Institutional Racism: Where assumptions about race are structured into the social and economic institutions in our society. Institutional racism occurs when organizations, businesses, or institutions like schools and police departments discriminate, either deliberately or indirectly against certain groups of people to limit their rights. This type of racism reflects the cultural assumptions of the dominant group.
- Structural Racism: While most of the legally based forms of racial discrimination have been outlawed, many of the racial disparities originating in various institutions and practices continue and accumulate as major forces in economic and political structures and cultural traditions. Structural racism refers to the ways in which social structures and institutions, over time, perpetuate and produce cumulative, durable, race-based inequalities. This can occur even in the absence of racist intent on the part of individuals.
- Racialization: This refers to the process through which 'race' (and its associated meanings) is attributed to something –an individual, community, status, practice, or institution. Institutions that appear to be neutral can be racialized, shaped by previous racial practices and outcomes so that the institution perpetuates racial disparities, or makes them worse. This is true of the criminal justice system, the education and health systems in our country, and so on.[20]
- "Reverse" Racism: Sometimes used to characterize 'affirmative action' programs, but this is inaccurate. Affirmative action programs are attempts to repair the results of institutionalized racism by setting guidelines and establishing procedures for finding qualified applicants from all segments of the population. The term 'reverse racism' is also sometimes used to characterize the mistreatment that individual whites may have experienced at the hands of individuals of color. This too is inaccurate. While any form of humans harming other humans is wrong, because no one is entitled to mistreat anyone, we should not confuse the occasional mistreatment experienced by whites at the hands of people of color with the systematic and institutionalized mistreatment experienced by people of color at the hands of whites.
- Racial Justice: Racial justice refers to a wide range of ways in which groups and individuals struggle to change laws, policies, practices and ideas that reinforce and perpetuate racial disparities. Proactively, it is first and foremost the struggle for equitable outcomes for people of color.

USEFUL LINKS

Haas Institute for a Fair and Inclusive Society: http://haasinstitute.berkeley.edu

Grassroots Policy Project: http://www.strategicpractice.org

Black Lives Matter: http://blacklivesmatter.com/

Unlearning Racism: http://www.unlearningracism.org/

Center for Social Inclusion: http://www.centerforsocialinclusion.org/

Growing Power: http://growingfoodandjustice.org/race-and-the-food-system/dismantling-racism-resources/

ENDNOTES

1 Alison Hope Alkon, Black, White and Green: Farmers Markets, Race, and the Green Economy (Atlanta: University of Georgia Press, 2012).

2 Michelle Alexander, The New Jim Crow: Mass Incarceration in the Age of Colorblindness, Revised Edition (New York: The New Press, 2012).

3 Roxanne Dunbar-Ortiz, An Indigenous People's History of the United States (Boston: Beacon Press, 2014).

4 Edward E. Baptist, The Half Has Never Been Told: Slavery and the Making of American Capitalism (New York, NY: Basic Books, 2014).

5 Sven Beckert, "Slavery and Capitalism," The Chronicle of Higher Education, December 12, 2014, http://chronicle.com/article/SlaveryCapitalism/150787/.

6 Nell Irvin Painter, The History of White People (New York: W.W. Norton and Company, Inc., 2010).

7 Noel Ignatiev, How the Irish Became White (New York, London: Routledge, 1995).

8 Alexander, op. cit.

9 Center for History and News Media, "Bracero History Archive," 2014, http://braceroarchive.org/.

10 Pete Daniel, Dispossession: Discrimination Against African American Farmers in the Age of Civil Rights (Chapel Hill: University of North Carolina Press, 2013).

11 Anuradha Mittal with Joan Powell, "The Last Plantation," Backgrounder (Oakland, CA: Food First/Institute for Food and Development Policy, Winter 2000).

12 john powell, "Poverty and Race Through a Belongingness Lens," Policy Matters, Volume 1, Issue 5 (Northwest Area Foundation, April 2012).

13 Eric Holt-Giménez, "This Land Is Whose Land? Dispossession, Resistance and Reform in the United States," Backgrounder (Oak-land, CA: Food First/Institute for Food and Development Policy, Spring 2014), http://foodfirst.org/publication/this-land-is-whose-land/.

14 "Food Insecurity of Restaurant Workers" (Food First, Food Chain Workers Alliance, Restaurant Opportunities Center, 2014), http://foodfirst.org/publication/food-insecurity-of-restaurant-workers/.

15 Carmen DeNavas-Walt, Bernadette D. Proctor, and Jessica C. Smith, "Income, Poverty, and Health Insurance Coverage in the United States (2012)" (Washington, D.C.: US Census Bureau, September 2013) in The US Farm Bill: Corporate Power and Structural Racialization in the United States Food System (Berkeley, CA: Haas Institute for a Fair and Inclusive Society, UC Berkeley, 2015), http://haasinstitute.berkeley.edu

16 Elsadig Elsheikh and Nadia Barhoum, "Structural Racialization and Food Insecurity in the United States: A Report to the U.N. Human Rights Committee on the International Covenant on Civil and Political Rights" (Haas Institute for a Fair and Inclusive Society, UC Berkeley, August 2013).

17 Centers for Disease Control and Prevention, "National Diabetes Statistics Report: Estimates of Diabetes and Its Burden in the United States, 2014." (Atlanta, GA: US Department of Health and Human Services; 2014). http://www.cdc.gov/diabetes/pubs/statsreport14/national-diabetes-report-web.pdf.

18 Julie Guthman, "If They Only Knew: Color Blindness and Universalism in California Alternative Food Institutions," in Taking Food Public: Redefining Foodways in a Changing World (New York, London: Routledge, 2012), 211–23.

19 Paulo Freire, Pedagogy of the Oppressed (New York: Herder and Herder, 1970).

20 Sandra Hinson, Richard Healey, and Nathaniel Weisenberg, "Race, Power and Policy: Dismantling Structural Racism" (National People's Action, n.d.).

CHAPTER SEVEN

Environmental Justice

This chapter on environmental justice asks a fundamental question: Why do some communities get more environmental goods and fewer environmental harms than other communities? Environmental goods are the pleasant and beneficial aspects of nature—clean air, clean water, clean soil that grows healthy food, and access to parks and green spaces for recreation and activities. Environmental harms describe the challenges of air pollution, toxic waste dumps, urban decay, and lack of access to good food and green spaces. In this chapter, we examine how communities that are marginalized by income and race are more likely to struggle to access beneficial nature and more likely to live in the midst of the harms and hazards of multiple types of toxicity and pollution. Environmental justice is about the quest for a safe and healthy environment that equally includes and benefits all people in society.

It would seem that activism for biodiversity conservation, land preservation, and overall environmental improvement would be a steady partner of the quest for environmental justice. This has not always been the case, and, in fact, the two movements—environmentalism and environmental justice—have remained stubbornly segregated along lines of race and class. The selected reading by Phaedra Pezzullo and Ronald Sandler, "Introduction: Revisiting the Environmental Justice Challenge to Environmentalism" from their book *Environmental Justice and Environmentalism: The Social Justice Challenge to the Environmental Movement* (2007), describes the history of the separation of these two movements for better human-nature relationships, why they continue to be addressed by different groups in society, and the challenges of bringing environmentalism and environmental justice into an enduring partnership.

Robert D. Bullard is known as the "Father of Environmental Justice" for his extensive research on the distribution of environmental harms in poor and racially segregated communities and his work to correct these issues. Bullard's (1990) reading selected for this chapter, "Environmentalism, Economic Blackmail, and Civil Rights: Competing Agendas Within the Black Community" from the book *Communities in Economic Crisis* edited by John Gaventa, is considered a classic depiction of the challenges of environmental justice, especially in the southern states of America. One of the critical examples that Bullard writes about took place in Afton, North Carolina, in 1978. The Exchange Project recommended reading, "Real People, Real Stories" (2006), is a summary of that well-known environmental justice case. What is evident as we review these cases and read the recommended Energy Justice Network's "Principles of Environmental Justice" (1991) is that there is overlap between environmental justice and the other issues in the text, especially the climate crisis in Chapter 5, agricultural and food justice in Chapter 6, and urbanization and population growth in Chapter 8.

Finally, Lauret Savoy's recommended reading, pages 1–5 of her book *Still an American Dilemma* (2013), picks up on an issue from Chapter 3 about environmental history, namely, that underlying the split between environmentalism and environmental justice is the circumstance that different groups of people have different concepts of and access to environmental decision-making.

RECOMMENDED READING

"The Principles of Environmental Justice (EJ)." First National People of Color Environmental Leadership Summit, October 24–27, 1991, Washington DC. Retrieved from: https://www.nrdc.org/resources/principles-environmental-justice-ej.

Savoy, L. 2013. *Still an American Dilemma*, 1–5 (Tucson, AZ: Terrain Publishing). Retrieved from: https://www.terrain.org/2013/a-stones-throw/still-an-american-dilemma/.

"Real People—Real Stories." 2006. In *The Exchange Project Case Study, Afton, North Carolina*, 2–17. *Exchange Project at The University of North Carolina at Chapel Hill.*

RECOMMENDED VIEWING

Grist. 2016. "Environmental Justice—Explained" (3:33).

WATCH AT https://www.youtube.com/watch?v=dREtXUij6_c.

Prince Ea. 2015. "Dear Future Generations: Sorry" (6:02).

WATCH AT https://www.youtube.com/watch?v=eRLJscAlk1M.

READING AND DISCUSSION PROMPTS

1. Pezzullo and Sandler list criticisms of the "Group of Ten" by environmental justice groups that highlight the focus of the Group of Ten on reductionist environmental protections that ignore "social, racial, and economic justice." Which organizations are in the Group of Ten? Are they familiar to you?
2. Since the movements Pezzullo and Sandler describe started in the 1990s, do you think the Group of Ten has made significant progress incorporating social, racial, and economic justice into their agendas? If you have no idea, investigate this issue online!
3. In his classic 1990 article, Robert Bullard writes that "The 'jobs versus environment' argument has held Black Southerners captive to a system that often forces them to choose between employment and a clean work environment." This is Bullard's main argument in the article. Bullard is describing environmental justice as a civil rights issue in communities of color. What do you think Bullard means by jobs versus environment? What relationships can you find between civil rights and environmental rights? Between social justice and environmental justice?
4. Bullard gave a powerful example of environmental injustice in his description of the waste disposal facilities in Houston in the 1920s–1970s. Briefly explain what was unjust and inequitable about the city's waste disposal operations.

READING 7.1

Revisiting the Environmental Justice Challenge to Environmentalism

By Phaedra C. Pezzullo and Ronald Sandler

> The two environmental movements could not be more different as black and white is truer than it sounds.
>
> —M. Dowie[1]

> People don't get all the connections. They say the environment is over here, the civil rights group is over there, the women's group is over there, and the other groups are here. Actually all of them are one group, and the issues we fight become null and void if we have no clean water to drink, no clean air to breathe and nothing to eat.
>
> —C. Tucker[2]

The environmental and environmental justice movements would seem to be natural allies. Indeed, one might expect that a social movement dedicated to environmental integrity and preservation and a social movement dedicated to justice in the distribution of environmental goods and decision making would not be two distinct social movements, but rather two aspects of one encompassing movement. After all, both have chosen the core term of "environment" to name their passions, mobilize their constituents, and send their message to those they aim to persuade. Moreover, there are ample opportunities for joint efforts in the cause for environmental health, sustainability, and integrity. All of our environments—from urban to wilderness areas—are being stressed, polluted, and commodified, while corporations and governmental agencies increasingly are challenging the general public and local communities for control over them. So it would seem reasonable that the movements would be, at minimum, coalition partners in a broad array of social and political struggles. Therefore, it is somewhat unexpected that the relationship between the environmental movement and the environmental justice movement in the United States often has been characterized as one of division and even hostility, rather than one of cooperation.

Since at least the early 1990s, activists from the environmental justice movement consistently have criticized what they consider the "mainstream" environmental movement's racism, classism, and limited activist agenda, charges against which environmental organizations have responded in ways ranging from defiance to varying degrees of acceptance.[3] For its part, the academic community's reaction to these critiques, both initially and in subsequent years, primarily has been to investigate the validity of the various charges, as well as to try to better understand the sources—the social, cultural, racial, economic, conceptual, institutional, historical, and rhetorical factors—that generate the tensions between the two movements. This scholarship was and remains important work, and it provides the basis for the next step: exploring how the two movements might be able to overcome, move beyond, or dissolve what divides them, to foster productive cooperation toward accomplishing their goals. The aim of this volume is to provide a stimulus for moving academic dialog in that direction. It consists of ten original essays, each of which considers some aspect of the environmental justice challenge to environmentalism and the relationship between the two movements in terms of what divisions remain, how interactions between the movements have fared in the past, and what the limits and possibilities are for the future. Without neglecting significant conceptual and practical points of tension, and while recognizing that there are times when collaboration is not appropriate or desirable, the collection as a whole emphasizes productive responses to the challenges environmental justice poses to environmentalism and the ways both movements have the potential to accomplish a great deal when they work together.

That the goals of both the environmental justice movement and the environmental movement are urgent and worth advancing is something all the contributors to this volume embrace. What is ultimately at issue is *not* whether one movement has more worthwhile goals or moral authority over the other, but, rather, *how the goals of both movements might be achieved together effectively*. As such, the contributors to this collection do not approach their topics from the "side" of either the environmental or environmental justice movement. Nor do they all approach the theme of this volume from one particular academic discipline. Among the fields represented are anthropology, environmental studies, natural resource sciences, philosophy, public policy, rhetoric, and sociology. The contributing authors thus provide a range of scholarly perspectives, methods, and frames. This diversity is appropriate to the multifaceted relationship between the two movements and the complexity of the social, political, conceptual, evaluative, historical, and rhetorical terrain in which they operate. A comprehensive assessment of the prospects for these two movements to work together requires that each of these perspectives be considered, without encumbrances from disciplinary boundaries.

The remainder of this introduction is intended to serve, first, as a primer for those who are not already familiar with two key events in the early 1990s—the letters to the "Group of Ten" and the First National People of Color Environmental Leadership Summit—that have since then largely framed the relationship between the two movements and significantly oriented the scholarship regarding the challenges that environmental justice poses to environmentalism. It then provides a brief discussion of what both activists and scholars have identified as major sources of division between the two movements. Finally, it provides a brief overview of the chapters, locating them within the questions, issues, and themes that drive this volume.

THE LETTERS

On January 16, 1990, the Gulf Coast Tenant Leadership Development Project sent a letter to the "Group of Ten"[4] national environmental organizations, declaring, "Racism and the 'whiteness' of the environmental movement is our Achilles heel."[5] Two months later, on March 16, 1990, the Southwest Organizing Project sent a second letter to the Group of Ten. This letter, which included 103 signatories, invited "frank and open dialogue" regarding the following charges:

> Although environmental organizations calling themselves the "Group of Ten" often claim to represent our interests, in observing your activities it has become clear to us that your organizations play an equal role in the disruption of our communities. There is a clear lack of accountability by the Group of Ten environmental organizations towards Third World communities in the Southwest, in the United States as a whole, and internationally.

The letters accused the Group of Ten of ignorance, ambivalence, and complicity with the environmental exploitation of communities of color within the United States and abroad. Although they often emphasized that environmental tenets are universal, the Group of Ten's pursuit of their conception of environmentalism had failed, according to the letters, to take into account the ramifications of their agenda for "working people in general and people of color in particular." The letters also claimed that the voices and representatives of communities of color too often were marginalized from environmental decision making by the very organizations that claimed to be representing their interests on a variety of issues ranging from grazing of sheep on public lands to "debt-for-nature swaps," in which Third World countries are invited to trade some rights over parts of their land for reduction of their national debt. Overall, the letters called for the environmental movement to review comprehensively and address its own culpability in patterns of environmental racism and undemocratic processes, including its hiring practices, lobbying agenda, political platforms, financial backers, organizing practices, and representations of Third World communities within the United States and abroad.

This was not the first time such concerns were expressed, but in this case environmental justice activists succeeded in raising the social, political, ethical, and institutional challenges to environmentalism in a way that gained the attention of the national mainstream press.[6] In light of the bluntness of these public allegations, it seemed impossible for the environmental movement to plead ignorance any longer about accusations of its own responsibility in patterns of racism and elitism. Meanwhile, the environmental justice movement only seemed to be gaining momentum.

THE FIRST SUMMIT

One year later, on October 24–27, 1991, the First National People of Color Environmental Leadership Summit (Summit I) was held in Washington, DC. The gathering brought together more than a thousand activists from across the United States, as well as Canada, Central America, and the Marshall Islands. In the words of then Executive Director of the United Church of Christ Commission for Racial Justice, Reverend Benjamin F. Chavis, Jr., Summit I was "not an independent 'event' but a significant and pivotal step in a crucial process whereby people of color are organizing themselves and their communities for self-determination and self-empowerment around the central issues of environmental justice" (1991, p. i).[7]

On the final day of the Summit, the delegates adopted the seventeen "Principles of Environmental Justice," which has since served as the defining document for the environmental justice movement. (The Principles of Environmental Justice can be found in Appendix A of this collection.) The Principles embody an expansive conception of environmental issues, and locate them within an encompassing social, political, and ethical outlook. They call for a robust activist agenda and a wide range of spiritual, ecological, sustainable, educational, and social justice commitments. They articulate a desire for universal protection and self-determination domestically and internationally. Overall, the Principles emphasize that the environmental justice movement is not only an effort for racial justice; it is a movement for justice for "all peoples."

At Summit I, a prominent corollary to articulating a vision for the environmental justice movement was addressing the relationship between environmental justice communities and environmental organizations. For example, Pat Bryant, executive director of the Gulf Coast Tenants Organization, outlined conditions for dialogue with environmental organizations.

> I think there is fertile ground for coalition and cooperation. But it cannot happen unless we adhere to some very basic principles . ... We cannot join hands with anybody who will not join with us and say that we have the right to live. And having the right to live means that we also have the right to housing, health care, jobs and education . ... We need our friends who are environmentalists to look at a total program for human uplift. (1991, p. 85)

During Summit I, a session was dedicated to the relationship between the environmental justice movement and the environmental movement. Moderated by Chavis, it was entitled "Our Vision of the Future: A Redefinition of Environmentalism." The speakers for that session included African American, Latino/a, Asian American, and tribal representatives of the environmental justice movement from across the United States, as well as two environmental movement leaders, John H. Adams, executive director of the Natural Resources Defense Council (NRDC), and Michael Fischer, executive director of the Sierra Club.

Both environmental leaders noted that their organizations had done previous work on pollution and public health campaigns. "The Sierra Club works a lot on rocks and trees and mountains and scenic beauty," Fischer acknowledged, but added, "[it] is not all we do. It is most important to know that, particularly in the last 10 to 15 years, much more of our energy has gone into a very broad mission" including toxics and urban sprawl (1991, p. 99). He also pointed out that the Sierra Club had recently given its highest award to Wangari Maathai, a Kenyan grassroots activist who established a women-led organization to reforest their lands. On a similar note, Adams reminded those attending the Summit that NRDC was an organizer of Summit I itself. A dedication to environmental justice, he argued, was not unusual for his organization: "For 20 years, NRDC has relentlessly confronted the massive problems associated with air, water, food and toxics. These issues form the core of NRDC's agenda, a public-health agenda" (1991, p. 101).

Nevertheless, both speakers could go only so far in situating their agenda within the emerging discourse of Summit I. Although both Fischer and Adams described the work of their organizations on what might be called "environmental justice issues" (for example, air quality and toxics), they stopped short of claiming that their groups' interests were equivalent to those voiced at the Summit. Instead, they claimed a desire to forge alliances. As NRDC's Adams put it, "I did not come here just to talk or just to listen, but I came here to engage in a new partnership" (1991, p. 101). Each insisted that this required efforts from not only environmentalists, but also from those delegates who attended Summit I. Adams observed, "What we need now is a common effort" (1991, p. 102). Fischer concurred:

> We know we have been conspicuously missing from the battles for environmental justice all too often, and we regret that fact sincerely. … I believe that this historic conference is a turning point, however, and while we can still say the *mea culpas* from time to time, this is a charge to all of us to work and look into the future, rather than to beat our breasts about the past. … We national environmental organizations are not the enemy. The divide-and-conquer approach is one that the Reagan and Bush administrations have used all too successfully for all too long. (1991, p. 99)

Thus, representatives of both movements hoped that the Summit might mark a starting point toward better communication, understanding, responsiveness, and alliances.

Cautious about any "quick fixes," however, Dana Alston, senior program officer of the Panos Institute of Washington, DC, responded with hesitation to the prospects of collaboration. First, she emphasized the importance of an expanded appreciation of "environmentalism," which involved a broader agenda than traditional conservation or preservation discourses included:

> For us, the issues of the environment do not stand alone by themselves. They are not narrowly defined. Our vision of the environment is woven into an overall framework of social, racial and economic justice. The environment, for us, is where we live, where we work, and where we play. (1991, p. 103)

Second, she described what a basis for a "just partnership" between the two movements would require:

> What we seek is a relationship based on equity, mutual respect, mutual interest, and justice. We refuse narrow definitions. It is not just ancient forests; it is not just saving the whales or saving other endangered species. These are all very important. We understand the life cycle and the inter-connectedness of life. But our communities and our people are endangered species, too. We refuse a paternalistic relationship. We are not interested in a parent-child relationship. Your organizations may be or may not be older than ours. Your

> organizations definitely have more money than ours. But if you are to form a partnership with us, it will be as equals and nothing else but equals. (1991, pp. 105–106)

UNDERSTANDING THE CHALLENGE

In the aftermath of the letters and Summit I, scholars began investigating further why these charges arose and analyzing the challenges they posed to the environmental movement. Several prominent themes emerged, including racism, classism, and sexism, as well as conceptual, rhetorical, historical, evaluative, and cultural differences.

As the letters and Summit I indicated, the primary impetus for the environmental justice movement's criticisms was the failure of the environmental movement to make racism a priority, internally or externally. Leading environmental justice scholars and activists Beverly A. Wright, Pat Bryant, and Robert D. Bullard echoed the letters by reiterating that a major barrier between the two movements is the whiteness of the environmental movement: "That seems to be the strategy of leaders of major environmental organizations. These groups cannot reach out to African Americans and people of color as long as they are nearly all white" (1994, p. 121).[8] In 1980, when the Group of Ten was established, the leaders of each organization were white.[9] One implication of this racial divide was the way it shaped agenda setting, particularly insofar as certain places became the focus of protection and other places—usually more populated and with more people of color inhabiting them—drew less attention from the environmental movement (Figueroa 2001; Lawson 2001). Moreover, by marginalizing the people, places, and issues important to those in the environmental justice movement, the environmental movement was limiting possibilities of alliance building, even when people of color approached them. "We knew we needed allies," Bryant explained, "but when we reached out to the Sierra Club, we found that only one Sierra Club member could understand us.... Somehow, racism has made itself palatable to the intellectuals and to the environmentalists" (1991, p. 84).[10]

Although race has been established as a separate, and often more significant, predicting factor of environmental discrimination and exclusion than economic status, elitism and economic disparity are also significant factors in the unequal siting of environmentally undesirable land uses, routine marginalization from environmental decision-making processes, and denial of just compensation and informed consent in environmental matters.[11] As environmental justice activist Lois Gibbs and others have noted, poor, white working-class communities also felt ignored by the Group of Ten. Despite occasional efforts to use the resources and clout of the more established movement—particularly in lobbying Capitol Hill—they found such attempts at collaboration often forced them to lose their own voices in setting the agenda (Schwab 1994, pp. 389, 391). As a result, the issues working-class communities wanted to focus on were often marginalized. And, although labor activists and environmentalists had worked together on some occupational health and safety legislation in the past, the often false choice of "jobs versus the environment" remained a dominant frame and influenced many local struggles (Obach 2004; Levenstein and Wooding 1998). In addition, "debt-for-nature" swaps were perceived as signals that, when the environmental movement engaged global issues of deforestation and global warming, it failed to take into account the needs of indigenous peoples and the Third World poor in those negotiations.[12]

Exacerbating the environmental justice movement's racial and economic critiques of the environmental movement was a sex and gender divide between the two movements. Although they have played various roles throughout the history of the U.S. environmental movement, women's contributions largely have been undervalued. Moreover, their roles have been more at the grassroots level, rather than in national or international leadership positions (Merchant 1996). Conversely, housewives and mothers, often mobilized by environmental health crises in their homes and communities, quickly emerged as leaders in the environmental justice movement and challenged traditional notions of gender roles. The attitudes and practices of the predominantly male leadership of the environmental movement further exacerbated tensions between the two movements when empowered, often self-taught grassroots leaders of the predominantly female-led or, at minimum, co-led environmental justice movement found themselves less respected and less represented by the environmental movement.[13]

In addition to challenges of race, class, and sex, there were also conceptual, cultural, and rhetorical differences. Both before and after the letters to the Group of Ten, environmental justice activists openly complained of the difficulties of articulating their views and concerns within the prevalent terms and conceptual frames of environmental organizations.[14] Although there was widespread awareness and concern about toxic pollution and public health within the environmental movement since at least the publication of Rachel Carson's (1962) best-seller *Silent Spring*, the Group of Ten remained most commonly identified by those both inside and outside the movement with the preservation of scenic wilderness areas and the protection of endangered species (Bullard and Wright 1992, p. 42). In her account of efforts to stop the location of a 1,600-ton-per-day solid waste incinerator in a South Central Los Angeles neighborhood in the mid-1980s, Giovanna Di Chiro reports, "These issues were not deemed adequately 'environmental' by local environmental groups such as the Sierra Club or the Environmental Defense Fund" (1996, p. 299ff.). Thus, when residents of the predominantly African American, low-income community approached these groups, "they were informed that the poisoning of an urban community by an incineration facility was a 'community health issue,' not an environmental one" (1996, p. 299).[15] On the other coast, in meetings in New York City, critics observed that it was clear "that the mainstream environmental community is reluctant to address issues of equity and social justice, within the context of the environment" (Alston 1990, p. 23). Episodes of this sort not only indicated to many in the environmental justice movement that the environmental movement was indifferent to their issues, they also suggested that the environmental movement was not interested in significantly challenging the established social and political power structure. Environmentalism failed, on this view, to provide a much-needed radical cultural critique (Bullard 1993; Hofrichter 1993).

Exasperated with the perceived narrowness of the environmental movement's social agenda and the marginalization of their issues and experiences, environmental justice activists began to emphasize self-definition (Di Chiro 1998). As is apparent from Alston's statement at Summit I, environmental justice activists were reinventing the concept of "environment" to reflect their diverse range of voices and cultures.[16] In *We Speak for Ourselves*, Alston (1990) insists that environmental justice "calls for a total redefinition of terms and language to describe the conditions that people are facing" (quoted in Di Chiro 1998, p. 105). And according to the National Environmental Justice Advisory Council, the movement "represents a new vision borne out of a community-driven process whose essential core is a *transformative public discourse* over what are truly healthy, sustainable and vital communities" (1996, p. 17). Indeed, one of the primary goals of the movement was, in the words of environmental justice activist Deehon Ferris, literally "shifting the terms of the debate" (1993). For example, the language of environmental justice activists drew on the legacy of the civil rights movement, but terms like "racism," "economic blackmail," "justice," and "rights" were not the predominant environmental discourse at the time. As Dorceta Taylor (2000) has argued, from the beginning the environmental justice movement effectively reframed environmental discourse by communicating its grievances and goals in a frame that inextricably linked social justice with the environment. This broadened dialogue about the "environment" worried some environmentalists, who wondered whether the already marginalized concerns for animals and wilderness would be placed even further on the back burner by this seemingly more anthropocentric set of values and terms.

In addition to redefining terms, the environmental justice movement also sought to redefine knowledge, by emphasizing how grassroots communities express their experiences and the knowledge they have to share. The environmental justice movement, for example, recognizes the importance of storytelling as an epistemology, in addition to more traditional scientific and economic discourses (Krauss 1994, p. 259). This way of knowing and critically interpreting the world contrasts with environmental reports that rely heavily on scientific and economic data and challenges particular conceptions of what an educated presentation entails.

As even this concise and selective discussion shows, in the 1990s the environmental justice movement was challenging the environmental movement in many ways and promised to do nothing short of transform the political and cultural landscape of environmental practice, theory, and discourse. Initial attempts by the environmental movement to respond to these charges were perceived with suspicion. For instance, when several large environmental organizations began environmental justice efforts, some environmental justice activists immediately expressed concern that such gestures were merely attempts to raise more money from foundations—money that environmental justice groups then would be unable to receive (Di Chiro, 1998, p. 112). Some environmental justice activists also questioned whether there was even a role for environmentalists in the environmental justice movement (Ferris and Hahn-Baker 1995). But all the criticisms, disappointments, and suspicions of the environmental movement not withstanding, this was a time of substantial optimism within the environmental justice movement. As Fred Setterberg and Lonny Shavelson have put it, "The 1990s, they hoped, would be their decade" (1993, p. xiii). Indeed, most scholars and activists seemed to agree. According to Jim Schwab, "The new movement had won a place at the table. The Deep South, the nation, would never discuss environmental issues in the same way again" (1994, p. 393).

TIME TO REASSESS

It now is well over a decade since the environmental justice critique of environmentalism was laid out in the 1990 letters to the Group of Ten and Summit I was convened. Much has changed within, transpired between, and happened around the two movements over that time. For example, in 1994 President Clinton signed Executive Order 12898, Federal Actions to Address Environmental Justice in Minority Populations and Low-Income Populations. Among the executive order's outcomes was the formation of the National Environmental Justice Advisory Council (NEJAC) to the EPA.[17] In this way, among others, the environmental justice movement has become increasingly institutionalized over the last ten years. Also, on October 23–27, 2002, a second National People of Color Environmental Leadership Summit (Summit II) was convened in Washington, DC, to mark a decade of accomplishments and to discuss directions for the future of the movement.

Moreover, there have been significant shifts in receptivity to environmental justice and environmental concerns within the national political landscape, particularly at the federal executive level. Whereas President Clinton was an outspoken advocate for environmental justice efforts targeted toward minority and low-income communities, President George W. Bush has reduced environmental justice efforts at the EPA and has proposed redefining environmental justice in a way that does not reference the historical environmental inequities and disproportionate environmental burdens of those communities.[18] Although neither President Clinton nor Vice President Gore became the leaders for which the environmental movement had hoped (there was widespread disappointment, for example, with their failure to support the Kyoto Protocol to curb global warming and with the signing of the North American Free Trade Agreement), both political leaders were preferable over the subsequent Bush administration, which has attempted to defund, roll back, revise or otherwise undermine many significant existing federal environmental policies and regulations and has stymied almost all new initiatives to expand environmental protections.[19] As a result of the current political climate, there are ongoing conversations within both movements regarding the viability and direction of their futures.

Other relevant changes to the environmental justice and environmentalism landscape since the early 1990s include: the emerging prominence of new issues, such as globalization, global warming, and human genetic research; the development by several environmental organizations, including the Sierra Club and Greenpeace, of active environmental justice campaigns and programs; the hiring of some people of color into prominent positions in environmental organizations[20]; and an increased circulation of the environmental justice framework globally, where it has begun to have an impact on transnational conversations, summits, and meetings.

Thus, it is time to reconsider the environmental justice challenge to environmentalism, as well as the relationship between the environmental and environmental justice movements more broadly to reassess the prospects for working together in the future. How and to what extent has the environmental movement responded to the challenges posed to it by the environmental movement? What are the points of division between the movements now, given the changes in the movements and the shifting social contexts in which they operate? Have new challenges, points of tension, or opportunities for cooperation emerged as a result of issues that have become increasingly urgent in recent years? Has the dialogue invited in the letters to the Group of Ten and in the speeches by Fischer and Adams at Summit I been realized to any significant degree, in at least some locales and on at least some issues? If so, what do these efforts teach us? How should the environmental movement respond to the challenges that remain? Are overcoming the divide, finding common ground, and promoting alliances or unity between the two movements appropriate aims? Do the two movements tend to work more productively when independent of one another, or have collaborations been effective in advancing both environmental and environmental justice goals? Do the events of the past decade signal future directions for the two movements? Do they adumbrate a collective or unified movement in which there is widespread appreciation of the importance of social justice to environmentalism and of environmentalism to social justice?

The essays in this collection address these and related questions. As noted, they do so from diverse academic perspectives and employ diverse research methodologies, including ethnographic participant observation, interviews, critical analysis of case studies, quantitative economic and ecological research, and philosophical analysis. Again, we believe this variety in perspectives and methods is appropriate to the multifarious dimensions of the dynamics between the movements. Only by expanding the dialogue within and beyond any one academic approach and bringing together various scholarly frames, techniques, and conceptual paradigms can an appropriately multifaceted understanding of the environmental justice challenge to environmentalism and the relationship between the two movements be achieved.

This is not to suggest that the selections in this collection represent all relevant perspectives. Rather than exhausting and closing down discussion, it is hoped that this polyvocal, but selective, gathering of academic voices will provide stimulus for a progressive and ongoing discussion of where the relationship between the two movements stands right now and how it might be developed to the benefit of both movements in the future.

NOTES

1 Dowie (1995, p. 127).

2 Environmental Justice Activist Cora Tucker, in Kaplan (1997, p. 69).

3 To differentiate between the environmental movement and the environmental justice movement, many scholars call the former the "mainstream environmental movement." We choose not to use the word "mainstream" because it suggests that the tenets of this movement have been widely accepted in dominant society. At this time, with the U.S. federal government ignoring or actively rolling back most initiatives of the environmental movement, environmentalism hardly appears "mainstream." For a discussion of additional limitations of this label, see Gottlieb (2005, p. 162).

4 "The Group of Ten" was the nickname for the major environmental organizations that met regularly to coordinate efforts to respond to the backlash against the environmental movement during the Reagan Administration. It included the Audubon Society, Environmental Defense Fund, Friends of the Earth, Izaak Walton League, National Parks and Conservation Association, National Wildlife Federation, Natural Resource Defense Council, Sierra Club, Sierra Club Legal Defense Fund, and The Wilderness Society.

5 "About the same time, the Network for Environmental and Economic Justice wrote to Greenpeace, the National Toxics Campaign, and the Citizens' Clearing House for Hazardous Wastes, expressing deep appreciation for their support of grassroots struggles in communities of color. The letter pointed out, however, that their organizations were still led and controlled by whites and were thus more likely to advocate *for* rather that [*sic*] *with* communities of color" (Dowie 1995, p. 147).

6 See, for example, Shabecoff (1990).

7 This and all subsequent quotes from the Summit are excerpted from a transcript of the Summit Proceedings compiled by the United Church of Christ Commission for Racial Justice.

8 It is interesting that this critique and many like it have been published by Sierra Club Books.

9 Gottlieb (2005, p. 165).

10 This "one Sierra Club member" is most likely Darryl Malek-Wiley, a European American who, at the time, was an employee of the Gulf Coast Tenants Association and one of the original signatures in the first letter to the Group of Ten. He also helped support the BASF lockout and the Great Louisiana Toxics March. In 2004, the Sierra Club hired him as an Environmental Justice Grassroots Organizing Program organizer for southern Louisiana.

11 The Council on Environmental Quality (CEQ) released a report in 1971 acknowledging a correlation between income and environmental quality. In 1982, protests in Warren County, North Carolina, prompted a U.S. General Accounting Office (GAO) study and a study commissioned by the United Church of Christ Commission, both of which established race to be a primary factor influencing waste siting. See, also Bullard (1990), Bullard and Wright (1987), United Church of Christ Commission for Racial Justice (1987), Lavelle and Coyle (1992), Moses (1993), and Faber and Kreig (2001).

12 Buttel (1995), Weissman (1993), and Bello (1993).

13 For more on the role of women as mothers and housewives in the environmental justice movement, see Freudenberg and Steinsapir (1992), Krauss (1993), Bullard (1994), and Kaplan (1997). For more about sex and gender divisions in the two movements, see Dunlap and Mertig (1992), Di Chiro (1992), and Gottlieb (1993, 2005).

14 For evidence of such complaints, see Austin and Schill (1994, pp. 58, 60), Bullard (1993), Dowie (1995, pp. 172–173), Pulido (1996, pp. 24–29), and Schwab (1994, p. 386).

15 Di Chiro notes, "Eventually, environmental and social justice organizations such as Greenpeace, the National Health Law Program, the Center for Law in the Public Interest, and Citizens for a Better Environment would join Concerned Citizens' campaign to stop [the proposed facility] LANCER" (1996, p. 527n).

16 Di Chiro, (1992, 1996, 1998); Dowie (1995, p. 124).

17 Executive Order 12898 requires "inter-agency coordination for eliminating discriminatory siting of polluting facilities." For more on NEJAC, see the government's official webpage: http://www.epa.gov/compliance/environmentaljustice/nejac/overview.html

18 A 2003 report issued by the U.S. Commission on Civil Rights called *Not In My Backyard: Executive Order 12898 and Title VI as Tools for Achieving Environmental Justice* notes that, despite the limited success of these legislative landmarks, their implementation has not yet been adequately realized (online at http://www.usccr.gov/pubs/envjust/ej0104.pdf). The commission reiterated this assessment of the progress of implementation in *Redefining Rights in America: The Civil Rights Record of the George W. Bush Administration, 2001–2004* (online at http://www.usccr.gov/pubs/bush/bush04.pdf, pp. 72–79). According to the report, the Bush administration has yet put in place a comprehensive strategic plan for realizing the

order, has yet to establish performance measures for assessing implementation, has yet to make Executive Order 12898 part of the EPA's core mission (and has instead deemphasized the disproportionate exposure of minority and low-income communities in its approach to addressing environmental hazards), and has failed to increase participation of affected minority and low-income communities in meaningful decision making processes. This evaluation echoes many of the concerns raised by the EPA Office of Inspector General's March 1, 2004, evaluation report: *EPA Needs to Consistently Implement the Intent of the Executive Order on Environmental Justice, Report No. 2004-P-00007* (online at http://www.epa.gov/oigearth/reports/2004/20040301-2004-P-00007.pdf). And on June 22, 2005, Bush's EPA introduced an "Environmental Justice Strategic Plan Outline" and "Framework for Integrating Environmental Justice," which do not include mention of the history of unequal protection in its definition of environmental justice.

19 For an accessible summary of the antienvironmental policies of the Bush administration's first term, see Kennedy (2004).

20 Most notably, in 2005, Jerome Ringo became the first African American chair of a major environmental organization, the National Wildlife Federation.

REFERENCES

Alston, D. *We Speak for Ourselves: Social Justice, Race, and Environment*. London: Panos Institute, 1990.

Austin, R., and M. Schill. "Black, Brown, Red and Poisoned," in R. D. Bullard, ed., *Unequal Protection: Environmental Justice and Communities of Color*. (San Francisco Sierra Club Books, 1994), 53–76.

Bello, W. "Global Economic Counterrevolution: The Dynamics of Impoverishment and Marginalization," in R. Hofrichter, ed., *Toxic Struggles: The Theory and Practice of Environmental Justice*. New Society Publishers, 1993, 197–208.

Bryant, B. *Environmental Justice: Issues, Policies, and Solutions*. Washington, D.C.: Island Press, 1995.

Bullard, R. D. *Unequal Protection: Environmental Justice and Communities of Color*. San Francisco: Sierra Club Books, 1994.

Bullard, R. D. *Confronting Environmental Racism: Voices from the Grassroots*. Boston: South End Press, 1993.

Bullard, R. D. *Dumping in Dixie: Race, Class, and Environmental Quality*. Boulder, Colo.: Westview Press, 1990.

Bullard, R. D., and B. H. Wright. "The Quest for Environmental Equity: Mobilizing the African-American Community for Social Change," in R. E. Dunlap and A. G. Mertig, eds., *American Environmentalism: The U.S. Environmental Movement, 1970–1990*. New York: Taylor and Francis, 1992, 39–49.

Bullard, R. D., and B. H. Wright. "Environmentalism and the Politics of Equity: Emergent Trends in the Black Community," *Mid-American Review of Sociology*, 12 (1987): 21–37.

Buttel, F. H. "Rethinking International Environmental Policy in the Late Twentieth Century," in B. Bryant, ed., *Environmental Justice: Issues, Polities, and Solutions*. Washington, D.C.: Island Press, 1995, 187–207.

Carson, R. *Silent Spring*. New York: Houghton Mifflin, 1962.

Di Chiro, G. "Environmental Justice from the Grassroots: Reflections on History, Gender, and Expertise," in D. Faber, ed., *The Struggle for Ecological Democracy: Environmental Justice Movements in the United States*. New York: Guilford Press, 1998, 104–136.

Di Chiro, G. "Nature as Community: The Convergence of Environment and Social Justice," in William Cronon, ed., *Uncommon Ground: Rethinking the Human Place in Nature*. New York: W.W. Norton, 1996, 298–320, 527–531.

Di Chiro, G. "Defining Environmental Justice: Women's Voices and Grassroots Politics," *Socialist Review*, 22, no. 4 (1992): 92–130.

Dowie, M. *Losing Ground: American Environmentalism at the Close of the Twentieth Century*. Cambridge, Mass.: MIT Press, 1995.

Dunlap, R. E., and A. G. Mertig. *American Environmentalism: The U.S. Environmental Movement, 1970–1990*. New York: Taylor and Francis, 1992.

Faber, D., and E. Kreig. *Unequal Exposure to Ecological Hazards: Environmental Injustices in the Commonwealth of Massachusetts*. Boston: Philanthropy and Environmental Justice Research Project, Northeastern University, 2001.

Ferris, D. "Environmental Justice: Continuing the Dialogue." Audio tape of presentations by D. Ferris, R. M. Augustine, et al., at a meeting of the Society of Environmental Journalists, Third National Conference, Duke University, Durham, N.C., October 21–24, 1993.

Ferris, D., and D. Hahn-Baker. "Environmentalists and Environmental Justice Policy," in B. Bryant, ed., *Environmental Justice: Issues, Policies, and Solutions*. Washington, D.C.: Island Press, 1995.

Figueroa, R. M. "Other Faces: Latinos and Environmental Justice," in L. Westra and B. E. Lawson, eds., *Faces of Environmental Racism: Confronting Issues of Global Justice*, 2nd ed. Lanham, Md.: Rowman & Littlefield, 2001, 167–184.

Freudenberg, N., and C. Steinsapir. "Not in Our Backyards: The Grassroots Environmental Movement," in R. E. Dunlap and A. G. Mertig, eds., *American Environmentalism: The U.S. Environmental Movement, 1970–1990*. New York: Taylor and Francis, 1992, 27–38.

Gottlieb, R. *Forcing the Spring: The Transformation of the American Environmental Movement*. Washington, D.C.: Island Press, 1993.

Gottlieb, R. *Forcing the Spring: The Transformation of the American Environmental Movement*, revi. and updated ed. Washington D.C.: Island Press, 2005.

Hofrichter, R. "Introduction," in R. Hofrichter, ed., *Toxic Struggles: The Theory and Practice of Environmental Justice*. New Society Publishers, 1993, 1–11.

Kaplan, T. *Crazy for Democracy: Women in Grassroots Movements.* New York: Routledge, 1997.

Kennedy, R. F., Jr. *Crimes Against Nature: How George W. Bush and His Corporate Pals Are Plundering the Country and Hijacking our Democracy.* New York: Harper Collins, 2004.

Krauss, C. "Women of Color on the Front Line," in R. D. Bullard, ed., *Unequal Protection: Environmental Justice and Communities of Color.* San Francisco, Sierra Club Books, 1994, 256–271.

Krauss, C. "Blue-Collar Women and Toxic-Waste Protests: The Process of Politicization," in R. Hofrichter, ed., *Toxic Struggles: The Theory and Practice of Environmental Justice.* Philadelphia: New Society Publishers, 1993, 107–117.

Lavelle, M., and M. Coyle. "Critical Mass Builds on Environmental Equity." *National Law Journal,* Washington Briefs, sec. 5 (September 21, 1992).

Lawson, B. "Living for the City: Urban United States and Environmental Justice," in L. Westra and B. E. Lawson, eds., *Faces of Environmental Racism: Confronting Issues of Global Justice,* 2nd ed. Lanham, Md.: Rowman and Littlefield, 2001, 41–56.

Lester, J. P., D. W. Allen, and K. M. Hill. *Environmental Injustice in the United States: Myths and Realities.* Boulder, Colo.: Westview, 2001.

Levenstein, C., and J. Wooding. "Dying for a Living: Workers, Production, and the Environment," in D. Faber, ed., *The Struggle for Ecological Democracy: Environmental Justice Movements in the United States.* New York: Guilford Press, 1998, 60–80.

Merchant, C. *Earthcare: Women and the Environment.* New York: Routledge, 1996.

Moses, M. "Farmworkers and Pesticides," in R. D. Bullard, ed., *Confronting Environmental Racism: Voices from the Grassroots.* Boston: South End Press, 1993, 161–178.

National Environmental Justice Advisory Council Subcommittee on Waste and Facility Siting, *Environmental Justice, ban Revitalization, and Brownfields: The Search for Authentic Signs of Hope* (Washington, D.C.: U.S. Environmental Protection Agency, 1996).

Obach, B. K. *Labor and the Environmental Movement: The Quest for Common Ground.* Cambridge, Mass.: MIT Press, 2004.

Pulido, L. *Environmentalism and Economic Justice: Two Chicano Struggles in the Southwest.* Tempe: University of Arizona Press, 1997.

Schwab, J. *Deeper Shades of Green: The Rise of Blue-Collar and Minority Environmentalism in America.* San Francisco: Sierra Club Books, 1994.

Setterberg, F., and L. Shavelson. *Toxic Nation: The Fight to Save Our Communities from Chemical Contamination.* New York: John Wiley and Sons, 1993.

Shabecoff, P. "Environmental Groups Told They Are Racists in Hiring," *New York Times* (February 1, 1990): 20A.

Taylor, D. "The Rise of the Environmental Justice Paradigm," *American Behavioural Scientist,* 43 no. 4 (2000): 508–580.

United Church of Christ Commission for Racial Justice. *Toxic Wastes and Race in the United States,* B. A. Goldman and L. Fitton, eds. Cleveland, Ohio: United Church of Christ, 1987.

U.S. General Accounting Office [GAO]. *Siting of Hazardous Waste Landfills and Their Correlation with Racial and Economic Status of Surrounding Communities.* Washington, D.C.: Government Printing Office, 1983.

Weissman, R. "Corporate Plundering of Third-World Resources," in R. Hofrichter, ed., *Toxic Struggles: The Theory and Practice of Environmental Justice.* Philadelphia: New Society Publishers, 1993, 186–196.

Wright, B. H., P. Bryant, and R. D. Bullard. "Coping with Poisons in Cancer Alley," in R. D. Bullard, ed., *Unequal Protection: Environmental Justice and Communities of Color.* San Francisco: Sierra Club Books, 1994, 110–129.

READING 7.2

Environmentalism, Economic Blackmail, and Civil Rights

COMPETING AGENDAS WITHIN THE BLACK COMMUNITY

By Robert D. Bullard

There is abundant evidence that blacks and low-income people are subjected to a disproportionately large amount of pollution in their neighborhoods and in their workplaces. This is especially true in the southern United States. Black communities in the South have become the dumping grounds for all types of toxins. Why has this happened? What are blacks doing to combat this threat? What is government doing to ensure that everyone has equal access to an unpolluted environment?

First of all, the black community in the South does not have extensive experience with environmental issues when compared with its white counterpart Blacks were actively involved in the civil rights movement during the peak period of the environmental movement, roughly during the late 1960s and early 1970s. On the other hand, civil rights advocates and boosters of unrestrained economic development became closely aligned. This alliance often brought them in direct conflict with environmentalists. Pollution and health risks were the price thousands of unemployed and marginally skilled blacks had to pay for employment.

In a desperate attempt to attract new industry and jobs, and in turn broaden their tax base, many poor communities in the South relaxed their enforcement of pollution and environmental regulations or simply looked the other way when violations were discovered. Polluting industries were brought into poor black communities with little input from local leaders When questions were raised by concerned citizens, the argument of jobs for local residents (a form of economic blackmail) was used to quell dissent. Many business firms, especially waste-disposal companies, came to view the South as a "pushover, lacking community organization, environmental consciousness, and with strong and blind pro-business politics."[1] Residents of these economically impoverished areas were often powerless against private and government polluters.

The strong pro-jobs stance, a kind of "don't bite the hand that feeds you" sentiment, permeated the black community and helped institutionalize high risks and inequities. The South's unique history, traditions, and laws institutionalized discrimination in employment, education, housing, and other areas. A plethora of federal civil rights legislation was enacted to remedy inequities that resulted from Jim Crow laws. The South during the 1950s and 1960s was the center of the civil rights movement. The 1970s catapulted the region into the national limelight again, but for different reasons. The South was now becoming a major population and economic center. Growth in the region during the 1970s was stimulated by a number of factors, including a climate pleasant enough to attract workers from other regions and the "underemployed" work force already in the region, weak labor unions and strong right-to-work laws, cheap labor and cheap land, aggressive self-promotion campaigns, and weak enforcement of environmental regulations. The South beginning in the mid-1970s was transformed from a "net exporter of people to a powerful human magnet."[2]

The South desperately attempted to rid itself of its image as a socially and economically backward region. It was vigorously promoted as the "New South." However, many of its old problems related to underdevelopment—poor education, large pool of unskilled labor, high unemployment, low wages—remained while the influx of polluting industry created new environmental problems. For example, four of the five states that led the nation in attracting polluting industry (paper, chemicals, waste disposal, and others) in the 1970s were located in the South: Texas, South Carolina, North Carolina, and Florida. Some Southern leaders continued to display a Third World approach to development: any industry is better than no industry at all. By one measure their efforts were successful: the South led all regions of the country in the number of jobs created. More than 17 million new nonagricultural jobs were added in the South between 1960 and 1985, compared with 11 million in the West and a combined total of 13 million in the Midwest and Northeast.[3]

The benefits and burdens of industrial growth were not equally shared by all Southerners. Although blacks received some of the economic benefits of the South's growth, they received more than their share of the growing industrial pollution burden,[4] For example, the South became a favorite location for hazardous-waste "superdumps," large facilities that can accept waste from other regions of the country. Not surprisingly, black communities were targeted for these facilities. Some examples of these superdumps include Chemical Waste Management's landfills in Sumter County, Alabama (the "Cadillac" of superdumps) and Lake Charles. Louisiana; Genstar's Pinewood site outside Columbia, South Carolina; the Browning-Ferris Industries site in Willow Spring, Louisiana; and the Rollins landfill in Scotlandville, Louisiana.

Local Sumter County black residents have been fighting the Chemical Waste Management facility for years. The company's 2,400-acre landfill in Emelle, however, contributes more than $2 million annually into the economies of Sumter and Greene counties, located in the western Alabama Black Belt. Local residents are paying a price for having the facility in their community. Pesticides and volatile solvents have shown up in the company's monitoring wells outside the site after less than ten years of operation.

ENVIRONMENTALISM AS CIVIL RIGHTS

Why are black communities burdened with so many of these waste facilities? Black and lower-income neighborhoods often occupy the "wrong side of the tracks" and receive different treatment when it comes to enforcement of environmental regulations. The sociospatial groupings that emerge in the South are a result of "the distribution of wealth, patterns of racial and economic discrimination, access to jobs, housing, and a host of other variables." Housing discrimination artificially restricts millions of blacks to poorer neighborhoods and areas that pose health risks from pollution and other environmental problems. Political power and economic clout are also key factors that influence the spatial distribution of nonresidential land use. Siting dilemmas involving noxious facilities, such as municipal and hazardous-waste landfills, garbage incinerators and transfer stations, and sewage treatment plants, could be resolved with a strategy based on the "politics of equity."[5]

Although there has been considerable overlap between the agendas of civil rights advocates and those of economic boosters, these agendas often conflicted with those of environmentalists. The interplay between civil rights advocacy and environmentalism has been minimal. Historically, black civil rights organizations have not been on the cutting edge of environmental issues, even those that directly affect the black community. On the other hand, many of the battles that mainstream environmentalists waged during the height of the movement had marginal effect on deteriorating conditions in inner-city areas.

The "jobs versus environment" argument has held black Southerners captive to a system that often forces them to choose between employment and a clean work environment. This either-or choice is tantamount to economic blackmail. The correlation between factors associated with disadvantage (poverty, occupations below management and professional levels, low rent, and high concentration of black residents) and poor environmental quality has been clearly documented.[6] Various forms of pollution take a heavy toll on inner-city neighborhoods as a result of the high concentration of industry and power plants, disparate enforcement of pollution laws, heavy vehicle traffic, and congested freeway systems, which often crisscross lower-income and minority neighborhoods.

Middle- and upper-class citizens have been more successful in changing the course of freeways and the siting of industrial facilities than their lower-income counterparts. Air and water pollution in central cities can be found at levels up to five times greater than in suburban areas. Exhaust fumes from automobiles are especially troublesome to neighborhoods adjacent to the heavily traveled freeways. Black children in the United States suffer from lead toxicity six times more frequently than white children.[7] Although the source of elevated lead levels in children can be difficult to pinpoint, leaded gasoline, lead-based paint, and industrial smelters are the major culprits.

Lead in the environment is caused largely by human activities. Individuals who live near lead smelters run a high risk of exposure to harmful pollutants. Residents of the mostly black and low-income West Dallas (Texas) neighborhood, for example, have for years lived with the constant bombardment of health-threatening pollutants from the nearby lead smelters.[8] As early as 1981, toxicologists in the U.S. Environmental Protection Agency (EPA) knew that air emissions from the smelters posed an immediate threat to area residents. Children who lived in nearby public housing were especially at risk.

In 1983 EPA's Office of Toxic Integration and the Center for Disease Control studied children who lived near the smelters and found high levels of lead in their blood. Contact with contaminated soil and workers who brought the toxic material home on their clothes were the major sources of lead toxicity in the children. The West Dallas Lead Pollution Task Force, a black grassroots organization, used a number of strategies to close the smelters, including litigation, lobbying for effective enforcement of the city's zoning ordinance, political pressure, and citizen protests.[9] After years of litigation, an out-of-court settlement estimated at nearly $20 million was reached in 1985 between the now-defunct RSR Corp., operator of one of the smelters, and the blacks whose children suffered irreversible brain damage from exposure to lead pollutants.

Individuals and businesses that can afford to flee do so, while the poor and less advantaged stay behind and suffer from poverty, pollution, and potential health problems. The problem for blacks is exacerbated by the factor of access to medical and health care One in six black families had trouble getting medical care in 1982, compared with one in eleven white families. Institutional barriers (employment and housing discrimination; disparate treatment by banks, mortgage companies, and insurance firms based on geographic location—"redlining", public policies that tend to favor the affluent over the poor; and disparate enforcement of land use and environmental regulations) relegate a large segment of the black community to less than desirable physical environments, reduce housing and residential options, limit mobility, and increase risks from exposure to potentially health-threatening toxic material.

THE DUMPING GROUNDS

The hazardous waste problem has been described as the most "serious problem facing the industrial world." The United States generates more than 250 million metric tons, of hazardous waste each year, and EPA regulations cover only a fraction of this waste. Potential Love Canals are waiting to be discovered. More than 80 percent of hazardous wastes is disposed of on land; only about 10 percent is disposed of properly. Millions of tons of unregulated hazardous wastes end up at municipal landfills designed for household garbage, are released from tank trucks onto back roads, or are dumped directly into sewer systems. The practices of "moonlight dumpers" create health and environmental time bombs that may explode years later.[10]

The location of off-site hazardous-waste landfills poses an even greater threat to the minority community. Toxic-waste facilities are often located in communities with high percentages of poor, elderly, young, and black residents. An inordinate concentration of uncontrolled toxic-waste sites are found in urban areas with a high percentage of minorities; large commercial hazardous-waste landfills are more likely to be found in rural communities in the Southern Black Belt.[11] The nation's largest commercial hazardous-waste landfill is located in Emelle, Alabama (Sumter County), where blacks constitute 78.9 percent of the population. The fourth-largest is located in Scotlandville. Louisiana, where blacks make up 93 percent of the population Together, the Emelle and Scotlandville sites account for more than one-third of the estimated landfill capacity in the United States.

The racial and economic dimension of hazardous-waste landfill siting in the southern United States was documented in a 1983 study by the U.S. General Accounting Office (GAO).[12] The study identified four off-site hazardous-waste landfills in the eight states that make up EPA's Region IV (Alabama, Florida, Georgia, Kentucky, Mississippi, North Carolina, South Carolina, and Tennessee). Blacks make up one-fifth of the population of Region IV, but three of the four hazardous-waste landfills are located in mostly black communities. Residents of these Black Belt counties are victims of a "triple whammy"—they arc rural, poor, and politically powerless.

The Warren County PCB (polychlorinated biphenyl) landfill is one of the four off-site hazardous-waste landfills located in EPA's Region IV. In 1982 Warren County, North Carolina, was selected as the burial site for more than 32,000 cubic yards of soil contaminated with the highly toxic PCBs that had been illegally dumped along the roadways in fourteen North Carolina counties in 1978. The decision to select this largely black and economically poor county made more political sense than environmental sense.[13] For a while Warren County received national attention. A host of well-known black civil rights activists, political leaders, and area residents marched and protested against the construction of the disposal facility, and more than 400 protesters were arrested.

Although the 1982 protest demonstrations were unsuccessful in blocking the landfill operation, they were significant in another way: they marked the first national attempt by blacks to link environmental issues to the mainstream civil rights agenda. The demonstrations prompted Congressman Walter E. Fauntroy (Congressman from the District of Columbia), who had been active in the protest demonstrations, to initiate the 1983 GAO study of hazardous landfill siting in the South. The protest demonstrations were later instrumental in setting the stage for the Commission for Racial Justice's 1987 national study on Toxic Wastes and Race.[14] The Reverend Ben Chavis (Commission for Racial Justice) and the Reverend Joseph Lowery (Southern Christian Leadership Conference) were two of the many civil rights activists who led marches against the Warren County PCB landfill. The demonstrations translated into something more than mere protest marches: they ushered in a new era, when blacks and the poor demanded their rights to equal protection from the ravages of pollution. It is not coincidental that the National Association for the Advancement of Colored People (NAACP), the premier civil rights organization, in 1983 passed its first resolution on the hazardous-waste issue.

THE POLITICS OF FACILITY SITING

Finding suitable sites for municipal and hazardous-waste landfills has become a critical problem, mainly because people are anxious about living near a facility where household garbage and toxic substances are dumped. The standard public reaction to landfill site selection has been "not in my back yard," abbreviated as the "NIMBY" principle. Public officials and private industry have in many cases responded using the "PIBBY" principle—"place in blacks' back yards."[15]

Because of the illegal dumping of toxic substances at "sanitary" landfills, black and lower-income neighborhoods are especially at risk, since they are burdened with a disproportionately large share of such facilities. The waste-disposal facility siting practices of cities and private companies have contributed to black and lower-income communities becoming the dumping grounds for household garbage and illegally dumped toxic materials. From Houston to Atlanta to Tampa, black neighborhoods have been burdened with a disproportionately large share of municipal waste-disposal facilities.

The disparate landfill siting pattern is probably best illustrated in Houston, the nation's fourth-largest city, with a population of more than 1.7 million.[16] Houston has the distinction of being the only major U.S. city which has no zoning. In addition, it has the largest black population, nearly one-half million, of any city in the South; blacks make up about 28 percent of the city's population. The city's blacks remain residentially segregated. More than 81 percent of them lived in majority black areas in 1980.

From the mid-1920s through the early 1970s, Houston operated its own solid-waste disposal facilities, including five municipal landfills and eight garbage incinerators. All the city-owned landfills and six of the eight garbage incinerators were located in black neighborhoods. In other words, although blacks constituted just over one-fourth of the city's population, eleven of the thirteen city-owned solid-waste disposal facilities were located in mostly black neighborhoods.

The Houston City Council, which had remained all-white until 1972, systematically targeted black neighborhoods for the city's solid-waste disposal facilities. Black protests against these practices went unheeded until the late 1970s, when black Houstonians began a frontal assault on the siting practices of the city, the state of Texas, and private waste-disposal companies.

In 1979 residents from a predominantly black northeast Houston subdivision filed a federal lawsuit to stop the construction of a sanitary landfill in their neighborhood. This action came after they were deliberately misinformed about the clearing of land on a construction site near their subdivision. Residents were under the impression that the removal of trees on the site was in preparation for new homes, not a sanitary landfill for Houston's garbage. Residents and their attorney, Linda McKeever Bullard, charged the Texas Department of Health (the permitting agency) and Browning-Ferris Industries (the General Motors of garbage) with racial discrimination in the selection of the landfill site so close to a densely populated subdivision.

Residents were upset because the landfill site was not only near their homes but within 1,400 feet of their high school (which was not equipped with air conditioning), their athletic stadium, and their school district's administration building. The North Forest Independent School District is a small suburban district where blacks make up more than 85 percent of the student population. The district is also one of the poorest in the Houston area Seven North Forest schools, which form a cluster, are located within a two-mile radius of the landfill Two of the three sanitary landfills currently used to dispose of Houston's solid waste are located within this mostly black district.

After long delays and numerous attempts by the landfill proponents to disrupt and divide the community, the case finally went to trial in 1985. Although the federal judge ruled against the residents and the landfill was built, local organized resistance produced some important changes in waste-disposal siting practices and policies in Houston. First, the Houston city council, acting under intense political pressure from blacks, passed a resolution in 1980 prohibiting city-owned solid-waste trucks from dumping at the controversial landfill. Second, the Texas Department of Health updated its requirements of landfill permit applicants to include detailed land use, economic, and socioeconomic data of the area near proposed sanitary landfill sites. Third, black Houstonians sent a clear signal to the state and city government and private disposal companies that they would fight any future attempts to place garbage dumps, landfills, incinerators, and any other type of waste-disposal facility in their neighborhood.[17] From 1979 to 1987, the Texas Department of Health did not grant a single sanitary landfill permit for a disposal site in a Houston black neighborhood.

CONCLUSION

The 1980s have seen the emergence of a small but growing cadre of blacks who see environmental issues as civil rights issues. An alliance has been forged between organized labor, minorities, and environmental groups, as exhibited by the 1983 Urban Environment Conference workshops held in New Orleans, Environmental and civil rights issues were presented as compatible agenda items by this coalition Environmental protection and social justice are now seen as essential parts of the same struggle. A growing number of grassroots organizations and their leaders have begun to incorporate more action-oriented strategies, such as protests, neighborhood demonstrations, picketing, political pressure, and litigation, to reduce and eliminate the toxic-waste threat. National black political leadership has also demonstrated a willingness to take a strong pro-environment stance. The League of Conservation Voters, for example, assigned the Congressional Black Caucus high marks for having one of the best pro-environment voting records.

Many black communities, however, still do not have the organization, financial resources, or personnel to mount and sustain long-term challenges to such unpopular facilities as municipal and hazardous-waste landfills, garbage incinerators. toxic-waste storage facilities. and industrial plants that may pose a threat to their health and safety. This problem is complicated by the fact that blacks in many cases have to go outside their communities to find the technical experts—toxicologists, hydrologists, epidemiologists, environmental engineers, land use planners, demographers, and lawyers—that may be needed to challenge the siting process. Moreover, the talent at historically black colleges and universities (most of which are located in the South and in black communities) is still untapped when it comes to providing leadership and expertise on environmental issues in the minority community. The underutilization of experts at these institutions must end if they are to remain viable partners in strengthening and improving the quality of life for people of color.

Finally, black communities in the South need to incorporate environmental safeguards into their agendas for economic development. The promise of jobs may provide short-term solutions to economically depressed black communities, but health and environmental risks can often overshadow the benefits derived from hazardous, low-paying occupations. The black community needs to use its institutions, churches, civic clubs, professional associations, civil rights and political organizations, colleges and universities to develop a network of advocates and experts who can develop and articulate long-term environmental strategies for the black community. Black Southerners, like all Americans, have a right to live and work in an unpolluted environment.

NOTES

Acknowledgment: Research for this study was supported in part by a grant from Resources for the Future.

1 Will Collette, "Somewhere Else USA: Fighting Back Against Chemical Dumpers," *Southern Neighborhoods* 9 (September 1985): 1.

2 John D. Kasarda, Michael D. Irvin, and Holly L. Hughes, "The South Is Still Rising," *American Demographics* 8 (June 1986): 34; *The President's National Urban Policy Report 1980* (Washington, D.C.: U.S. Department of Housing and Urban Development, 1980). 165–69; John D. Kasarda. "The Implications of Contemporary Trends for National Urban Policy," *Social Science Quarterly* 61 (December 1980): 373–400.

3 David R. Goldfield. *Promised Land: The South Since 1945* (Arlington Heights, Ill.: Harlan Davidson, 1987), 197. Kasarda, Irvin, and Hughes, "The South Is Still Rising." 32–40.

4 See Robert D. Bullard and Beverly H. Wright. "The Politics of Pollution: Implications for the Black Community." *Phylon* 47 (March 1985): 71–78.

5 Robert L Lineberry, *Equality and Urban Policy: The Distribution of Municipal Public Services* (Beverly Hills. Calif.: Sage, 1977), 11. David Morell. "Siting and Politics of Equity," in *Resolving Locational Conflict*, ed. Robert W. Lake (New Brunswick. N.J.: Rutgers University Center for Urban Policy Research, 1987), 118.

6 See Robert D. Bullard and Beverly H. Wright, "Blacks and the Environment," *Humboldt Journal of Social Relations* 14 (Summer 1987): 165–84

7 K. Mahaffey, J. L. Annest, J. Roberts, and R. S. Murphey, "National Estimates of Blood Lead Levels: United States, 1976-1960," *New England Journal of Medicine* 307 (September 1982): 572–79.

8 Jonathan Lash, Katherine Gillman, and David Sheridan. *A Season of Spoils: The Story of the Reagan Administration's Attack on the Environment* (New York: Pantheon Books, 1984), 132–39.

9 Bullard and Wright, "The Politics of Pollution," 77.

10 See Samuel S. Epstein. Lester O. Brown, and Carl Pope, *Hazardous Waste in America* (San Francisco: Sierra Club Books, 1983). 33–39; Adeline Levine. *Love Canal: Science, Politics,*

and People (Lexington, Mass.: Lexington Books, 1982). Office of Technology Assessment, *Technologies and Management Strategies for Hazardous Waste Control* (Washington. D.C.: U.S. Government Printing Office, 1983), 3. Michael H. Brown, *Laying Waste: The Poisoning of America by Toxic Chemicals* (New York: Pantheon Books, 1982), 267.

11 *Siting of Hazardous Waste Landfills and Their Correlation with Racial and Economic Status in Surrounding Communities* (Washington, D.C.: U.S. General Accounting Office, 1983), 2: *Toxic Wastes and Race in the United States: A National Report on the Racial and Socioeconomic Characteristics of Communities with Hazardous Waste Sites* (New York: Commission for Racial Justice, 1987), 16; Robert D. Bullard and Beverly H. Wright. "Environmentalism and the Politics of Equity: Trends in the Black Community." *Mid-American Review of Sociology* 12 (Winter 1987): 21–38.

12 *Siting of Hazardous Waste Landfills*, 2–3.

13 Sue Pollack and JoAnn Grozuczak, *Reagan, Toxics, and Minorities* (Washington. D.C.: Urban Environment Conference, 1984), 20.

14 *Toxic Wastes and Race.* 23–27.

15 Robert D. Bullard, *Invisible Houston; The Black Experience in Boom and Bust* (College Station. Tex.: Texas A&M University Press, 1987), 70.

16 See Robert D. Bullard, "Solid Waste Sites and the Black Houston Community," *Sociological Inquiry* 53 (Spring 1983): 273–88; Robert D. Bullard. "Endangered Environs: The Price of Unplanned Growth in Boomtown Houston," *California Sociologist* 7 (Summer 1984): 85–101.

17 For a detailed account of the waste-disposal controversy in Houston see Bullard. *Invisible Houston*, chapter 6.

CHAPTER EIGHT

Human Population, Urbanization, and Land Use

This chapter examines some of the fundamental information about human populations: how exponential human population growth started, the history and effects of urbanization, and the effect of population growth on land use. The Dork Sahagian selected reading, "Human Population" from *A User's Guide for Planet Earth: Fundamentals of Environmental Science* (2018), provides a good overview of the history of human demography, "the study of human population change." Understanding changing population sizes in different countries can help us plan for more sustainable resource use in the future. As our economies require the input of natural resources, following the course of demographic transitions from high birth and death rates to low birth and death rates can help us predict the resource needs of different countries.

In order to manage the use of resources and to avoid excess pollution, tracking changes in human population size can be crucial. The selected reading by Paul R. Ehrlich and Anne H. Ehrlich, "Can a Collapse of Global Civilization Be Avoided" (2013), discusses the various causes of historical population collapses, such as the Classic Maya or Rapa Nui (Easter Island), and what our current global population needs to focus on to avoid the mistakes of the past. One of the main ideas of the article is overconsumption, which was explained visually in the documentary video "The Story of Stuff," introduced under sustainability in Chapter 2. However, we need to connect unsustainable overconsumption back to the various ideas for how we can manage all of our shared resources.

Collapse from overconsumption is not inevitable, and farmers, countries, and societies can and do cooperate with each other to manage their use of shared natural resources. There are many models to examine how to manage a common resource, such as fresh water, fields for grazing, or our global fisheries. To control atmospheric pollution, particularly carbon dioxide, it has been difficult but imperative to regulate the release of pollutants. Often countries that create very little pollution bear the brunt of climate change and sea level rise. The recommended reading by Thomas Dietz et al., "The Struggle to Govern the Commons," attempts to describe why it has been so difficult to govern global common resources over time. This article connects back to the discussion of human demography because as we create institutions to govern the commons—international treaties, national laws, and non-governmental agencies—we must understand the changing needs of different countries based on the size and growth of their human populations. These readings connect to our policy discussions in Chapter 10, and these ideas are part of how we decide to protect and consume resources and energy as discussed in Chapters 2, 4, and 9. At the end of this text, in Chapters 11 and 12, we will explore the ethics of resource consumption.

RECOMMENDED READING

Dietz, T., Ostrom, E., and Stern, P. C. 2003. "The struggle to govern the commons." *Science*, 302(5652): 1907–1912.

RECOMMENDED VIEWING

NOVA. 2004. *World in Balance: The People Paradox*. PBS Studios.
WATCH AT https://www.pbs.org/wgbh/nova/worldbalance/credits.html

PBS. 2007. "Bogota Building a Sustainable City." *e2 design: The Economies of Being Environmentally Conscious,* Season II, Episode 9, Tad Fettig (Director).
WATCH AT https://www.pbs.org/e2/episodes/209_bogota_building_sustainable_city_trailer.html

READING AND DISCUSSION PROMPTS

1. How many people can our planet really support? What do you think is Earth's carrying capacity for humans? Have we reached the carrying capacity yet? If not, what makes you think that? If you think we have reached carrying capacity, do you think humans must undergo a drastic decrease in population?
2. An urban ecosystem is very different from a natural ecosystem. But in what ways do you think the two ecosystems—urban and natural—are similar?

3. We seem to accept, as a matter of course, that human beings are driven to consume more and more. Is this the case, or rather are we socialized into a consumption mentality? What evidence from any of the readings in this chapter support your position? What are some effective ways to reduce material consumption in everyday life while maintaining livability?
4. One of the main ideas of both economic and environmental policy is the notion of sustainability. How does sustainability relate to overpopulation? Can we achieve sustainability without addressing overpopulation?

READING 8.1

Human Population

By Dork Sahagian

So many young people inhabit the land
Our proliferation was somewhat unplanned.
Our numbers keep growing
Increase hardly slowing
As resource imbalance gets way out of hand.

In 2018, there are over 7.5 billion people on the planet. This is remarkable in a number of ways. Most notable is the rate of growth, which is about 3 people per second, or an additional equivalent to the entire U.S. population every three years. This explosive rate of population growth (Figure 8.1.1), were it any other species on the earth, would be considered an infection or a plague (depending on organism size), and antibiotics or other sterilization measures would be applied immediately. Of this growth, 90% is in the developing world, or the poorer nations globally, where about 80% of the population already lives. As such, the spatial distribution is skewed, as is the distribution of wealth and security, shifting ever more toward an increasing fraction of the world population who are under food, water, health, and other stresses. Perhaps one of the most alarming observations is that about 50 to 100 billion modern humans have ever lived on Earth (depending on whether you count infant mortality during times of life expectancy of ten years or less over most of the last 50,000 years). Of those, 7.5 billion, or about 7% to 14% are alive today.

The history of humanity and precursors shows that there was a small (fewer than a couple hundred million) and stable population for the last 200,000 years or so, until the

Figure 8.1.1 Large family.

most recent thousand years or so (Figure 8.1.2). Population increase accelerated, and then exploded starting about 1850, or the time of the industrial revolution. In part, the stability of the early population was due (as for any species) to a balance between births and deaths. High mortality rates made it necessary to maintain high fertility rates (children born per woman) in order to maintain the population. These high fertility rates became the norm, and without them, the species would have been extinct long ago. About 10,000 years ago, a stabilizing climate enabled ecosystems to remain in one place for long periods, and this quickly led to the concept of agriculture, enabling the purposeful growth of crops and animals specifically (and increasingly) bred for human consumption. This enabled the onset of specialization, stationary communities, and the support of larger populations. It was not until the advent of antibiotics, uses for fossil fuels, and industrialization that the greatest imbalance between fertility and mortality began. With increasing global access to medicine and medical care, an unprecedented fraction of babies lived to reproduce. This caused a huge increase in the number of grandchildren born (Figure 8.1.2). (It is not the children born, but the grandchildren who determine growth or decline of a population. You could have twelve children, but if only one of them survives to bear you grandchildren, the population could still decline.)

Two hundred thousand years of "having as many children as possible" is a difficult habit to break, and even after most children born survived to maturity, cultural norms maintained high fertility. Eventually, in the most industrialized, wealthiest countries where medicine, food, water, sanitation, technology, and personal safety enabled almost every child to survive, people began to feel the confidence to bear fewer children and fertility declined to closer to constant population-maintenance levels. The delay between the ability for children to survive and the confidence of parents to bear fewer children is called the "**demographic transition**" (Figure 8.1.3), which is affected by both poverty and education (Bottencourt, 2018; Snopkoski et al., 2016).

Before the transition, population is held stable by high death rates matching high birth rates. After the transition, it is stabilized by low birth rates finally matching low death rates. In between, there is population explosion, and this is what happened in the previous century in Europe and America, and is happening in this century in the rest of the world (Figure 8.1.4).

WHAT IS THE CARRYING CAPACITY OF THE EARTH?

Carrying capacity is the limit of population that an ecosystem can sustainably support. For every other species (besides human), the carrying capacity is determined by the balance of reproductive rate, food, and habitat on the one hand, and mortality and predation on the other. Organisms use only as much food and other resources as needed to survive. With humans, however, there is a large range of resource consumption. Some, in very poor regions, consume a small fraction of the amount that others in rich areas do. The

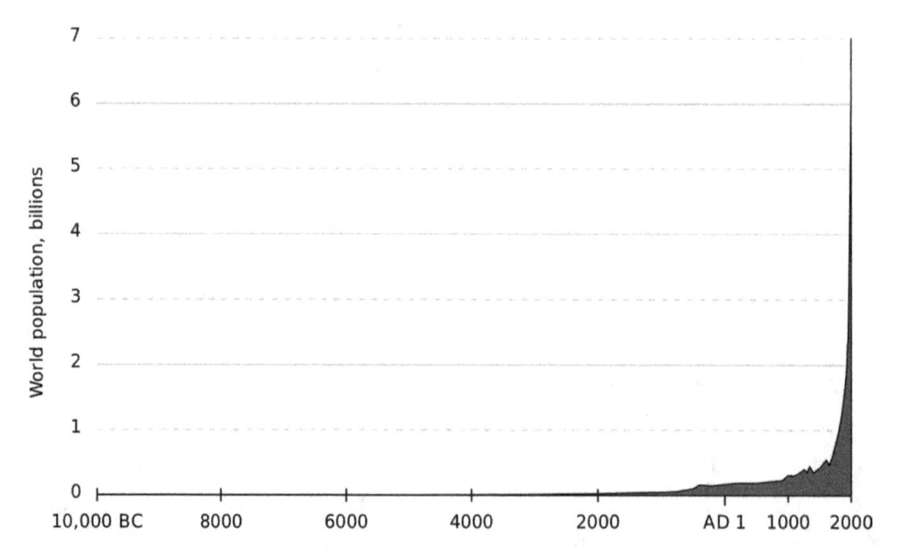

Figure 8.1.2 Population Curve
Human population remained stable for thousands of years until a recent explosion, surpassing 7 billion in 2012, and 7.5 billion in 2017.

planet can carry more people who consume very little than rich people who consume a lot. So the question of carrying capacity comes down to "How do people want to live?" While this is not a scientific question, it bears on the science of the environment in that human populations are responsible for the degradation of ecosystems throughout the world, and the more people there are, and the more each consumes, the more rapid the rate of environmental degradation. In general the overall environmental impact is just the product of the average impact of individual humans and the human population. The general feeling globally is that the exploding population of the developing world wishes to live and consume like Americans do, with orders of magnitude greater consumption of energy, food, and other resources than the poorest and most rapidly increasing populations of the world. This being the case, the carrying capacity declines dramatically. In effect, humans are the first species

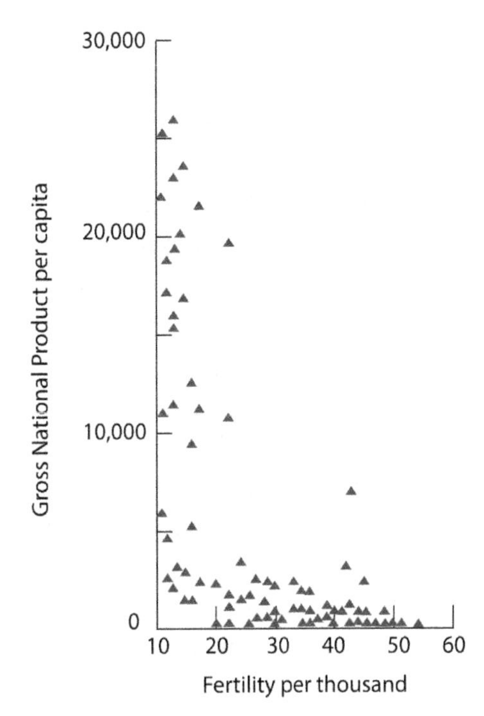

Figure 8.1.3 Strong correlation with poverty and birth rates.

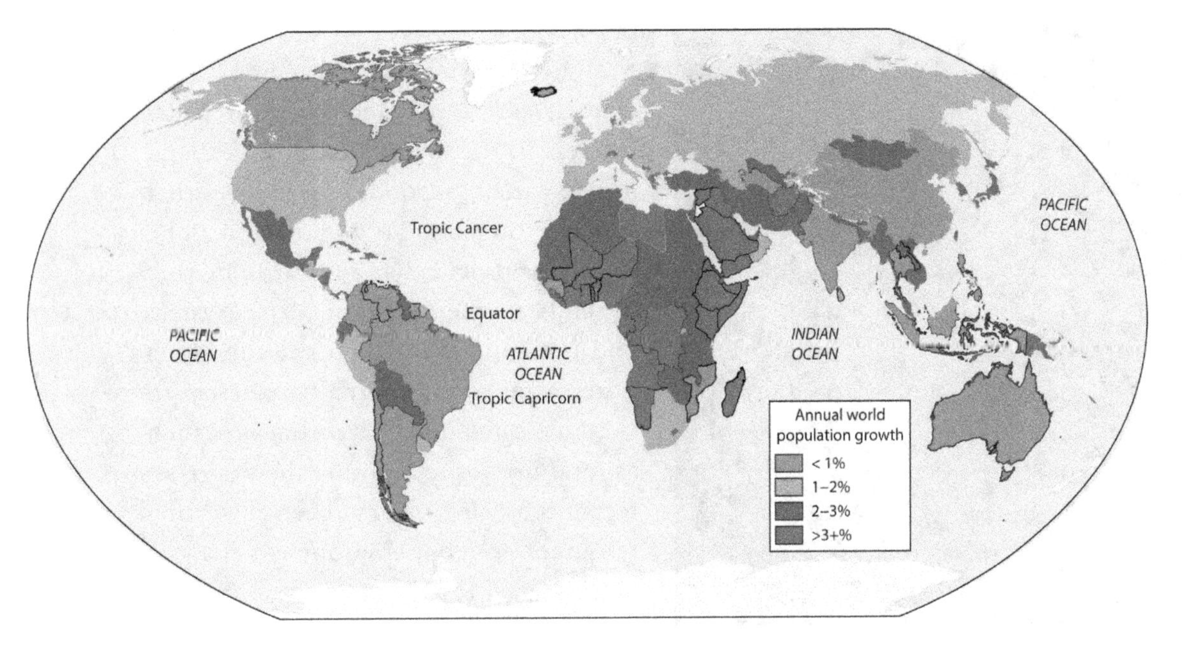

Figure 8.1.4 Regional population growth rates.

(that we know of) that can determine its own means of population control. It does not need to be starvation, disease, and predation, as it is for other species. If we choose not to reproduce right up to the available food (and other resource) supply, we can avoid "eating into the principal" and future decline of carrying capacity.

It has long been realized that human overpopulation and overconsumption is the root of all environmental problems. There are already more people in the world than can be sustained by the world's ecosystems, and degradation of soils (Figure 8.1.5), aquifers, fish (Figure 8.1.6), and biodiversity is already proceeding at an alarming pace.

The usual concern regarding this is the continued availability of food for human consumption. There are billions of people in the world who are undernourished, and technologic and economic advances could help to provide more food and better living conditions for a large segment of the human population. The problem is that if these populations are still within the demographic transition, prior to reducing fertility voluntarily (Battacharya and Chakraborty, 2017), more food and better conditions will merely enable more children to survive and will lead to further population explosion, potentially getting right back to where they started, but now with more mouths to feed. This same concept applies to all environmental problems caused by human activities. Essentially, "There is no solution to an environmental problem that cannot be negated by a concomitant increase in human population." With an increasing portion of the world getting through the demographic transition, the rate of population increase appears to be slowing down a bit, but population is still increasing rapidly (Figure 8.1.7).

Figure 8.1.5 Soil loss.

The global ecosystem can be considered as a bank account that bears interest in the form of food, water, and a wide variety of goods and services that support our human population. The interest is provided at a certain rate that depends on the health of the ecosystem and the extent to which the functions it performs are permitted to operate in the face of human perturbations such as land use for agriculture. However, in recent centuries, we have been extracting resources from our environment at a rate much greater than that at which they are restored. As such, we have been eating into the principal, a concept abhorrent to any financial manager. The result of this is that with more limited ecosystem function, the global environment bears less "interest" for us to use, and thus the carrying capacity actually declines. So the more people there are, the faster they use up the remaining resources, and the fewer people who can ultimately be supported in the long run. What happens in typical populations when they exceed their environment's carrying capacity is that they increase for a while, during which they deplete the resources upon which they depend, and then when the resources are stressed to a critical limit, the population crashes to a new and very low number, determined by the few remaining resources available (Figure 8.1.8).

If it took 30 days for an exponentially increasing population of bacteria to completely fill a test beaker, when would the beaker be only half full of bacteria? Answer: Day 29.

Figure 8.1.6 Overfishing.

About half of the world's primary productivity (the amount of biomass produced by plants) is already used by humans. This is used in an unsustainable manner that leads to soil loss, decline of fisheries, and reduction of biodiversity. If the population were to double (in just a few decades), the entire planet would be used for agriculture to support human life. This would quickly lead to reduction in the rate of provision of ecosystem goods and services, and subsequent reduction of carrying capacity, as humans need other resources besides food (e.g., clean fresh water, clean air, proper sanitation, etc.).

POPULATION BY THE NUMBERS

The difference between the number of deaths in a population and the number of births (per year) is the growth rate. At present, the global birth rate is about twenty-one people

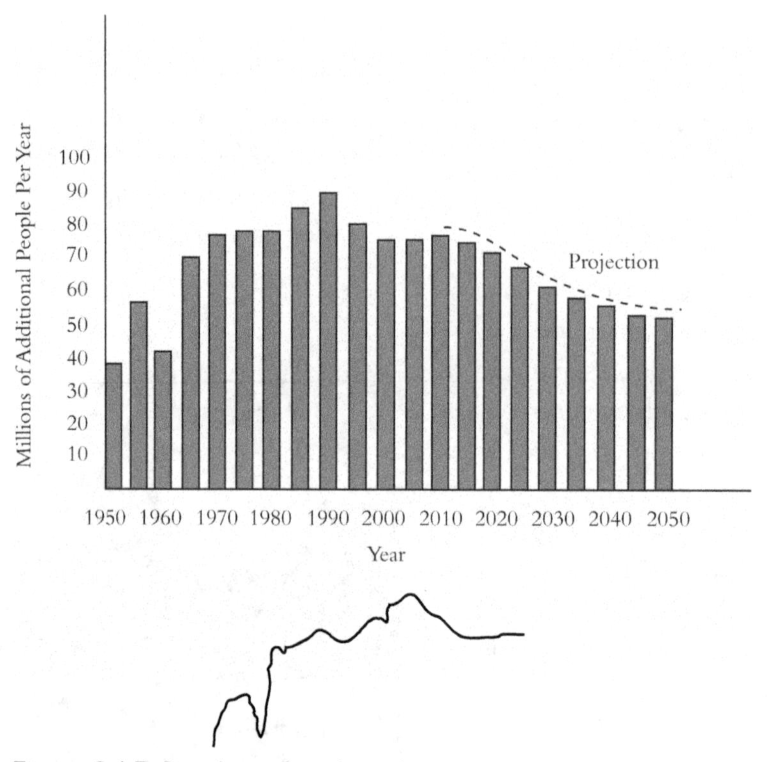

Figure 8.1.7 Population has slowed
The rate of population growth has slowed already and is projected to be further reduced. This should not be confused with a reduction in population. It is merely projected to increase as a slightly slower rate than it has to date. In order to population to decrease, the growth rate would need to become negative.

per thousand (per year), and the death rate is about nine people per thousand (per year). This makes a global growth rate of twelve per thousand per year, or 1.2% per year. While this may not sound like a very large number, it is. In 10 years the population increases by over 13%. In fact, one can easily calculate the time it would take the entire population to double—roughly 70/1.2 = 58 years. At a 3% growth rate, it would double in 23 years.

The history of birth and death rates of a segment of the population determines its age structure. If there are a great many babies born, but life expectancy is short, there is a very young average population. If, on the other hand, there are very few births and long life expectancy, but there were more births in the past, there would be a very old population with declining numbers. If the case of the young population gains medicine, security, and longer life expectancy, it would enter the demographic transition and population would explode. The current population of the world is unevenly distributed, with most in Asia,

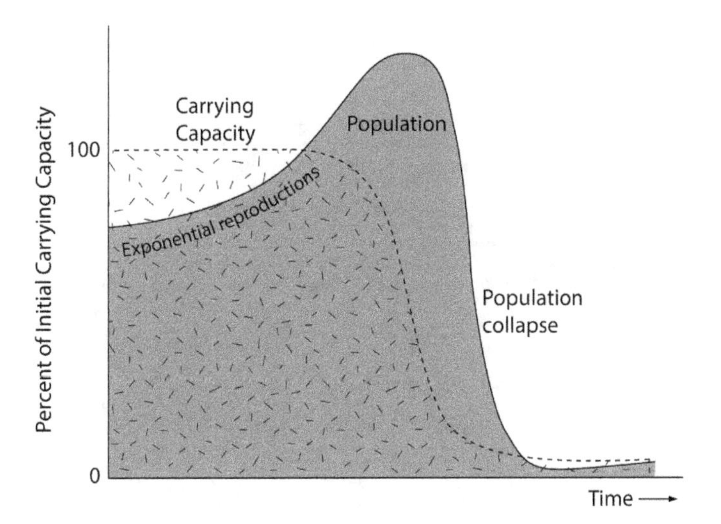

Figure 8.1.8 Population exceeds carrying capacity
A population can exceed its carrying capacity for a while. As long as it is beneath its carrying capacity, it is supported by the rate of provision of environmental goods and services (e.g., food) provided by the ecosystem, much like bearing interest on a bank account. The population can exceed the carrying capacity, at which point it reduces the amount of the ecosystem that provides support, like "eating into the principal" of a bank account. This causes fewer goods and services to be provided, reducing carrying capacity. When the ecosystem is exhausted in what the population needs, the population crashes to a new, much lower (maybe zero) level, according to the rate at which the remnants of the ecosystem can provide the necessary goods and services.

yet with the greatest rate of growth in Africa. In general, high birth rate is related to poverty (Figure 8.1.9). Historically, it has been advantageous for old people to be supported by a large number of young people. As our life expectancy increases, with more and older people, an inverted pyramid age structure would lead to a greater burden on younger, working people to support the aged. This is an inevitable and necessary, yet temporary, price to be paid for stabilizing populations that grew quickly in the previous generation.

REFERENCES

Bhattacharya, J., & Chakraborty, S. (2017). Contraception and the demographic transition. *Economic Journal*, 127(606), 2263–2301.

Bittencourt, M. (2018). Primary education and fertility rates: Evidence from Southern Africa. *Economics of Transition*, 26(2), 283–302.

Snopkowski, K., Towner, M. C., Shenk, M. K., & Colleran, H. Pathways from education to fertility decline: a multi-site comparative study. (2016). *Philosophical Transactions of the Royal Society B-Biological Sciences*, 371(1692), 20150156

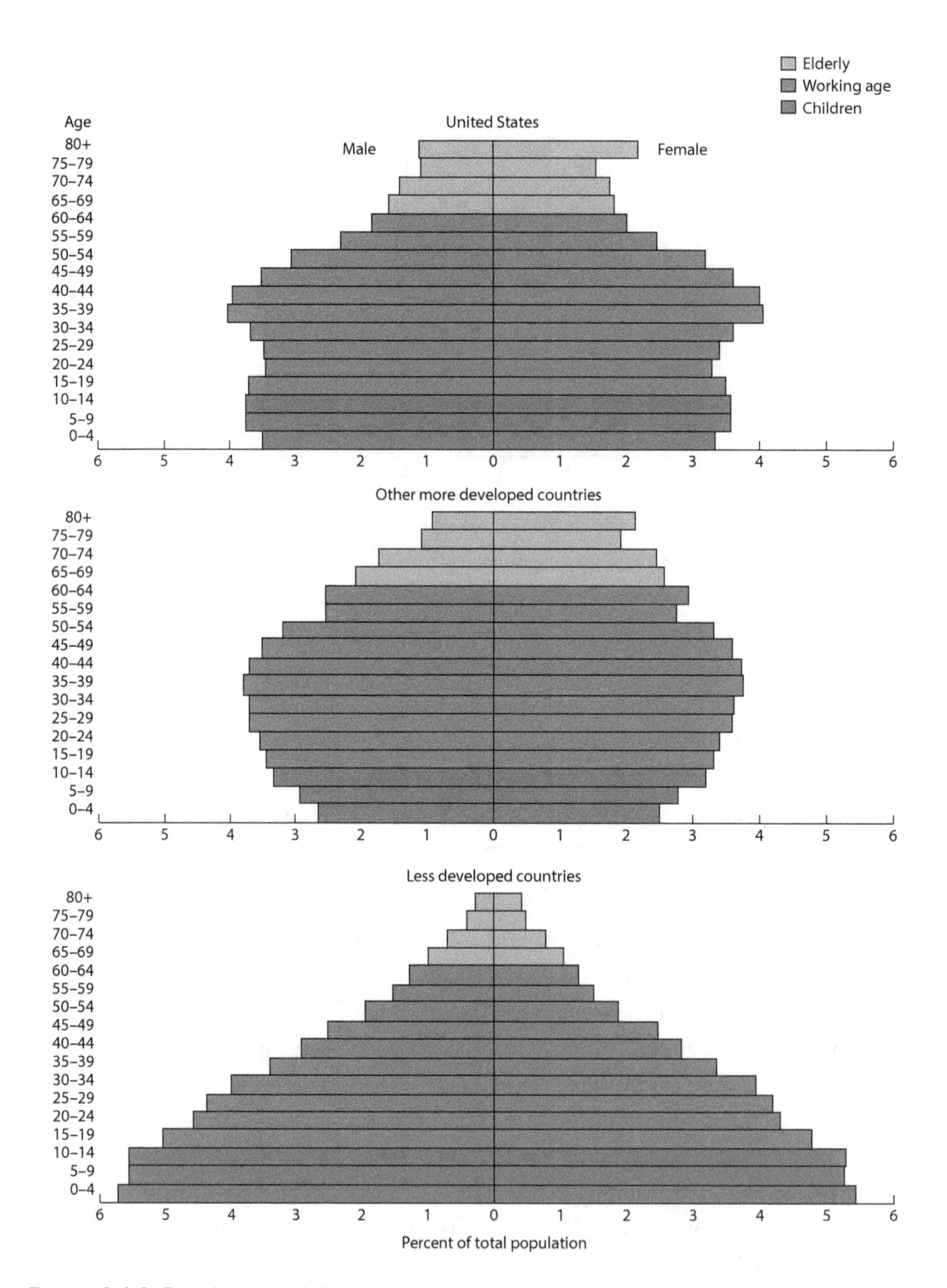

Figure 8.1.9 Population and Age graph

There is a strong correlation between poverty and birth rates. Wealthy nations are generally past the demographic transition, while parents in poorer nations are still unsure of children's survival. The cause and effect between having many children and poverty is not clear, and feedbacks may be involved.

FIGURE CREDITS

Fig. 8.1.1: Copyright © Ojedamd (CC BY-SA 3.0) at https://commons.wikimedia.org/wiki/File:FamiliaOjeda.JPG.

Fig. 8.1.2: https://commons.wikimedia.org/wiki/File:Population_curve.svg

Fig. 8.1.4: https://commons.wikimedia.org/wiki/File:BlankMap-World6.svg

Fig. 8.1.5: https://commons.wikimedia.org/wiki/File:STS007-03-0058.jpg

Fig. 8.1.6: Copyright © CSIRO (CC by 3.0) at https://commons.wikimedia.org/wiki/File:CSIRO_ScienceImage_3691_Fishermen_haul_a_catch_of_orange_roughy_aboard_a_fishing_vessel.jpg

Fig. 8.1.9: http://nationalatlas.gov/articles/people/IMAGES/int-fig5.gif

READING 8.2

Can a Collapse of Global Civilization Be Avoided?

By Paul R. Ehrlich and Anne H. Ehrlich

Environmental problems have contributed to numerous collapses of civilizations in the past. Now, for the first time, a global collapse appears likely. Overpopulation, overconsumption by the rich and poor choices of technologies are major drivers; dramatic cultural change provides the main hope of averting calamity.

INTRODUCTION

Virtually every past civilization has eventually undergone collapse, a loss of socio-political-economic complexity usually accompanied by a dramatic decline in population size [1]. Some, such as those of Egypt and China, have recovered from collapses at various stages; others, such as that of Easter Island or the Classic Maya, were apparently permanent [1,2]. All those previous collapses were local or regional; elsewhere, other societies and civilizations persisted unaffected. Sometimes, as in the Tigris and Euphrates valleys, new civilizations rose in succession. In many, if not most, cases, overexploitation of the environment was one proximate or an ultimate cause [3].

But today, for the first time, humanity's *global* civilization—the worldwide, increasingly interconnected, highly technological society in which we all are to one degree or another, embedded—is threatened with collapse by an array of environmental problems. Humankind finds itself engaged in what Prince Charles described as 'an act of suicide on a grand scale' [4], facing what the UK's Chief Scientific Advisor John Beddington called a 'perfect storm' of environmental problems [5]. The most serious of these problems show signs of rapidly escalating severity, especially climate disruption. But other elements could potentially also contribute to a collapse: an accelerating extinction of animal and plant populations and species, which could lead to a loss of ecosystem services essential for human survival; land degradation and land-use change; a pole-to-pole spread of toxic compounds; ocean acidification and eutrophication (dead zones); worsening of some aspects of the epidemiological environment (factors that make human populations susceptible to infectious diseases); depletion of increasingly scarce resources [6,7], including especially groundwater, which is being overexploited in many key agricultural areas [8]; and resource wars [9]. These are not separate problems; rather they interact in two gigantic complex adaptive systems: the biosphere system and the human socio-economic system. The negative manifestations of these interactions are often referred to as 'the human predicament' [10], and determining how to prevent it from generating a global collapse is perhaps *the* foremost challenge confronting humanity.

The human predicament is driven by overpopulation, overconsumption of natural resources and the use of unnecessarily environmentally damaging technologies and socio-economic-political arrangements to service *Homo sapiens*' aggregate consumption [11–17]. How far the human population size now is above the planet's long-term carrying capacity is suggested (conservatively) by ecological footprint analysis [18–20]. It shows that to support *today's* population of seven billion sustainably (i.e. with business as usual, including current technologies and standards of living) would require roughly half an additional planet; to do so, if all citizens of Earth consumed resources at the US level would take four to five more Earths. Adding the projected 2.5 billion more people by 2050 would make the human assault on civilization's life-support systems disproportionately worse, because almost everywhere people face systems with nonlinear responses [11,21–23], in which environmental damage increases at a rate that becomes faster with each additional person. Of course, the claim is often made that humanity will expand Earth's carrying capacity dramatically with technological innovation [24], but it is widely recognized that technologies can both add and subtract from carrying capacity. The plough evidently first expanded it and now appears to be reducing it [3]. Overall, careful analysis of the prospects does not provide much confidence that technology will save us [25] or that gross domestic product can be disengaged from resource use [26].

DO CURRENT TRENDS PORTEND A COLLAPSE?

What is the likelihood of this set of interconnected predicaments [27] leading to a global collapse in this century? There have been many definitions and much discussion of past 'collapses' [1,3,28–31], but a future global collapse does not require a careful definition. It could be triggered by anything from a 'small' nuclear war, whose ecological effects could quickly end civilization [32], to a more gradual breakdown because famines, epidemics and resource shortages cause a disintegration of central control within nations, in concert with disruptions of trade and conflicts over increasingly scarce necessities. In either case, regardless of survivors or replacement societies, the world familiar to anyone reading this study and the well-being of the vast majority of people would disappear.

How likely is such a collapse to occur? No civilization can avoid collapse if it fails to feed its population. The world's success so far, and the prospective ability to feed future generations at least as well, has been under relatively intensive discussion for half a century [33–40]. Agriculture made civilization possible, and over the last 80 years or so, an industrial agricultural revolution has created a technology-dependent global food system. That system, humanity's single biggest industry, has generated miracles of food production. But it has also created serious long-run vulnerabilities, especially in its dependence on stable climates, crop monocultures, industrially produced fertilizers and pesticides, petroleum, antibiotic feed supplements and rapid, efficient transportation.

Despite those food production miracles, today at least two billion people are hungry or poorly nourished. The Food and Agriculture Organization estimates that increasing food production by some 70 per cent would be required to feed a 35 per cent bigger and still growing human population adequately by 2050 [41]. What are the prospects that *H. sapiens* can produce and distribute sufficient food? To do so, it probably will be necessary to accomplish many or all of the following tasks: severely limit climate disruption; restrict expansion of land area for agriculture (to preserve ecosystem services); raise yields where possible; put much more effort into soil conservation [3]; increase efficiency in the use of fertilizers, water and energy; become more vegetarian; grow more food for people (not fuel for vehicles); reduce food wastage; stop degradation of the oceans and better regulate aquaculture; significantly increase investment in sustainable agricultural and aquacultural research; and move increasing equity and feeding everyone to the very top of the policy agenda.

Most of these long-recommended tasks require changes in human behaviour thus far elusive. The problem of food wastage and the need for more and better agricultural research have been discussed for decades. So have 'technology will save us' schemes such as building 'nuclear agro-industrial complexes' [42], where energy would be so cheap that it could support a new kind of desert agriculture in 'food factories', where crops would be grown on desalinated water and precisely machine fertilized. Unhappily, sufficiently cheap energy has never been produced by nuclear power to enable large-scale agriculture to move in that direction. Nor has agriculture moved towards feeding people protein extracted from leaves or bacteria grown on petroleum [43, pp. 95–112]. None of these schemes has even resulted in a coordinated development effort. Meanwhile, growing numbers of newly well-off people have increased demand for meat [44], thereby raising global demand for feedgrains.

Perhaps even more critical, climate disruption may pose insurmountable biophysical barriers to increasing crop yields. Indeed, if humanity is very unlucky with the climate, there may be reductions in yields of major crops [45], although near-term this may be unlikely to affect harvests globally [46]. Nonetheless, rising temperatures already seem to be slowing previous trends of increasing yields of basic grains [45,47], and unless greenhouse gas emissions are dramatically reduced, dangerous anthropogenic climate change [48] could ravage agriculture. Also, in addition to falling yields from many oceanic fish stocks because of widespread overfishing [49], warming and acidification of the oceans threaten the protein supply of some of the most nutritionally vulnerable people [50], especially those who cannot afford to purchase farmed fish.

Unfortunately, the agricultural system has complex connections with all the chief drivers of environmental deterioration. Agriculture itself is a major emitter of greenhouse gases and thus is an important cause of climate disruption as well as being exceptionally vulnerable to its consequences. More than a millennium of change in temperature and precipitation patterns is apparently now entrained [51], with the prospect of increasingly severe storms, droughts, heat waves and floods, all of which seem already evident and all of which threaten agricultural production.

Land is an essential resource for farming, and one facing multiple threats. In addition to the serious and widespread problems of soil degradation, sea-level rise (the most certain consequence of global warming) will take important areas out of production either by inundating them (a 1 m rise would flood 17.5% of Bangladesh [52]), exposing them to more frequent storm surges, or salinizing coastal aquifers essential for irrigation water. Another important problem for the food system is the loss of prime farmland to urbanization, a trend that seems certain to accelerate [53] as population growth steadily erodes the *per capita* supply of farmland.

The critical importance of substantially boosting the inadequate current action on the demographic problem can be seen in the time required to change the trajectory of population growth humanely and sensibly. We know from such things as the World War II mobilizations that many consumption patterns can be altered dramatically within a year, given appropriate incentives [54]. If food shortages became acute, then a rapid reaction would ensue as hunger became much more widespread. Food prices would rise, and diets would temporarily change (e.g. the number of meals consumed per day or amount of meat consumed) to compensate the shortage. Over the long term, however, expanding the global food supply and distributing it more equitably would be a slow and difficult process.

Even though a major famine might well provoke investment in long-needed improvements in food production and distribution, they would take time to plan, test and implement.

Furthermore, agriculture is a leading cause of losses of biodiversity and thus of the critical ecosystem services supplied to agriculture itself (e.g. pollination, pest control, soil fertility, climate stability) and other human enterprises. Farming is also a principal source of global toxification, as has been clear since the days of Carson [55], exposing the human population to myriad subtle poisons. These pose further potential risks to food production.

WHAT NEEDS TO BE DONE TO AVOID A COLLAPSE?

The threat from climate disruption to food production alone means that humanity's entire system for mobilizing energy needs to be rapidly transformed. Warming must be held well below a potential 58C rise in global average temperature, a level that could well bring down civilization [56]. The best estimate today may be that, failing rapid concerted action, the world is already committed to a 2.48C increase in global average temperature [57]. This is significantly above the 28C estimated a decade ago by climate scientists to be a 'safe' limit, but now considered by some analysts to be too dangerous [58,59], a credible assessment, given the effects seen already before reaching a one degree rise. There is evidence, moreover, that present models underestimate future temperature increase by overestimating the extent that growth of vegetation can serve as a carbon sink [60] and underestimating positive feedbacks [61].

Many complexities plague the estimation of the precise threats of anthropogenic climate disruption, ranging from heat deaths and spread of tropical diseases to sea-level rise, crop failures and violent storms. One key to avoiding a global collapse, and thus an area requiring great effort and caution is avoiding climate-related mass famines. Our agricultural system evolved in a geological period of relatively constant and benign climate and was well attuned to twentieth-century conditions. That alone is cause for substantial concern as the planet's climates rapidly shift to new, less predictable regimes. It is essential to slow that process. That means dramatically transforming much of the existing energy mobilization infrastructure [62] and changing human behaviour to make the energy system much more efficient. This *is* possible; indeed, sensible plans for doing it have been put forward [63,64], and some progress has been made. The central challenge, of course, is to phase out more than half of the global use of fossil fuels by 2050 in order to forestall the worst impacts of climate disruption, a challenge the latest International Energy Agency edition of World Energy Outlook makes look more severe [65]. This highlights another dilemma. Fossil fuels are now essential to agriculture for fertilizer and pesticide manufacture, operation of farm machinery, irrigation (often wasteful), livestock husbandry, crop drying, food storage, transportation and distribution. Thus, the phase-out will need to include at least partial substitution of non-fossil fuels in these functions, and do so without greatly increasing food prices.

Unfortunately, essential steps such as curbing global emissions to peak by 2020 and reducing them to half of present levels by 2050 [66] are extremely problematic economically and politically. Fossil fuel companies would have to leave most of their proven reserves in the ground, thus destroying much of the industry's economic value [67]. Because the ethics of some businesses include knowingly continuing lethal but profitable activities [68], it is hardly surprising that interests with large financial stakes in fossil fuel burning have launched a gigantic and largely successful disinformation campaign in the USA to confuse people about climate disruption [69,70] and block attempts to deal with it [71].

One recurrent theme in analyses of the food problem is the need for closing 'yield gaps' [72–74]. That means raising yields in less productive systems to those typical of industrial agriculture. But climatic conditions may change sufficiently that those industrial high yields can themselves no longer be sustained [45]. Thus, reducing the chances of a collapse calls for placing much more effort into genetic and ecological research related to agriculture [75] and adopting already known environmental-friendly techniques, even though that may require trading off immediate corporate profits for social benefits or long-term sustainability [3].

Rationalizing energy mobilization alone may not be enough to be enough to maintain agricultural production, let alone allow its great expansion. Human water-handling infrastructure will have to be re-engineered for flexibility to bring water to crops in an environment of constantly changing precipitation patterns [51]. This is critical, for although today only about 15 per cent of agricultural land is irrigated, it provides some 40 per cent of the grain crop yield. It seems likely that farming areas now rain-fed may someday need to be irrigated, whereas irrigation could become superfluous elsewhere, and both could change more or less continually. For this and many other reasons, the global food system will need to quickly evolve an unprecedented flexibility, never before even contemplated.

One factor making the challenges more severe is the major participation in the global system of giant nations whose populations have not previously enjoyed the fossil energy abundance that brought Western countries and Japan to positions of affluence. Now they are poised to repeat the West's energy 'success', and on an even greater scale. India alone, which recently suffered a gigantic blackout affecting 300 million people, is planning to bring 455 new coal plants on line. Worldwide more than 1200 plants with a total installed capacity of 1.4 million megawatts are planned [76], much of that in China, where electricity demand is expected to skyrocket. The resultant surge in greenhouse gases will interact with the increasing diversion of grain to livestock, stimulated by the desire for more meat in the diets of Indians, Chinese and others in a growing global middle class.

DEALING WITH PROBLEMS BEYOND FOOD SUPPLY

Another possible threat to the continuation of civilization is global toxification. Adverse symptoms of exposure to synthetic chemicals are making some scientists increasingly nervous about effects on the human population [77–79]. Should a global threat materialize, however, no planned mitigating responses (analogous to the ecologically and politically risky 'geoengineering' projects often proposed to ameliorate climate disruption [80]) are waiting in the wings ready for deployment.

Much the same can be said about aspects of the epidemiological environment and the prospect of epidemics being enhanced by rapid population growth in immune-weakened societies, increased contact with animal reservoirs, high-speed transport and the misuse of antibiotics [81]. Nobel laureate Joshua Lederberg had great concern for the epidemic problem, famously stating, 'The survival of the human species is not a preordained evolutionary program' [82, p. 40]. Some precautionary steps that should be considered include forbidding the use of antibiotics as growth stimulators for livestock, building emergency stocks of key vaccines and drugs (such as Tamiflu), improving disease surveillance, expanding mothballed emergency medical facilities, preparing institutions for imposing quarantines and, of course, moving as rapidly as possible to humanely reduce the human population size. It has become increasingly clear that security has many dimensions beyond military security [83,84] and that breaches of environmental security could risk the end of global civilization.

But much uncertainty about the human ability to avoid a collapse still hinges on military security, especially whether some elements of the human predicament might trigger a nuclear war. Recent research indicates that even a regional-scale nuclear conflict, as is quite possible between India and Pakistan, could lead to a global collapse through widespread climatic consequences [32]. Triggers to conflict beyond political and religious strife easily could include cross-border epidemics, a need to gain access to food supplies and farmland, and competition over other resources, especially agricultural water and (if the world does not come to its energy senses) oil. Finding ways to eliminate nuclear weapons and other instruments of mass destruction must move even higher on civilization's agenda [85], because nuclear war would be the quickest and surest route to a collapse [86].

In thinking about the probability of collapse, one must obviously consider the social disruptions associated with elements of the predicament. Perhaps at the top of the list should be that of environmental refugees [87]. Recent predictions are that environmental refugees could number 50 million by 2020 [88]. Severe droughts, floods, famines and epidemics could greatly swell that number. If current 'official' predictions of sea-level rise are low (as many believe they are), coastal inundations alone could generate massive human movements; a 1 m rise would directly affect some 100 million people, whereas a 6 m rise would displace more than 400 million [89]. Developing a more comprehensive system of international governance with institutions planning to ameliorate the impacts of such catastrophes would be a major way to reduce the odds of collapse.

THE ROLE OF SCIENCE

The scientific community has repeatedly warned humanity in the past of its peril [90–102], and the earlier warnings [93,103–107] about the risks of population expansion and the 'limits to growth' have increasingly been shown to be on the right track [108–111] (but see Hayes [17]). The warnings continue [109,112–119]. Yet many scientists still tend to treat population growth as an exogenous variable, when it should be considered an endogenous one—indeed, a central factor [120]. Too many studies asking 'how can we possibly feed 9.6 billion people by 2050?' should also be asking 'how can we humanely lower birth rates far enough to reduce that number to 8.6?' To our minds, the fundamental cure, reducing the scale of the human enterprise (including the size of the population) to keep its aggregate consumption within the carrying capacity of Earth [121], is obvious but too much neglected or denied. There are great social and psychological barriers in growthmanic cultures to even considering it. This is especially true because of the 'endarkenment'—a rapidly growing movement towards religious orthodoxies that reject enlightenment values such as freedom of thought, democracy, separation of church and state, and basing beliefs and actions on empirical evidence. They are manifest in dangerous trends such as climate denial, failure to act on the loss of biodiversity and opposition to condoms (for AIDS control) as well as other forms of contraception [122]. If ever there was a time for evidence-based (as opposed to faith-based) risk reduction strategies [123], it is now.

How can scientists do more to reduce the odds of a collapse? Both natural and social scientists should put more effort into finding the best ways of accomplishing the necessary re-modelling of energy and water infrastructure. They should develop better ways of evaluating and regulating the use of synthetic chemicals, a problem that might abate somewhat as availability of their fossil fuel sources fades (even though only about 5% of oil production flows into petrochemical production). The protection of Earth's remaining biodiversity (especially the crucial diversity of *populations* [124,125]) must take centre stage for both scientific specialists and, through appropriate education, the public [126,127]. Scientists must continually call attention to the need to improve the human epidemiological environment, and for control and eventual elimination of nuclear, chemical and biological weapons. Above all, they should expand efforts to understand the mechanisms through which cooperation evolves [128], because avoiding collapse will require unusual levels of international cooperation.

Is it too late for the global scientific community to collect itself and start to deal with the nexus of the two complex adaptive systems [129] and then help generate the necessary actions to move towards sustainability? There are certainly many small-scale science-based efforts, often local, that can provide hope if scaled up [121]. For example, environmental non-governmental organizations and others are continually struggling to halt the destruction of elements of biodiversity (and thus, in some cases, of vital ecosystem services [7]), often with success. In the face of the building extinction crisis, they may be preserving nuclei from which Earth's biota and humanity's ecosystem services, might eventually be regenerated. And some positive efforts *are* scaling up. China now has some 25 per cent of its land in ecosystem function conservation areas [130] designed to protect both natural capital and human well-being. The Natural Capital Project [131] is helping improve the management of these areas. This is good news, but in our view, many too few scientists are involved in the efforts needed, especially in re-orienting at least part of their research towards mitigating the predicament and then bringing their results to the policy front.

THE NEED FOR RAPID SOCIAL/POLITICAL CHANGE

Until very recently, our ancestors had no reason to respond genetically or culturally to long-term issues. If the global climate were changing rapidly for *Australopithecus* or even ancient Romans, then they were not causing it and could do nothing about it. The forces of genetic and cultural selection were not creating brains or institutions capable of looking generations ahead; there would have been no selection pressures in that direction. Indeed, quite the opposite, selection probably favoured mechanisms to keep perception of the environmental background steady so that rapid changes (e.g. leopard approaching) would be obvious [132, pp. 135–136]. But now slow changes in that background are the most lethal threats. Societies have a long history of mobilizing efforts, making sacrifices and changes, to defeat an enemy at the gates, or even just to compete more successfully with a rival. But there is not much evidence of societies mobilizing and making sacrifices to meet gradually worsening conditions that threaten real disaster for future generations. Yet that is exactly the sort of mobilization that we believe is required to avoid a collapse.

Perhaps the biggest challenge in avoiding collapse is convincing people, especially politicians and economists, to break this ancient mould and alter their behaviour relative to the basic population-consumption drivers of environmental deterioration. We know that simply informing people of the scientific consensus on a serious problem does not ordinarily produce rapid changes in institutional or individual behaviour. That was amply demonstrated in the case of cigarettes [68], air pollution and other environmental problems [69] and is now being demonstrated in the obesity epidemic [133] as well as climate disruption.

Obvious parallels exist regarding reproduction and over-consumption, which are especially visible in what amounts to a cultural addiction to continued economic growth among the already well-off [134]. One might think that the mathematics of compound interest would have convinced everyone long ago that growth of an industrialized economy at 3.5 per cent annually cannot long continue. Unfortunately, most 'educated' people are immersed in a culture that does not recognize that, in the real world, a short history (a few centuries) of exponential growth does not imply a long future of such growth.

Besides focusing their research on ways to avoid collapse, there is a need for natural scientists to collaborate with social scientists, especially those who study the dynamics of social movements. Such collaborations could develop ways to stimulate a significant increase in popular support for decisive and immediate action on the predicament. Unfortunately, awareness among scientists that humanity is in deep trouble has not been accompanied by popular awareness and pressure to counter the political and economic influences implicated in the current crisis. Without significant pressure from the public demanding action, we fear there is little chance of changing course fast enough to forestall disaster.

The needed pressure, however, might be generated by a popular movement based in academia and civil society to help guide humanity towards developing a new multiple intelligence [135], 'foresight intelligence' to provide the long-term analysis and planning that markets cannot supply. Foresight intelligence could not only systematically look ahead but also guide cultural changes towards desirable outcomes such as increased socio-economic resilience. Helping develop such a movement and foresight intelligence are major challenges facing scientists today, a cutting edge for research that must slice fast if the chances of averting a collapse are to be improved.

If foresight intelligence became established, many more scientists and policy planners (and society) might, for example, understand the demographic contributions to the predicament [136], stop treating population growth as a 'given' and consider the nutritional, health and social benefits of humanely ending growth well below nine billion and starting a slow decline. This would be a monumental task, considering the momentum of population growth. Monumental, but not impossible if the political will could be generated globally to give full rights, education and opportunities to women, and provide all sexually active human beings with modern contraception and backup abortion. The degree to which those steps would reduce fertility rates is controversial [137–139], but they are a likely win-win for societies [140].

Obviously, especially with the growing endarkenment, there are huge cultural and institutional barriers to establishing such policies in some parts of the world. After all, there is not a single nation where women are truly treated as equal to men. Despite that, the population driver should not be ignored simply because limiting overconsumption can, at least in theory, be achieved more rapidly. The difficulties of changing demographic trajectories mean that the problem should have been addressed sooner, rather than later. That halting population growth inevitably leads to changes in age structure is no excuse for bemoaning drops in fertility rates, as is common in European government circles [141]. Reduction of population size in those over-consuming nations is a very positive trend, and sensible planning can deal with the problems of population aging [142].

While rapid policy change to head off collapse is essential, fundamental institutional change to keep things on track is necessary as well. This is especially true of educational systems, which today fail to inform most people of how the world works and thus perpetuate a vast culture gap [54]. The academic challenge is especially great for economists, who could help set the background for avoiding collapse by designing steady-state economic systems [107,134,143], and along the way destroying fables such as 'growth can continue forever if it's in service industries', or 'technological innovation will save us'. Issues such as the importance of comparative advantage under current global circumstances [144], the development of new models that better reflect the irrational behaviour of individuals and groups [145], reduction of the worship of 'free' markets that infests the discipline, and tasks such as making information more symmetrical, moving towards sustainability and enhancing equity (including *redistribution*) all require re-examination. In that re-examination, they would be following the lead of distinguished economists [146–148] in dealing with the real world of biophysical constraints and human well-being.

At the global level, the loose network of agreements that now tie countries together [149,150], developed in a relatively recent stage of cultural evolution since modern nation states appeared, is utterly inadequate to grapple with the human predicament. Strengthening global environmental governance [151] and addressing the related problem of avoiding failed statehood [152] are tasks humanity has so far refused to tackle comprehensively even as cultural evolution in technology has rendered the present international system (as it has educational systems) obsolete. Serious global environmental problems can only be solved and a collapse avoided with an unprecedented level of international cooperation [122]. Regardless of one's estimate of civilization's potential longevity, the time to start restructuring the international system is right now. If people do not do that, nature will restructure civilization for us.

Similarly, widely based cultural change is required to reduce humanely both population size and overconsumption by the rich. Both go against cultural norms, and, as long feared [153], the overconsumption norm has understandably been adopted by the increasingly rich subpopulations of developing nations, notably India and China. One can be thrilled by the numbers of people raised from poverty while being apprehensive about the enormous and possibly lethal environmental and social costs that may eventually result [154,155]. The industrial revolution set civilization on the road to collapse, spurring population growth, which contributed slightly more than overconsumption to environmental degradation [136]. Now population combined with affluence growth may finish the job.

Needless to say, dealing with economic and racial inequities will be critically important in getting large numbers of people from culturally diverse groups [156] to focus their minds on solving the human predicament, something globalization should help [157]. These tasks will be pursued, along with an emphasis on developing 'foresight intelligence', by the nascent *Millennium Alliance for Humanity and the Biosphere* (the MAHB; http://mahb.stanford.edu). One of its central goals is to try to accelerate change towards sustainability. Since simply giving the scientific facts to the public will not do it, among other things, this means finding frames and narratives to convince the public of the need to make changes.

We know that societies can evolve fundamentally and unexpectedly [158, p. 334], as was dramatically demonstrated by the collapse of communist regimes in Europe in 1989 [159]. Rather than tinkering around the edges and making feeble or empty gestures towards one or another of the interdependent problems we face, we need a powerful and comprehensive approach. In addressing climate change, for instance, developing nations need to be convinced that they (along with the rest of the world) cannot afford (and do not need) to delay action while they 'catch up' in development. Indeed, development on the old model is counterproductive; they have a great opportunity to pioneer new approaches and technologies. All nations need to stop waiting for others to act and be willing to do everything they can to mitigate emissions and hasten the energy transition, regardless of what others are doing.

With climate and many other global environmental problems, polycentric solutions may be more readily found than global ones. Complex, multi-level systems may be better able to cope with complex, multi-level problems [160], and institutional change is required at many levels in many polities. What scientists understand about cultural evolution suggests that, while improbable, it may be possible to move cultures in such directions [161,162]. Whether solutions will be global or polycentric, international negotiations will be needed, existing international agencies that deal with them will need strengthening, and new institutions will need to be formed.

CONCLUSIONS

Do we think global society can avoid a collapse in this century? The answer is yes, because modern society has shown some capacity to deal with long-term threats, at least if they are obvious or continuously brought to attention (think of the risks of nuclear conflict). Humanity has the assets to get the job done, but the odds of avoiding collapse seem small because the risks are clearly not obvious to most people and the classic signs of impending collapse, especially diminishing returns to complexity [28], are everywhere. One central psychological barrier to taking dramatic action is the distribution of costs and benefits through time: the costs up front, the benefits accruing largely to unknown people in the future. But whether we or more optimistic observers [17,163] are correct, our own ethical values compel us to think the benefits to those future generations are worth struggling for, to increase at least slightly the chances of avoiding a dissolution of today's global civilization as we know it.

REFERENCES

1 Diamond J. 2005 *Collapse: how societies choose to fail or succeed.* New York, NY: Viking.

2 Morris I. 2011 *Why the west rules for now: the patterns of history, and what they reveal about the future.* New York, NY: Picador.

3 Montgomery DR. 2012 *Dirt: the erosion of civilizations.* Berkeley, CA: University of California Press.

4 Brown J. 2012 Mankind must go green or die, says Prince Charles. *The Independent (London).* See http://ind.pn/R5WZgl (accessed 23 November).

5 Sample I. 2009 World faces 'perfect storm' of problems by 2030, chief scientist to warn. *The Guardian.* See http://www.guardian.co.uk/science/2009/mar/18/perfect-storm-john-beddingtonenergy-food-climate.

6 Klare MT. 2012 *The race for what's left: the global scramble for the world's last resources.* New York, NY: Metropolitan Books.

7 Heinberg R. 2007 *Peak everything: waking up to the century of declines.* Gabriola Island, BC: New Society Publishers.

8 Gleeson TT, Wada YY, Bierkens MFP, van Beek LPH. 2012 Water balance of global aquifers revealed by groundwater footprint. *Nature* 488, 197–200. (doi:10.1038/nature11295)

9 Klare MT. 2001 *Resource wars: the new landscape of global conflict.* New York, NY: Henry Holt.

10 Ehrlich PR, Ehrlich AH. 2012 Solving the human predicament. *Int. J. Environ. Stud.* 69, 557–565. (doi:10.1080/00207233.2012.693281)

11 Ehrlich PR, Holdren J. 1971 Impact of population growth. *Science* 171, 1212–1217. (doi:10.1126/science.171.3977.1212)

12 Holdren JP, Ehrlich PR. 1974 Human population and the global environment. *Am. Sci.* 62, 282–292.

13 Dietz T, Rosa E. 1994 Rethinking the environmental impacts of population, affluence and technology. *Hum. Ecol. Rev.* 1, 277–300.

14 Rosa EA, York R, Dietz T. 2004 Tracking the anthropogenic drivers of ecological impacts. *Ambio* 333, 509–512.

15 Dietz T, Rosa EA, York R. 2010 Human driving forces of global change: dominant perspectives. In *Human footprints on the global environment: threats to sustainability* (eds EA Rosa, A Diekmann, T Dietz, CC Jaeger), pp. 83–134. Cambridge, MA: MIT Press.

16 Alcott B. 2010 Impact caps: why population, affluence and technology strategies should be abandoned. *J. Cleaner Prod.* 18, 552–560. (doi:10. 1016/j.jclepro.2009.08.001)

17 Hayes B. 2012 Computation and the human predicament. *Am. Sci.* 100, 186–191. (doi:10.1511/2012.96.186)

18 Wackernagel M, Rees W. 1996 *Our ecological footprint: reducing human impact on the Earth.* Gabriola Island, BC: New Society Publishers.

19 Global Footprint Network 2012 World footprint: do we fit the planet. See http://www.footprintnetwork.org/en/index.php/GFN/page/world_footprint/.

20 Rees WE. In press. Ecological footprint, concept of. In *Encyclopedia of biodiversity* (ed. S Levin), 2nd edn. San Diego, CA: Academic Press.

21 Harte J. 2007 Human population as a dynamic factor in environmental degradation. *Popul. Environ.* 28, 223–236. (doi:10.1007/s11111-007-0048-3)

22 Liu J, Daily G, Ehrlich PR, Luck G. 2003 Effects of household dynamics on resource consumption and biodiversity. *Nature* 421, 530–533. (doi:10.1038/nature01359)

23 Yu E, Liu J. 2007 Environmental impacts of divorce. *Proc. Natl Acad. Sci. USA* 104, 20 629–20 634. (doi:10.1073/pnas.0707267104)

24 Rosner L. 2004 *The technological fix: how people use technology to create and solve problems.* New York, NY: Routledge.

25 Huesemann M, Huesemann J. 2012 *Techno-fix: why technology won't save us or the environment.* Gabriola Island, BC: New Society Publishers.

26 Brown JH *et al.* 2011 Energetic limits to economic growth. *BioScience* 61, 19–26. (doi:10.1525/bio. 2011.61.1.7)

27 Liu J *et al.* 2007 Complexity of coupled human and natural systems. *Science* 317, 1513–1516. (doi:10.1126/science.1144004)

28 Tainter JA. 1988 *The collapse of complex societies.* Cambridge, UK: Cambridge University Press.

29 McAnany PA, Yoffee N. 2010 *Questioning collapse: human resilience, ecological vulnerability, and the aftermath of empire.* New York, NY: Cambridge University Press.

30 Tainter J. 2006 Archaeology of overshoot and collapse. *Ann. Rev. Anthropol.* 35, 9–74. (doi:10.1146/annurev.anthro.35.081705.123136)

31 Butzer KW, Endfield GH. 2012 Critical perspectives on historical collapse. *Proc. Natl Acad. Sci. USA* 109, 3628–3631. (doi:10.1073pnas.1114772109)

32 Toon O, Robock A, Turco RP, Bardeen C, Oman L, Stenchikov G. 2007 Consequences of regional-scale nuclear conflicts. *Science* 315, 1224–1225. (doi:10.1126/science.1137747)

33 Paddock W, Paddock P. 1967 *Famine: 1975!* Boston, MA: Little Brown & Co.

34 Brown LR. 1968 *Seeds of change: the green revolution and development in the 1970s.* New York, NY: Frederick A. Praeger.

35 Bardach J. 1968 *Harvest of the sea.* New York, NY: Harper and Row.

36 Borgstrom G. 1969 *Too many.* Toronto, Canada: Collier-Macmillan.

37 Frankel O, Agble WK, Harlan JB. 1969 Genetic dangers in the green revolution. *Areas* (FAO) 2, 35–37.

38 Pirie NW. 1969 *Food resources, conventional and novel.* Baltimore, MD: Penguin.

39 Ryther JH. 1969 Photosynthesis and fish production in the sea. *Science* 166, 72–76. (doi:10.1126/science.166.3901.72)

40 Daily GC, Ehrlich PR. 1990 An exploratory model of the impact of rapid climate change on the world food situation. *Proc. R. Soc. Lond. B* 241, 232–244. (doi:10.1098/rspb.1990.0091)

41 Food and Agriculture Organization (FAO) 2009 *How to feed the world in 2050.* See http://www.fao.org/fileadmin/templates/wsfs/docs/expert_paper/How_to_Feed_the_World_in_2050.pdf. Rome, Italy.

42 Weinberg AM. 1969 Nuclear energy and the agro-industrial complex. *Nature* 222, 17–21. (doi:10.1038/222017a0)

43 Ehrlich PR, Ehrlich AH. 1970 *Population, resources, environment: issues in human ecology.* San Francisco, CA: W.H. Freeman and Co.

44 York R, Gossard MH. 2004 Cross-national meat and fish consumption: exploring the effects of modernization and ecological context. *Ecol. Econ.* 48, 293–302. (doi:10.1016/j.ecolecon.2003.10.009)

45 Lobell DB, Schlenker W, Costa-Roberts J. 2011 Climate trends and global crop production since 1980. *Science* 333, 616–620. (doi:10.1126/science.1204531)

46 Lobell DB, Gourdji SM. In press. The influence of climate change on global crop productivity. *Plant Physiol.*

47 Lobell DB, Field CB. 2007 Global scale climate–crop yield relationships and the impacts of recent warming. *Environ. Res. Lett.* 2, 014002. (doi:10.1088/1748-9326/2/1/014002)

48 Hansen J *et al.* 2012 Scientific case for avoiding dangerous climate change to protect young people and nature. See http://pubs.giss.nasa.gov/docs/notyet/submitted_Hansen_etal.pdf.

49 Rowland D. 2012 World fish stocks declining faster than feared. *Financial Times*. See http://www.ft.com/cms/s/2/73d14032-088e-11e2-b37e-00144feabdc0.html#axzz28KxPEqPr.

50 Lemonick MD. 2012 Ocean acidification threatens food security, report. *Climate Central*. See http://www.climatecentral.org/news/ocean-acidificationthreatens-food-security-in-developing-world-studyfinds-15036.

51 Solomon S, Plattner G-K, Knutti R, Friedlingstein P. 2009 Irreversible climate change due to carbon dioxide emissions. *Proc. Natl Acad. Sci. USA* 106, 1704–1709. (doi:10.1073/pnas.0812721106)

52 Md. Golam Mahabub Sarwar. 2005 Impacts of sea level rise on the coastal zone of Bangladesh. See http://static.weadapt.org/placemarks/files/225/golam_sarwar.pdf.

53 Seto K, Güneralp B, Hutyra LR. 2012 Global forecasts of urban expansion to 2030 and direct impacts on biodiversity and carbon pools. *Proc. Natl Acad. Sci. USA* 109, 16 083–16 088. (doi:10.1073/pnas. 1211658109)

54 Ehrlich PR, Ehrlich AH. 2010 The culture gap and its needed closures. *Int. J. Environ. Stud.* 67, 481–492. (doi:10.1080/00207233.2010.510825)

55 Carson R. 1962 *Silent spring*. Boston, MA: Houghton Mifflin.

56 World Bank 2012 *Turn down the heat: why a 48C warmer world must be avoided*. Washington DC: World Bank.

57 Schellnhuber HJ. 2008 Global warming: stop worrying, start panicking. *Proc. Natl Acad. Sci. USA* 105, 14 239–14 240. (doi:10.1073/pnas.0807331105)

58 Anderson K, Bows A. 2011 Beyond 'dangerous' climate change: emission: scenarios for a new world. *Phil. Trans. R. Soc. A* 369, 20–44. (doi:10.1098/rsta.2010.0290)

59 Fischetti M. 2011 28 global warming limit called a 'prescription for disaster'. *Sci. Am.* See http://blogs. scientificamerican.com/observations/2011/12/06/two-degree-global-warming-limit-is-called-aprescription-for-disaster/.

60 Reich PB, Hobbie SE. 2012 Decade-long soil nitrogen constraint on the CO2 fertilization of plant biomass. *Nat. Clim. Change*. (doi:10.1038/nclimate1694)

61 Torn MS, Harte J. 2006 Missing feedbacks, asymmetric uncertainties, and the underestimation of future warming. *Geophys. Res. Lett.* 33, L10703. (doi:10710.11029/12005GL025540)

62 Alexander S. 2012 Degrowth, expensive oil, and the new economics of energy. *Real-world Econ. Rev.* 61, 40–51. See http://www.energybulletin.net/stories/2012-08-07/degrowth-expensive-oil-and-neweconomics-energy.

63 Makhijani A. 2007 *Carbon-free and nuclear-free; a roadmap for US energy policy*. Takoma Park, MD: IEER Press.

64 Harte J, Harte ME. 2008 *Cool the earth, save the economy: solving the climate crisis is easy*. See http://cooltheearth.us/.

65 Klare M. 2012 World energy report 2012: the good, the bad, and the really, truly ugly. *Truthout*. See http://bit.ly/TrCGWA.

66 Mann ME. 2009 Defining dangerous anthropogenic interference. *Proc. Natl Acad. Sci. USA* 106, 4065–4066. (doi:10.1073/pnas.0901303106)

67 McKibben B. 2012 Global warming's terrifying new math. *Rolling Stone*. See http://www.rollingstone.com/politics/news/global-warmings-terrifying-newmath-20120719 1–11.

68 Proctor RN. 2011 *Golden holocaust: origins of the cigarette catastrophe and the case for abolition*. Berkeley, CA: University of California Press.

69 Oreskes N, Conway EM. 2010 *Merchants of doubt: how a handful of scientists obscured the truth on issues from tobacco smoke to global warming*. New York, NY: Bloomsbury Press.

70 Klein N. 2011 Capitalism versus the climate. *Nation* 293, 11–21.

71 Eilperin J. 2012 Climate skeptic group works to reverse renewable energy mandates. *Washington Post*. See http://wapo.st/UToe9b (accessed 24 November).

72 Godfray HCJ *et al.* 2010 Food security: the challenge of feeding 9 billion people. *Science* 327, 812–818. (doi:10.1126/science.1185383)

73 Foley JA *et al.* 2011 Solutions for a cultivated planet. *Nature* 478, 332–342. (doi:10.1038/nature10452)

74 Foley JA. 2011 Can we feed the world and sustain the planet? A five-step global plan could double food production by 2050 while greatly reducing environmental damage. *Sci. Am.* 305, 60–65. (doi:10.1038/scientificamerican1111-60)

75 Ziska LH *et al.* 2012 Food security and climate change: on the potential to adapt global crop production by active selection to rising atmospheric carbon dioxide. *Proc. R. Soc. B* 279, 4097–4105. (doi:10.1098/rspb.2012.1005)

76 Friedman L. 2012 India has big plans for burning coal. *Sci. Am.* See http://www.scientificamerican.com/article.cfm?id=india-has-big-plans-forburning-coal (accessed 17 September).

77 Colborn T, Dumanoski D, Myers JP. 1996 *Our stolen future*. New York, NY: Dutton.

78 Myers P, Hessler W. 2007 Does 'the dose make the poison'? extensive results challenge a core assumption in toxicology. *Environ. Health News*. See http://www. environmentalhealthnews.org/sciencebackground/2007/2007-0415nmdrc.html.

79 Vandenberg LN *et al.* 2012 Hormones and endocrine-disrupting chemicals: low-dose effects and nonmonotonic dose responses. *Endocr. Rev.* 33, 378–455. (doi:10.1210/er.2011-1050)

80 Battersby S. 2012 Cool it. *New Sci.* 2883, 31–35.

81 Daily GC, Ehrlich PR. 1996 Impacts of development and global change on the epidemiological environment. *Environ. Dev. Econ.* 1, 309–344. (doi:10.1017/S1355770X00000656)

82 Wald P. 2008 *Contagious: cultures, carriers, and the outbreak narrative*. Durham, NC: Duke University Press.

83 Pirages DC, DeGeest TM. 2003 *Ecological security: an evolutionary perspective on globalization*. Lanham, MD: Rowman & Littlefield.

84 Ehrlich PR. 1991 Population growth and environmental security. *Georgia Rev.* 45, 223–232.

85 Shultz GP, Perry WJ, Kissinger HA, Nunn S. 2011 Deterrence in the age of nuclear proliferation: the doctrine of mutual assured destruction is obsolete in the post-Cold War era. *Wall Street J.* See http://on.wsj.com/FLYQco.

86 Ehrlich PR *et al.* 1983 Long-term biological consequences of nuclear war. *Science* 222, 1293–1300. (doi:10.1126/science.6658451)

87 Myers N. 1993 Environmental refugees in a globally warmed world. *BioScience* 43, 752–761. (doi:10.2307/1312319)

88 Zelman J. 2011 50 million environmental refugees by 2020, experts predict. *Huff Post Green.* See http://www.huffingtonpost.com/2011/02/22/environmental-refugees-50_n_826488.html (accessed 22 February).

89 Rowley RJ. 2007 Risk of rising sea level to population and land area. *EOS* 88, 105–116. (doi:10.1029/2007EO090001)

90 Osborne F. 1948 *Our plundered planet.* Boston, MA: Little, Brown and Company.

91 Vogt W. 1948 *Road to survival.* New York, NY: William Sloan.

92 Brown H. 1954 *The challenge of man's future: an inquiry concerning the condition of man during the years that lie ahead.* New York, NY: Viking.

93 Borgstrom G. 1965 *The hungry planet.* New York, NY: Macmillan.

94 Cloud P. 1968 Realities of mineral distribution. *Texas Q.* 11, 103–126.

95 Georgescu-Rogen N. 1974 *The entropy law and the economic process.* Cambridge, MA: Harvard University Press.

96 Myers N. 1979 *The sinking ark.* New York, NY: Pergamon Press.

97 Dunlap RE, Catton WR. 1979 Environmental sociology. *Annu. Rev. Sociol.* 5, 243–273. (doi:10.1146/annurev.so.05.080179.001331)

98 Ehrlich PR, Ehrlich AH. 1981 *Extinction: the causes and consequences of the disappearance of species.* New York, NY: Random House.

99 Union of Concerned Scientists 1993 *World scientists' warning to humanity.* Cambridge, MA: Union of Concerned Scientists.

100 National Academy of Sciences USA 1993 A joint statement by fifty-eight of the world's scientific academies. In *Population summit of the world's scientific academies.* New Delhi, India: National Academy Press.

101 Homer-Dixon T. 1994 Environmental scarcities and violent conflict: evidence from cases. *Int. Security* 19, 5–40. (doi:10.2307/2539147)

102 Lovejoy TE. 1994 The quantification of biodiversity: an esoteric quest or a vital component of sustainable development? *Phil. Trans. R. Soc. Lond. B* 345, 81–87. (doi:10.1098/rstb.1994.0089)

103 Ehrlich PR. 1968 *The population bomb.* New York, NY: Ballantine Books.

104 Boulding KE. 1966 The economics of the coming spaceship earth. In *Environmental quality in a growing economy* (ed H Jarrett), pp. 3–14. Baltimore, MD: Johns Hopkins University Press.

105 Daly HE. 1968 On economics as a life science. *J. Polit. Econ.* 76, 392–406. (doi:10.1086/259412)

106 Meadows DH, Meadows DL, Randers J, Behrens III WW. 1972 *The limits to growth.* Washington, DC: Universe Books.

107 Daly HE. 1973 *Toward a steady-state economy.* San Francisco, CA: W.H. Freeman and Co.

108 Hall CAS, Day Jr JW. 2009 Revisiting the limits to growth after peak oil. *Am. Sci.* 97, 230–237. (doi:10.1511/2009.78.230)

109 Hall CAS, Powers R, Schoenberg W. 2008 Peak oil, EROI, investments and the economy in an uncertain future. In *Biofuels, solar and wind as renewable energy systems* (ed D Pimentel), pp. 109–132. Berlin, Germany: Springer.

110 Kiel K, Matheson V, Golembiewski K. 2010 Luck or skill? An examination of the Ehrlich–Simon bet. *Ecol. Econ.* 69, 1365–1367. (doi:10.1016/j.ecolecon.2010.03.007)

111 Ehrlich PR, Ehrlich AH. 2009 The population bomb revisited. *Electron. J. Sustainable Dev.* 1, 63–71.

112 Millennium Ecosystem Assessment 2005 *Ecosystems and human well-being: synthesis.* Washington, DC: Island Press.

113 Homer-Dixon T. 2006 *The upside of down: catastrophe, creativity, and the renewal of civilization.* Washington, DC: Island Press.

114 Rockström J *et al.* 2009 Planetary boundaries: exploring the safe operating space for humanity. *Ecol. Soc.* 14, 32.

115 Bradshaw C, Giam X, Sodhi N. 2010 Evaluating the relative environmental impact of countries. *PLoS ONE* 5, e10440. (doi:10.1371/journal.pone.0010440)

116 Barnosky AD *et al.* 2010 Has the Earth's sixth mass extinction already arrived? *Nature* 471, 51–57. (doi:10.1038/nature09678)

117 Burger JR *et al.* 2012 The macroecology of sustainability. *PLoS Biol.* 10, e1001345. (doi:10.1371/journal.pbio.1001345)

118 Barnosky AD *et al.* 2012 Approaching a state shift in Earth's biosphere. *Nature* 486, 52–58. (doi:10. 1038/nature11018)

119 Gerken J. 2012 Arctic ice melt, sea level rise may pose imminent threat to island nations, climate scientist says. *Huff Post Green.* See http://www. huffingtonpost.com/2012/10/05/arctic-ice-melt-sealevel-rise_n_1942666.html?utm_hp_ref=green&ncid=edlinkusaolp00000008.

120 Turner A. 2009 Population priorities: the challenge of continued rapid population growth. *Phil. Trans. R. Soc. B* 364, 2977–2984. (doi:10.1098/rstb.2009.0183)

121 Ehrlich PR, Kareiva PM, Daily GC. 2012 Securing natural capital and expanding equity to rescale civilization. *Nature* 486, 68–73. (doi:10.1038/nature11157)

122 May RM. 2006 Threats to tomorrow's world. *Notes Rec. R. Soc.* 60, 109–130. (doi:10.1098/rsnr.2005.0134)

123 Kennedy D. 2005 Twilight for the enlightenment? *Science* 308, 165. (doi:10.1126/science.1112920)

124 Hughes JB, Daily GC, Ehrlich PR. 1997 Population diversity: its extent and extinction. *Science* 278, 689–692. (doi:10.1126/science.278.5338.689)

125 Hughes JB, Daily GC, Ehrlich PR. 2000 The loss of population diversity and why it matters. In *Nature and human society* (ed PH Raven), pp. 71–83. Washington, DC: National Academy Press.

126 Blumstein DT, Saylan C. 2011 *The failure of environmental education (and how we can fix it)*. Berkeley, CA: University of California Press.

127 Ehrlich PR. 2011 A personal view: environmental education—its content and delivery. *J. Environ. Stud. Sci.* 1, 6–13. (doi:10.1007/s13412-011-0006-3)

128 Levin SA. 2009 *Games, groups, and the global good*. London, UK: Springer.

129 Levin S. 1999 *Fragile dominion*. Reading, MA: Perseus Books.

130 Liu J, Li S, Ouyang Z, Tam C, Chen X. 2008 Ecological and socioeconomic effects of China's policies for ecosystem services. *Proc. Natl Acad. Sci. USA* 105, 9489–9494. (doi:10.1073/pnas.0706905105)

131 Daily GC, Kareiva PM, Polasky S, Ricketts TH, Tallis H. 2011 Mainstreaming natural capital into decisions. In *Natural capital: theory and practice of mapping ecosystem services* (eds PM Kareiva, H Tallis, TH Ricketts, GC Daily, S Polasky), pp. 3–14. Oxford, UK: Oxford University Press.

132 Ehrlich PR. 2000 *Human natures: genes, cultures, and the human prospect*. Washington, DC: Island Press.

133 James PT, Leach R, Kalamara E, Shayeghi M. 2001 Worldwide obesity epidemic. *Obes. Res.* 9(Suppl. 4), S228–S233. (doi:10.1038/oby. 2001.123)

134 Jackson T. 2009 *Prosperity without growth: economics for a finite planet*. London, UK: Earthscan.

135 Gardner H. 2008 *Multiple intelligences: new horizons in theory and practice*. New York, NY: Basic Books.

136 Holdren J. 1991 Population and the energy problem. *Popul. Environ.* 12, 231–255. (doi:10. 1007/BF01357916)

137 Potts M. 2009 Where next? *Phil. Trans. R. Soc. B* 364, 3115–3124. (doi:10.1098/rstb.2009.0181)

138 Sedgh G, Hussain R, Bankole A, Singh S. 2007 Women with an unmet need for contraception in developing countries and their reasons for not using a method. In *Occasional report*, pp. 1–80. New York, NY: Guttmacher Institute.

139 Singh S, Sedgh G, Hussain R. 2010 Unintended pregnancy: worldwide levels, trends, and outcomes. *Stud. Fam. Plann.* 41, 241–250. (doi:10.1111/j. 1728-4465.2010.00250.x)

140 O'Neill BC, Liddle B, Jiang L, Smith KR, Pachauri S, Dalton M, Fuchs R. 2012 Demographic change and carbon dioxide emissions. *Lancet* 380, 157–164. (doi:10.1016/S0140-6736(12)60958-1)

141 Ehrlich PR, Ehrlich AH. 2006 Enough already. *New Sci.* 191, 46–50. (doi:10.1016/S0262-4079(06)60615-5)

142 Turner A. 2009 Population ageing: what should we worry about? *Phil. Trans. R. Soc. B* 364, 3009–3021. (doi:10.1098/rstb.2009.0185)

143 Victor PA. 2008 *Managing without growth.* Northampton, MA: Edward Elgar.

144 Galbraith JK. 2008 *The predator state: how conservatives abandoned the free market and why liberals should to.* New York, NY: Free Press.

145 Ariely D. 2009 *Predictably irrational, revised and expanded edition.* New York, NY: Harper Collins.

146 Dasgupta P. 2001 *Human well-being and the natural environment.* Oxford, UK: Oxford University Press.

147 Dasgupta P. 2010 Nature's role in sustaining economic development. *Phil. Trans. R. Soc. B* 365, 5–11. (doi:10.1098/rstb.2009.0231)

148 Arrow K *et al.* 2004 Are we consuming too much? *J. Econ. Perspect.* 18, 147–172. (doi:10.1257/0895330042162377)

149 Barrett S. 2003 *Environment and statecraft: the strategy of environmental treaty-making.* New York, NY: Oxford University Press.

150 Barrett S. 2007 *Why cooperate: the incentive to supply global public goods.* Oxford, UK: Oxford University Press.

151 Dietz T, Ostrom E, Stern PC. 2003 The struggle to govern the commons. *Science* 302, 1902–1912. (doi:10.1126/science.1091015)

152 Acemoglu D, Robinson J. 2012 *Why nations fail: the origins of power, prosperity, and poverty.* New York, NY: Crown Business.

153 Pirages D, Ehrlich PR. 1972 If all Chinese had wheels. *New York Times* (16 March, 1972).

154 Klare MT. 2008 *Rising powers, shrinking planet: the new geopolitics of energy.* New York, NY: Henry Holt and Company.

155 Watts J. 2010 *When a billion Chinese jump.* New York, NY: Scribner.

156 Moghaddam FM. 2012 The omnicultural imperative. *Cult. Psychol.* 18, 304–330. (doi:10.1177/1354067X12446230)

157 Buchan NR, Grimalda G, Wilson R, Brewer M, Fatase E, Foddy M. 2009 Globalization and human cooperation. *Proc. Natl Acad. Sci. USA* 106, 4138–4142. (doi:10.1073/pnas.0809522106)

158 Ehrlich PR, Ehrlich AH. 2005 *One with nineveh: politics, consumption, and the human future, (with new afterword).* Washington, DC: Island Press.

159 Meyer M. 2009 *The year that changed the world: the untold story behind the fall of the Berlin Wall.* New York, NY: Scribner.

160 Ostrom E. 2009 A polycentric approach for coping with climate change. *World Bank Policy Research Working Paper no.* 5095.

161 Cialdini RB. 2008 *Influence: science and practice.* Boston, MA: Allyn & Bacon.

162 Barrett S, Dannenberg A. 2012 Climate negotiations under scientific uncertainty. *Proc. Natl Acad. Sci. USA* 109, 17 372–17 376. (doi:10.1073/pnas. 1208417109)

163 Matthews JH, Boltz F. 2012 The shifting boundaries of sustainability science: are we doomed yet? *PLoS Biol.* 10, e1001344. (doi:10.1371/journal.pbio.1001344)

CHAPTER NINE

Energy and the Environment

Fossil fuels are involved in nearly every aspect of our daily lives. They provide us with the energy to heat and light our homes; drive our vehicles; produce our goods; and grow, harvest, and distribute our food. However, our fossil-fuel-based economy is not sustainable. In addition to being the main driver of climate change, motivating countless wars around the world, and concentrating money and power in the hands of a few global corporations, fossil fuels have a final, fatal flaw: they are not renewable, at least not on a timeline that is relevant to humans. A wide range of experts predict that at some point between 2020 and 2050, we will hit "peak fossil fuels" which means that we will be extracting the maximum amount of fossil fuels possible. After this time, fossil fuel extraction will go into terminal decline.

In this chapter, we focus not on fossil fuel decline but, instead, on the next step for our future: finding economically feasible, environmentally sound, and socially just alternatives to fossil fuels, thereby building a more sustainable society. A huge part of the next step to sustainable energy use is transitioning to renewable energy sources. The current barriers to this transition are more political than technological. In Carla S. Jones's and Stephen Mayfield's selected reading, "Methods for Reducing Our Fossil Fuel Usage: Renewable Energy Sources and Uses" from *Our Energy Future: Introduction to Renewable Energy and Biofuels*, we read about diverse renewable energy technologies that we already have the ability to harness at large scale, including solar, wind, geothermal, tidal energy, and biomass.

As fossil fuels decline, the political motivation to shift to renewables will become stronger, but it is critically important that we break not just from the fossil fuels themselves, but from the unjust ownership and distribution models that were established as we became dependent on fossil fuels. For example, Indigenous American leader and activist Winona LaDuke points out in her recommended article, "Indigenous Power:

A New Energy Economy" from *Race, Poverty & the Environment* (2006), that "at least 10 percent of the US energy market and its reserves [are] dependent on tribal resources," and yet tribal governments receive only a tiny fraction of the profits from the sale of fossil fuels extracted from their lands. These lands have immense potential for solar and wind renewable energy as well; consequently, as we transition to these energy types, we must also transition to a more equitable distribution of profits, an issue related to the environmental justice topics in Chapter 7. Charles Fanniel's recommended article from *The Arizona Republic*, "My Turn: Put solar power in the poor's hands. It'll pay off for all" (2017), provides insight into how renewables can be more equitably owned and managed through systems like community solar and net metering.

RECOMMENDED READING

Fanniel, C. 2017. "My Turn: Put solar power in the poor's hands. It'll pay off for all." *The Arizona Republic*. Retrieved from: https://www.azcentral.com/story/opinion/op-ed/2017/08/25/solar-in-poor-hands-will-pay-off-for-everyone/591369001/.

LaDuke, W. 2006. "Indigenous Power: A New Energy Economy." *Race, Poverty & the Environment* 13(1): 6–10.

READING AND DISCUSSION PROMPTS

1. What are the three primary energy sources from which all other energy on Earth is derived? Connect each type of renewable energy with its primary energy source.
2. Describe some advantages and disadvantages of first-generation biofuels.
3. Do you think 100 percent renewable energy can power our global society? Why or why not?
4. Unlike fossil fuels, many renewables like solar, wind, and hydro are distributed fairly evenly around the world. As the world transitions to renewable energy, how do you think these distribution patterns will affect the balance of power between countries?
5. In the Fanniel (2017) article, the author explains why energy is an environmental justice issue. Describe the solution Fanniel proposes for making solar power available in a more equitable way than it is currently.

READING 9.1

Methods for Reducing Our Fossil Fuel Usage

RENEWABLE ENERGY SOURCES AND USES

By Carla S. Jones and Stephen Mayfield

Over the past century, society's expanding consumption of energy has mainly focused on energy derived from fossil fuels. Fossil fuels are abundant and relatively cheap resources, and they are remarkably energy dense fuels. However, for the greater part of human history, people have actually relied mostly on other natural resources for energy. For instance, humans first used wood and dung to produce fire for warmth and cooking, the ancient Egyptians used boats with sails powered by the wind to travel the Nile River, and the Romans used running water to turn waterwheels for irrigation and for grinding grain (Nersesian, 2010). These natural resources are still widely available and used in a similar manner around the world today, but their consumption is significantly less due to the prevalence and efficiency of fossil fuels for energy production.

RENEWABLE AND SUSTAINABLE ENERGY RESOURCES FOR THE FUTURE

How are wood, wind, and water different from fossil fuels? All are essentially natural energy resources derived from the Earth, and all can be used as a type of fuel, but a key difference between some natural resources and others comes down to two simple words, **renewable** and **sustainable**. These terms are commonly used interchangeably, but their meanings are not precisely the same: a renewable resource is defined as a resource that can be exploited from the Earth and then replaced within a short period of time, while a sustainable resource refers to a resource that is utilized in such a way that the use does not impact its availability for future generations. Consider the wind. Humans have used wind power for many centuries, yet there is no shortage of wind today. Wind is created from the heat of the sun on Earth; it is constantly produced and the Earth's generation of wind is not directly impacted by human activity. Thus, wind is both renewable and sustainable. Fossil fuels, while naturally created, cannot be sustained in the face of rapidly increasing consumption and therefore cannot be guaranteed to be an available resource in the future. In addition, as you learned previously, fossil fuels take millions of years to develop, meaning these resources cannot be replaced in a short period of time; therefore, fossil fuels are both non-sustainable and nonrenewable. The development of an ideal energy resource to replace fossil fuels will need to be both renewable and sustainable to support all generations in the future and maintain environmental quality.

All of the energy that is consumed today, regardless of whether it is from a finite or infinite resource, comes from only one of three **primary energy sources**: the sun, the moon, or the core of the Earth. For example, fossil fuels, which are a product of millions of years of decayed plant matter, are ultimately derived from the sun since plants capture solar energy through photosynthesis. As other renewable energy sources like water, wind, waves, and tides are discussed, it is important to remember that they can all be tracked back to one of these three primary energy sources.

Two of these primary energy sources, the sun and the core of the Earth, generate their energy through **thermonuclear reactions**. Thermonuclear reactions involve the combination or dissociation of atomic nuclei, either of which results in the release of large amounts of energy. These reactions are classified as either nuclear **fission** reactions when the nuclei dissociate (i.e., break apart) or nuclear **fusion** reactions when two atomic nuclei combine (i.e., fuse). Figure 9.1.1 shows examples of nuclear fission and fusion reactions. Nuclear fission reactions usually involve the breaking apart of larger atomic elements into smaller elements. An example of a nuclear fission reaction is when uranium is split into two smaller atoms like krypton and barium as shown. Also diagrammed in the figure, nuclear fusion reactions involve the combination of very small atomic elements like the combination of two hydrogen atoms to form a helium atom. Whether the reaction is a result of fission or fusion, the changing atomic structure releases a huge amount of energy. This is obvious if you consider the colossal amount of energy produced through thermonuclear fusion by both the sun and the core of the Earth. Nuclear fusion reactions in the core of the sun produce the energy that lights and warms Earth externally, while

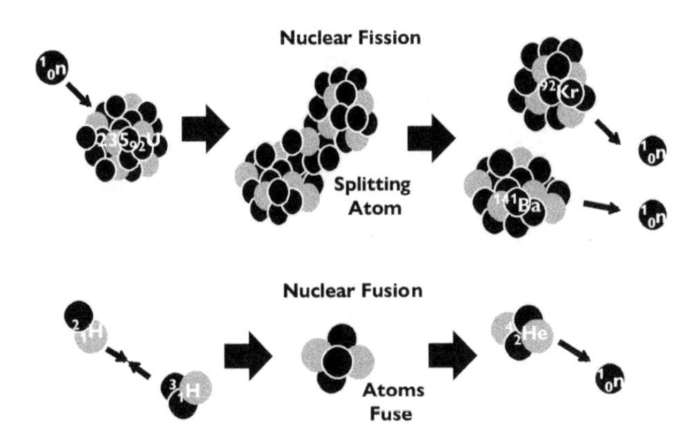

Figure 9.1.1 Diagram of thermonuclear fission and fusion reactions. In this example, nuclear fission occurs when a neutron (n) collides with a Uranium (U) atom, causing it to split into one atom of krypton (Kr) and one atom of barium (Ba). This results in the release of two neutrons that can continue the cycle by colliding with other atoms of uranium. Nuclear fusion occurs when two atoms of hydrogen (H) collide with one another and fuse to generate one atom of helium (He) and release one neutron. Both reactions produce large quantities of energy due to the loss of neutrons during the reactions.

fusion within the core of the Earth heats the Earth from the inside out. The sun alone is estimated to produce a level of energy equivalent to 3.8×10^{26} joules per second. To put this into perspective, the United States consumed only about 1.00×10^{23} joules total during 2014. Therefore, the sun produces an amount of energy in one second that is more than 1,000 times the amount of energy consumed in the United States in one year (Barbier, 2012; EIA, 2015). While these reactions occur naturally, scientists and engineers have also been able to reproduce thermonuclear fission reactions to generate nuclear power.

NUCLEAR ENERGY: AN ALTERNATIVE ENERGY RESOURCE, BUT IS IT REALLY RENEWABLE?

When we think of thermonuclear reactions, it is probably not the sun or center of the Earth that comes to mind but rather nuclear energy production. Nuclear energy is a form of energy that results from mass-to-energy conversion within the nucleus of an atom. Because atoms use a lot of energy to hold the protons, neutrons, and electrons inside and around their nuclei, the splitting or combining of individual atomic nuclei can release an immense quantity of energy, generally in the form of heat. As a reminder, nuclear fission reactions occur when large atoms such as uranium or plutonium are split into smaller products such as krypton and barium. During this reaction, a neutron is released from the splitting nucleus. This neutron can then impact another atomic nucleus, causing it to split. The splitting process results in a chain reaction leading to the continuous splitting of atomic nuclei and release of extremely large amounts of energy (Bodansky, 2005). Nuclear fission is the type of reaction usually involved in the production of commercial nuclear energy today in nuclear power plants.

In 2013, nuclear energy provided about 4.4% of the world's total energy consumption and 8.3% of US primary energy. Despite a fairly low percentage of total energy, this nuclear energy consumption is significant because it represents the second-highest consumed nonfossil-fuel-based energy resource with only hydropower having a higher consumption at 6.7% of the world's primary energy (British Petroleum, 2014). In addition, as a nonfossil fuel, no carbon dioxide is released into the atmosphere from nuclear reactions.

The utilization of nuclear energy today has its origins in the concept of the atom initially proposed by Greek philosophers in about 370 BC. However, it was not until early in the twentieth century that physicists began to fully grasp the quantities of energy contained within an atomic nucleus. In 1911, Ernest Rutherford, a British scientist, discovered that an atom has a nucleus and wrote about the heat produced as radium decayed. In 1934, a physicist named Enrico Fermi demonstrated the interactions between neutrons and nuclei that led to the discovery of nuclear fission. This discovery was quickly followed by the first self-sustaining nuclear reaction in 1942 focused mostly on the use of this technology for military purposes including nuclear weapons. The obvious risks associated with the use of this technology for weapons development led to the establishment of the Atomic Energy Commission in 1946. Their goal was to create a nuclear energy program for peaceful civilian use. In 1951, the world's first electricity-generating nuclear power plant came on line (Bodansky, 2005; WNA, 2014).

Energy generated from nuclear reactions today is largely a product of the fission of uranium. Uranium is an atomic element that naturally occurs in most rocks and in seawater. Uranium nuclei are naturally found as two different radioactive isotopes, ^{238}U (99.3%) and ^{235}U (0.7%). The difference between these two isotopes is based on a variation in the number of neutrons and protons present in the nucleus where ^{238}U has three more neutrons than ^{235}U. ^{235}U is the most utilized of the uranium isotopes for regular nuclear fission reactions. When the uranium atom captures a stray neutron, it will split into isotopes such as krypton (^{92}Kr) and barium (^{142}Ba). Although this is a volatile reaction, scientists have learned to sustain and control the reaction allowing for the energy to be captured and used in the production of electricity (Mudd, 2011).

This ability to control and harness energy from nuclear reactions is largely based on the design of a nuclear reactor. If nuclear reactions containing uranium were allowed to take place without control mechanisms, there would eventually be a nuclear meltdown, releasing radioactivity and heat without capturing any energy. Instead, the nuclear reactor is specifically designed to control the fission reaction. The uranium is formed into pellets and then placed in rods, about the diameter of a dime, called fuel rods. The rods are attached together and submerged in water within the center of the reactor known as the nuclear core. The water is crucial in keeping the rods cool during the reaction and avoiding an uncontrolled chain reaction resulting in a nuclear meltdown; however, the water alone is not enough to control the nuclear reaction. In order to truly control a nuclear reaction, scientists use control rods made of materials designed to absorb excess neutrons. These control rods are raised or lowered to control the number of neutrons that are coming in contact with the fuel rods. In this way, if the control rod is lifted, then the uranium rods are exposed to more neutrons and more energy is produced in the form of heat, but as the control rods are lowered, some of the neutrons are blocked, lowering the amount of energy released. When a nuclear reactor is shut down, usually in case of an emergency or maintenance, these control rods are completely lowered to stop the reaction (Nersesian, 2010).

The energy from a nuclear reaction is usually in the form of heat. This heat energy can be utilized to heat water and generate steam. The steam is then used in a traditional steam-turbine-driven power plant designed to produce electrical power as described in chapter 2. Once the steam has been utilized in power generation, it cannot simply be released into the environment due to the detrimental environmental effects that would result from the direct release of the extremely hot water. To avoid environmental damage, large distinctly shaped cylindrical towers, often associated with nuclear power plants and called cooling towers, are assembled. These cooling towers allow the gaseous steam to condense into cooler water before being released into the environment.

Nuclear energy has become an alternative to fossil fuel energy due to its release of large amounts of energy with much lower greenhouse gas emissions. Reactor grade uranium has an energy density of 3.7×10^6 megajoules per kilogram, enough to power a 100 watt lightbulb for 1,171 years. When compared to the energy density of coal (32.5 megajoules per kilogram) or crude oil (41.9 megajoules per kilogram), the difference in magnitude is immediately recognizable. The same amount of coal or crude oil could only power that same lightbulb for 3–5 days (Touran, 2012). The potential of nuclear energy has resulted in the development of many nuclear power plants. In 2015, there were 438 operating nuclear reactors in 30 countries, producing 378,870 megawatts of energy, an additional 69 reactors under construction, and 184 reactors ordered or planned in the future (WNA, 2015). As mentioned previously, these nuclear reactors supply about 4.4% of the world's total primary energy (British Petroleum, 2014). Figure 9.1.2 compares nuclear energy consumption in the various regions of the world where Europe, Eurasia, and north America clearly consume the most nuclear energy. Within these regions, the united states is the leading consumer of nuclear energy, accounting for about 33% of the world's nuclear energy consumption (British Petroleum, 2014). Most of the nuclear power plants located in the united states have been in operation for a few decades, and they continue

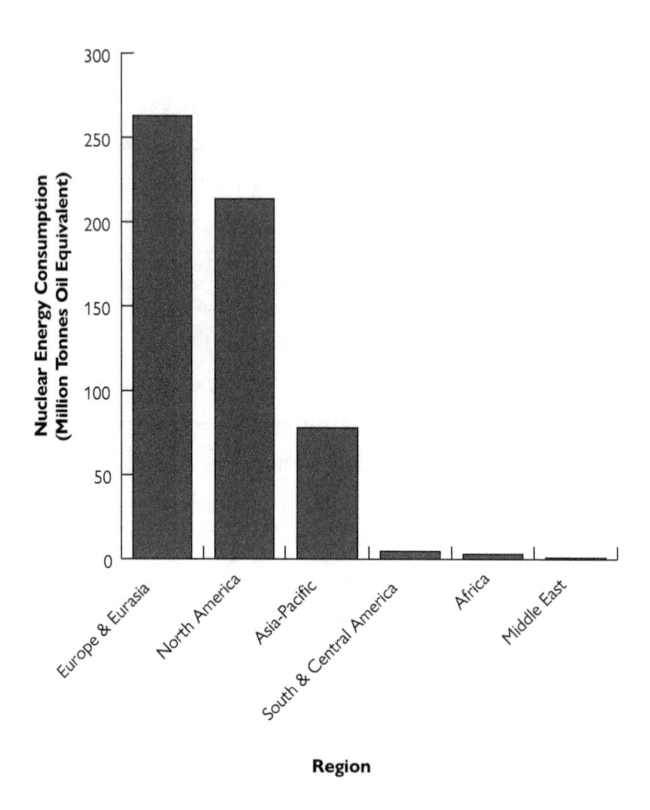

Figure 9.1.2 Comparison of nuclear energy consumption by region in 2013. Europe and Eurasia are the leading consumers of nuclear energy at 263 million tonnes oil equivalent (mtoe), followed by north America at 213.7 mtoe and Asia-Pacific consuming 77.8 mtoe. Within these regions, the united states, France, and south Korea are the highest individual nuclear energy consuming countries, respectively. Other regions including south and central America, Africa, and the Middle east are minor contributors to global nuclear energy consumption (data from British Petroleum, 2014).

to become more efficient and produce more power. In the united states, 99 nuclear reactors produce 98,756 megawatts of total nuclear energy including 790.2 billion kilowatt-hours of electricity. This is about 19.4% of the total electric power generated in the united states (EIA, 2015; WNA, 2015).

Despite its sometimes-confusing classification as a sustainable energy resource due to its potential to produce power for a very long period of time without carbon dioxide emissions, nuclear energy is not a renewable energy source by the traditional definition. Nuclear energy requires uranium or some other radioactive atomic element found within the Earth. These sources are finite and must be mined. Once these resources run out, nuclear power will no longer be possible. Currently, scientists estimate there to be enough uranium to provide nuclear power to the existing nuclear power plants for only the next

90 years. These uranium reserves are located largely in mines found in Australia, Kazakhstan, Russia, and Canada (WNA, 2014). So why would this resource sometimes be classified with the other truly sustainable resources? One of the answers lies in the development and implementation of a second type of nuclear reactor known as the **breeder reactor.** In a breeder reactor, more fissile material is produced than consumed. In these reactors, nuclear material undergoes fission reactions to produce energy and also generates new material capable of additional rounds of fission, thereby continuing the energy generation cycle. In the end, this continuous reaction is predicted to be able to provide the substrate for energy production for a much longer period of time, possibly 1,000 years (Nersesian, 2010; Sevior et al., 2010).

NEXT-GENERATION NUCLEAR REACTORS

Travis L. Johnson

Nuclear fission reactors have been designed and built since the mid-twentieth century and nuclear technologies have advanced through the years. The oldest reactor designs are called Generation I and were built in the 1950s and 1960s as prototypes. Most current nuclear reactors are Generation II, which were built from the late 1960s to the late 1990s and are based on the light water reactor (LWR) concept. In this design, the reactor core is immersed in water and the heat from the reactor is transferred to a secondary water system that transforms into steam and turns a turbine generator. This reactor type has high power densities and requires high safety redundancy to minimize loss of coolant (water) in the reactor, which could lead to a meltdown. Generation III reactors are newer designs built in the 2000s and Generation III+ reactors are improved versions that will be built in the 2020s and 2030s. These are based on LWR, but also include passive safety systems such as natural convection air discharge, outside cooling air intake, internal condensation, and natural recirculation. These designs are safer and less complex than Generation II reactors and make it less likely for a meltdown to occur. Looking forward, the next-generation reactors would be Generation IV and nuclear fusion reactors. Generation IV would take the passive safety design to the extreme, making a meltdown physically impossible as well as improving the economics of the reactor and reducing the amount of long-lived waste products. Finally, scientists are researching fusion reactors, which would never have meltdowns, would not produce long-lived waste, and would have life spans of up to 100 years rather than the 40–60 year life spans of current reactors, but fusion reactors appear to still be several decades away.

source: Tynan (2014).

While nuclear energy is an important source of power and one that could likely replace coal- and natural-gas-generated electricity easier and faster than some of the other truly renewable energy resources, nuclear power does have some significant problems including public safety, vulner-abilities to terrorism, and significant issues with long-term storage of the radioactive waste. In order to continue developing nuclear technology and to expand the utilization of nuclear power, it will be necessary for the entire global community to address each of these concerns.

GEOTHERMAL ENERGY

Nuclear energy used in nuclear power plants is not truly a sustainable resource due to the reliance upon a finite supply of uranium from the Earth. However, another energy source that does have the potential to be sustainable is derived directly from the Earth's core in the form of **geothermal energy**. Geothermal energy is the result of heat transferred from the core of the Earth to its surface. The energy is initiated from radioactive isotopic decay and other potential nuclear reactions at the core that heat the surrounding rock and turn it into magma. The heated magma then moves up through the various layers of the Earth until it gets closer to the surface, becoming cooler within every layer. As magma gets closer to the surface, it heats the land and water at the surface (Isherwood, 2011). Sometimes hot magma is released from the Earth through volcanoes and at other times it is trapped within the Earth and acts to heat its surroundings. One common way to experience how magma heats the Earth is to enjoy a natural springs thermal bath. These warm waters are naturally created when heat energy from the core of the Earth acts to warm waters trapped within the Earth before they seep to the surface. Sometimes these waters can be warmed by magma to such an extent that steam is created. If this highly energetic steam is funneled toward a small exit within the Earth, it can create an explosion of water vapor known as a geyser.

The warming of water trapped just below the surface of the Earth is actually the exact way we use geothermal energy as an energy resource. In some simple cases, piping is laid down under a home or building, allowing water to be pumped underground where it is warmed by the Earth, and then brought back up to be used to heat a home or building. Other larger-scale commercial power stations use steam generated from within the Earth to produce electricity. Some power stations can rely directly on natural water trapped deep in the Earth as steam. These stations simply place a pipe deep into the Earth, creating an exit for the pressurized steam. This high-energy steam will shoot to the surface with plenty of velocity to spin a turbine and generate electricity. Once the pressure of the natural water supply becomes too low, water can be injected into the Earth to replenish the water supply and rebuild the pressure. This technique was successfully employed by the largest natural steam field in the world north of San Francisco known as the geysers. Here, they used processed wastewater from local communities to replenish the natural water supply allowing for continued generation of energy from this field (Nersesian, 2010).

The creation of pressurized steam generally requires temperatures above 300 degrees Fahrenheit; however, there are geothermal resources closer to the surface that are below this temperature and can still be used to produce power. In these situations, a heat exchange occurs where the heat from the geothermal water is transferred to a second fluid with a lower boiling point such as isopentane. The vapor from this second fluid can then be used to drive the power-generating process (Nersesian, 2010).

The most active areas for geothermal energy are those areas where hot rocks are close to the surface, which often occurs where tectonic plates come together. These areas are also associated with volcanoes and earthquakes. The ring of fire, located around the rim of the Pacific Ocean, is one of these geothermally active regions. Figure 9.1.3a shows a map of geothermally active regions in the united states. The darker red and orange areas, representing many regions in the western united states, are areas where the prospect of geothermal power generation is favorable. In 2013, the united states produced a total of 16.5 million watts of power using geothermal energy, an amount equivalent to 0.4% of total us power generation (EIA, 2015). Nearly 80% of this geothermal power is generated in the state of California, with the remainder produced largely in Nevada, Hawaii, Idaho, and Utah as shown in Figure 9.1.3B (Roberts, 2014).

The generation of power utilizing geothermal energy is a sustainable manner of power production that could play a continued and larger role in replacing coal and natural gas for electricity generation. While certainly less detrimental than fossil-fuel-based energy resources, the consumption of geothermal energy also has environmental consequences. Geothermal power plants can release both hydrogen sulfide and carbon dioxide, but generally at much lower levels than coal or natural gas power plants. By using a scrubbing system to remove contaminants from the steam, hydrogen sulfide can be limited to about 3% of that released by fossil fuel power plants. In addition, carbon dioxide from a geothermal power plant is less than 4% of that released by the dirtier fossil fuel plants (Kagel et al., 2007). Another potential environmental consequence to consider related to geothermal energy is the locations of good steam fields. In some cases, these steam fields may be located in regions that are designated national parks like Yellowstone National Park. The development of these natural regions to fulfill our desire for energy could result in a significant level of ecological destruction. With the continued development of geothermal energy, it will be necessary to figure out ways to use the heat from the Earth without ruining delicate ecosystems at the Earth's surface.

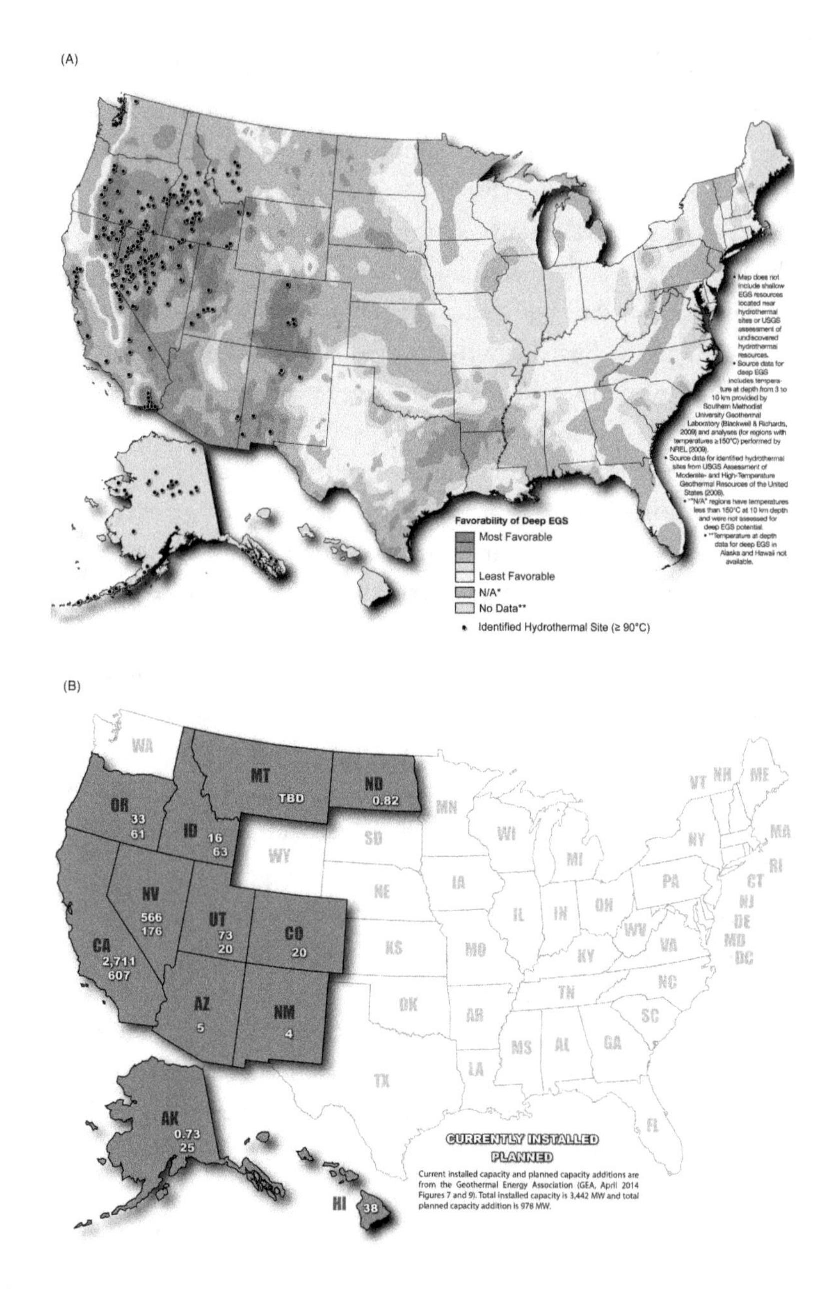

Figure 9.1.3 Geothermal resources in the United States. (A) Map of potential geothermal resources within the United States, showing locations of identified hydrothermal sites and favorability of deep enhanced geothermal systems (EGS). Areas shown in red and dark orange, largely in the western portion of the country, represent areas favorable for the development and implementation of geothermal systems. (B) Map of current and planned geothermal power generation capacity (in megawatts) in each state. Installed capacity shown in white and planned capacity shown in yellow (images by Roberts, 2009, 2014).

SOLAR ENERGY

Perhaps the most powerful primary energy resource available on Earth comes from the sun. The sun continuously produces an average of 340.4 watts per square meter of energy, and 163.3 watts per square meter of this energy arrives at the surface of the Earth (Canright, 2011). The sun produces this energy through nuclear fusion reactions that are released in the form of photons. These photons travel toward the outer boundaries of the sun and into space and eventually come in contact with the Earth. Photons that are not absorbed by the Earth's atmosphere impact the surface of the planet and can either be absorbed by vegetation and inorganic materials on the surface or be reflected back into the atmosphere. The continued reflection of energy between the surface of the Earth and the Earth's atmosphere results in the warming of the planet due to the greenhouse effect as discussed in the previous chapter. Considering solar energy in terms of individual photons may not reveal the impact of energy from the sun on the Earth, but in fact, one hour's worth of solar energy striking the Earth is greater than all of the energy consumed by the world's population in one year (Lewis and Nocera, 2006). This means that the sun is easily capable of sustaining all of the Earth's energy needs if the proper technologies were developed to harness this energy.

One of the most common of these technologies available today is solar power. Solar power can be classified into one of three subcategories: passive, active, and photovoltaic.

Passive solar energy occurs when a structure such as a house, apartment, or dorm room absorbs heat from the sun and that heat is used to replace heat usually obtained by methods derived from fossil fuels such as a space heater. Passive solar energy is the easiest type of solar energy to use because it does not require any mechanical equipment but rather takes advantage of the inherent properties built into a structure. These properties may include south-facing windows or insulation. To better understand this concept, imagine a car left parked in the sun with the windows rolled up for a period of time. Within a matter of minutes, the interior will have become warm if not outright hot. The capture of thermal energy inside the car is an example of passive solar heating. The same thing can occur in a home where glass windows, particularly those facing south, can trap heat inside and thereby warm the room. Once the room gets too warm, the window can be opened allowing the air to flow out and be replaced by cooler air from the outside. In this way, passive solar energy can be used for heating without the need for fossil-fuel-derived energy supplementation.

Active solar energy is the next logical step beyond passive solar energy, where instead of relying on the structure inherent in a building itself, mechanical structures are built to actively absorb and collect the sunlight. The heat from this sunlight can then be used for a specific purpose like heating water or generating steam. Thermal solar energy uses solar collectors to collect sunlight in ideal locations, which is then used to heat water (Gabbard, 2011). The simplest of solar collectors are those often associated with heating water for individual home use, generally either a swimming pool or a shower. These solar collectors are made of rubber or plastic and designed in a tube-like structure to allow water to flow through. As the water flows through, it is warmed by the sun then returned to its original source. In a swimming pool, for instance, it will raise the temperature of the water within the pool, thus creating a heated swimming pool without the use of large amounts of electricity.

More complicated solar collectors are designed to collect enough solar energy to actually produce electricity from heated water and other materials (Philibert et al., 2010). These solar collectors come in three main forms: a solar dish, a solar trough, and a solar power tower. An example of a solar trough collector is shown in Figure 9.1.4. All of these solar

Figure 9.1.4 Photograph of parabolic solar trough at Harper Lake in California. These troughs reflect the sunlight to a central line where the increased intensity of the light and heat can be used to heat a fluid that can be used for many purposes including as an energy resource (image by "Parabolic trough at Harper Lake in California" by Z22, own work. Licensed under CC BY-SA 3.0 via Wikimedia commons, http://commons.wikimedia.org/wiki/file:Parabolic_trough_at_harper_lake_in_california.jpg#/media/file:Parabolic_trough_at_harper_lake_in_california.jpg).

SOLAR PHOTOVOLTAIC TECHNOLOGIES

Travis L. Johnson

The sun is an enormously important source of energy for Earth, and one way we are able to harness its power is by converting the sun's photons directly into electrons using photovoltaic (PV) cells. This power comes in the form of sunlight, which is also called solar irradiance, and it has different components at the Earth's ground level. One component is the direct normal irradiance that is the radiation from the sun coming directly from the sun's rays. If one pointed a tube straight at the sun and tracked it as it moved through the sky, one would be capturing the sun's direct normal irradiance. Another component is the diffuse irradiance, which is the radiation that has been scattered by atmospheric molecules and distributed throughout the sky.

The most common form of PV technology is the flat panel PV array, which can be found on watches, calculators, and residential and commercial roofs. This technology uses both diffuse and direct irradiances and converts photons to electrons at around 20% efficiency. Another PV technology is concentrated PV, which consists of a mirror system that concentrates direct irradiance into the PV cell. A first mirror is shaped like a dish and can capture more area of direct irradiance and reflect it to another smaller mirror in the middle of the dish that then reflects the sunlight into a multi-junction cell. The multi-junction cell can capture more wavelengths of light, converting 35–40% of the photons to electrons, making it more efficient than flat panel PV cell. Concentrated PV cells are typically about 100 times more expensive than a flat panel PV, but they are able to concentrate the solar radiation by 300–1,000 times.

sources: Coimbra (2014); 3Tier by Vaisala (2015).

collectors are designed so that they reflect sunlight to a designated point, either the apex of a solar dish or tower, or at the midline of a trough. These solar collectors will track the sun as it moves through the sky and reflect as much radiation energy as possible on to these individual points. In many cases, these points are directly associated with flowing water or other materials in a tube similar to the simpler thermal solar collectors. This water can be heated to such an extent that steam is formed, and just like with coal power generation, this solar-generated steam can be used to generate electricity (Nersesian, 2010).

Finally, photovoltaics represents another solar technology developed to take advantage of solar energy. Photovoltaics means "electricity from light" and is different than both passive and active solar power because a photovoltaic cell can skip the step of heating a material to produce steam that is used to generate electricity, and instead directly produce electricity from sunlight through the **photovoltaic effect** (Knier, 2011). The photovoltaic effect occurs when the semiconducting material of a photovoltaic solar cell absorbs photons of energy from the sun. Eventually the semiconducting material absorbs enough photons that it forces electrons to be ejected from atoms within the material. Due to the negative charge of electrons, these electrons are attracted to the front of the solar cell, which is coated in positive charges. The separation of the negatively charged electrons from the positively charged atomic nuclei creates a voltage potential. Once the front of the solar cell is connected to the back via an electric conductor, this voltage potential caused by the attraction between the positive charges and the negative charges will directly create a flow of electricity (Knier, 2002).

You may be familiar with photovoltaic technology if you have ever used a solar calculator that does not require a battery. While this is a small example, combining many photovoltaic cells can produce enough electricity to power a home or building. Sometimes this electricity exceeds what is needed by the individual structures and can be sent onto the electric grid. Photovoltaics are beneficial in that they reduce carbon dioxide emissions by replacing fossil fuel power-generating technologies like coal; however, they also have consequences for the environment. Photovoltaic cells have a lifetime of about 25 years and contain toxic materials such as lead, mercury, and cadmium. These are finite materials that can result in toxic emissions during their initial mining and preparation, and must be dealt with properly for disposal (Alsema et al., 2006). In order to expand photovoltaic technology for the replacement of coal-generated power, it will be necessary to find ways to safely dispose of these materials and in some cases find methods to recycle these finite resources.

The demand for solar photovoltaic power generation is growing. Figure 9.1.5 shows the net power generation from solar photovoltaic utilization in the united states since 2003. Beginning in 2008, solar photovoltaic power generation quickly began rising with net power generation of 76,000 megawatt-hours in 2008 and 8,327,000 megawatt-hours in 2013, an increase of 10,856%. This compares to a much slower increase in solar thermal power generation from 788,000 megawatt-hours in 2008 to only 926,000 megawatt-hours in 2013, an increase of just 17.5%. Despite the increase in power generation from photovoltaics, total solar technology is still only used to provide 2.3% of total power generation in the united states (EIA, 2015). The widespread use of photovoltaic technology is limited due to the initial economic burden or cost to the consumer. This is largely based on the initial cost of installation of solar cells. Photovoltaic solar cells cost about $4–10 per watt

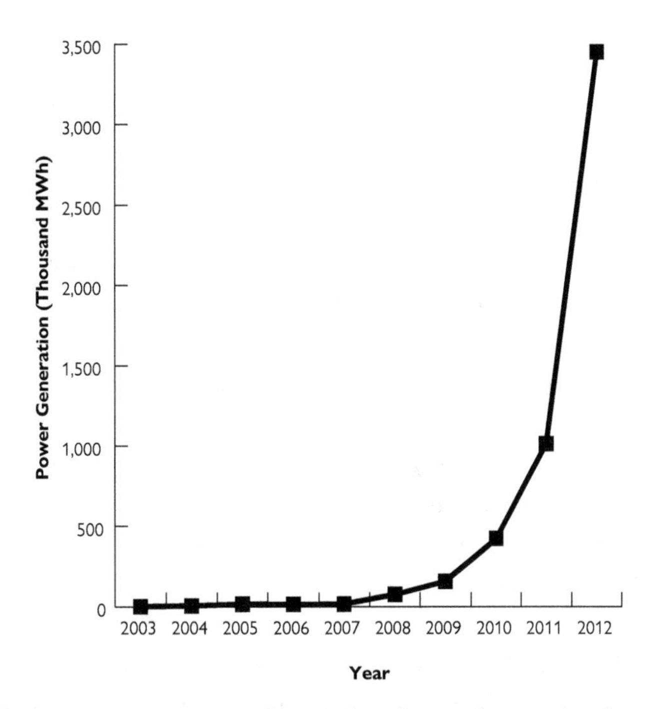

Figure 9.1.5 US net power generation from solar photovoltaic technology from 2003 to 2012. The expansion of photovoltaic power generation began in the United States in 2007 and has rapidly increased each year (data from EIA, 2015).

of installed capacity compared to a coal power plant of $3 per watt of installed capacity (Gabbard, 2011). In addition, the intensity of sunlight is not equivalent across the entire united states. NREL has shown that areas in the southwestern united states can produce more than 6.0 kilowatt-hours per square meter per day from a photovoltaic solar collector; however, regions in the northeast may only be able to produce less than 4.0 kilowatt-hours per square meter per day on average (Roberts, 2009). This difference in solar irradiance between these regions represents a potential differential in price and availability of power. Homes in the northeast may need to continue supplementing power generated from fossil fuels to meet their needs, while homes in the southwest that can produce more power than needed can get paid to put their extra power into the electric grid. While the installation costs today may keep some people from installing this technology, the continued decrease in the price of the technology, coupled with the ever-increasing price of fossil fuel electricity, will likely help push more people to use photovoltaics. Developing cheap and efficient methods to store photovoltaic power and creating a more ecologically sustainable process for solar cell generation would also allow photovoltaics to play a much larger role in the future of renewable energy.

WIND ENERGY

Wind is another renewable energy source that is ultimately derived from the sun. At first this may not seem intuitive, but the regional heating of the Earth by the sun generates wind. Warm air will rise, leading to a void that then pulls the cooler air in to replace the rising warm air. As this air rushes in, wind is created (Olanrewaju, 2011). This process is evident on a global scale by studying hemispheric wind patterns. As depicted in Figure 9.1.6, in the tropics near the equator, the sun is intense and heats the air, resulting in warm, moist tropical air. This air rises into the atmosphere near the equator in what is known as the intertropical convergence zone. However, this rising warm air must also be replaced by cooler air located closer to the Earth's surface in the subtropical regions. Subtropical cool air drops below the tropical warm air to create the easterlies or trade winds often found in the tropics and subtropics.

Wind can also be created on a much smaller regional scale as seen with ocean front climates. Daily sea breezes felt when visiting the beach are the result of variations in air temperatures. During the day, the sun warms the land more quickly than the water. This warm air over the land will rise and the cooler ocean air will flow in, creating the afternoon onshore sea breezes. However, at night the process is reversed as the air above the land cools much more quickly, while the air over the ocean remains warm, resulting

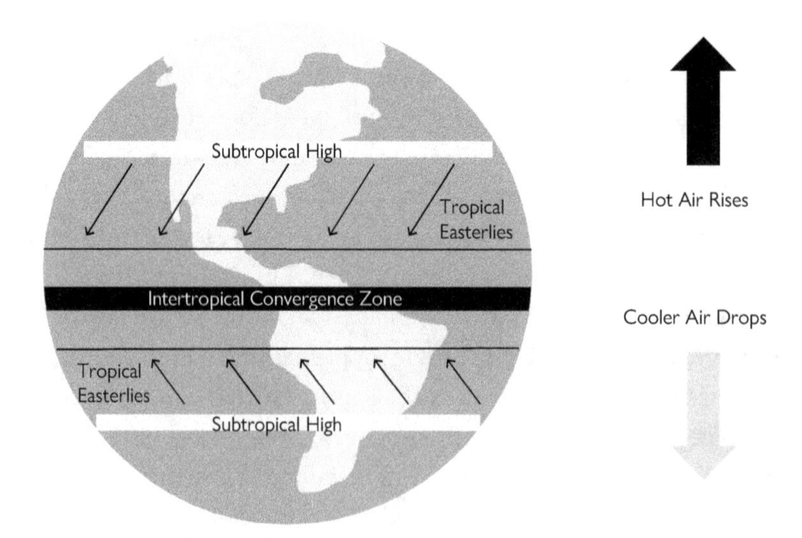

Figure 9.1.6 Basic diagram of hemispheric wind patterns. Warm, moist air in the tropics rises within the intertropical convergence zone, allows cooler air from the subtropics to be pulled under the warm air, and creates a global wind pattern known as the trade winds.

in an offshore flow. Whether on a global, regional, or local scale, wind is ultimately a manifestation of solar energy.

Wind as an energy resource is a very old concept dating back to the ancient Egyptians using sail power to navigate the Nile river. Civilizations have used windmills for the last 4,000 years for everything from grinding grain to pumping water. In the united states, the development of wind turbines resulted from the need to provide rural farms with electricity. Today, wind power has become an important sustainable resource for energy generation due to the rising prices of fossil fuels (Olanrewaju, 2011).

Wind power is generated using a wind turbine, the modern-day windmill. Wind turbines are fairly simple devices designed to capture the kinetic energy of the wind with long blades as shown in Figure 9.1.7. These turbines function when the wind turns the blades that are connected by a shaft to a gear box (equivalent to a turbine) that powers the generator and produces electricity. This electricity travels to the ground and can be used by individual buildings in rural areas or connected to the power grid to supply electricity over a much wider area (Olanrewaju, 2011). As you can see, this process is similar to the normal steam-generated power production process but without the need for fossil fuels. The largest wind turbines are built to tower over the land, sometimes at the height of nearly a 20 story building, in order to obtain higher wind speeds and less turbulent winds. These turbines can be very efficient and often have a rotating diameter nearly the length of a football field (BLM, 2012).

Figure 9.1.7 Example of wind turbines. The long blades are capable of capturing the kinetic energy of the wind and transferring this energy to the compartment at the base of the blades that houses a rotor. Spinning the rotor can be used to generate electricity. This electricity is transferred back to the ground down the pole where it can enter the power grid (image by ©istockphoto.com/globestock).

The best places to take advantage of wind energy are locations where wind turbines or groups of wind turbines (known as wind farms) can be placed on the tops of hills, across open plains, along shorelines, or within mountain gaps where wind funneling can occur. In general, wind speed increases with altitude, making regions at higher altitudes with these characteristics even more valuable (Nersesian, 2010).

Wind power has become the second most utilized renewable resource for power generation in the United States providing 4.1% of total power generation and 32.1% of renewable power generation. Figure 9.1.8 shows the growth of power generation from wind between 2002 and 2012. Like solar photovoltaics, wind energy production in the United States has also seen a huge increase in the past decade, growing from 10,354,000 megawatt-hours in 2002 to 167,665,000 megawatt-hours in 2013, with the largest increase in production occurring steadily since 2007. This amount of electricity is enough to power over 10 million households (EIA, 2015).

Wind energy is one of the cleanest and most environmentally friendly forms of renewable energy. Wind turbines do not release harmful emissions, they do not consume water, and they have a low land use footprint; however, just like any energy source, wind turbines also come with trade-offs. One of the greatest weaknesses of wind power is that wind does not blow all of the time, and in many cases when the wind does blow, it does not correspond to peak electricity usage periods. Finding a way to store power generated from wind turbines will be critical in the future development and implementation of this technology on a wider scale. Some people are also concerned that wind turbines are not

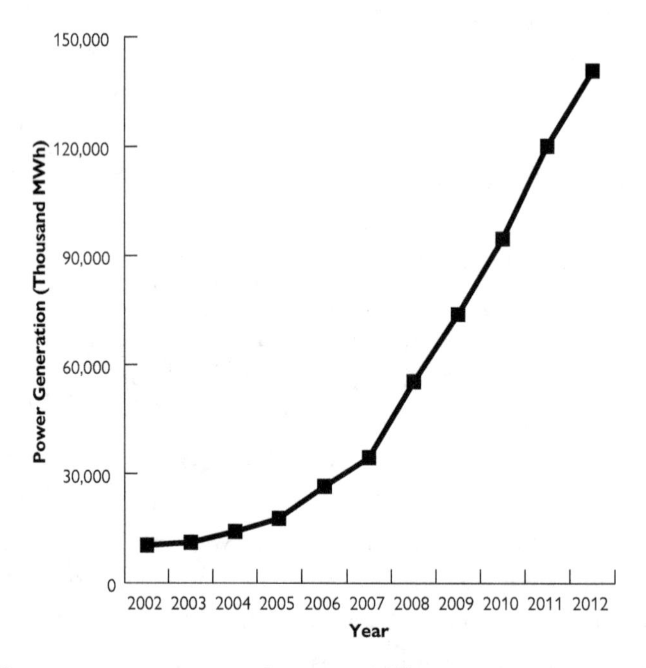

Figure 9.1.8 US net power generation from wind. The generation of wind power in the united states has seen a steady increase since 2002 with the most rapid increase after 2007 similar to the rapid increase of solar photovoltaic usage (data from EIA, 2015).

aesthetically pleasing and that they are a threat to wildlife, particularly migrating birds. Steps are being taken to improve wind turbines and the control of wind turbines to avoid disturbing bird migration patterns, but more birds are killed yearly by pesticides (estimated 72 million due to pesticides application in agriculture) than by wind turbines (33,000 bird deaths) (FWS, 2002).

Wind farms are also being built offshore where wind is often found to be more constant; however, these turbines must have added features to allow them to withstand the harsher oceanic elements such as wave action and powerful storms. Although wind turbines may not have a huge land footprint, they are still unrealistic for large-scale use in urban areas; thus, new urban wind turbines are also being developed with designs appropriate to urban environments, such as vertical wind turbine shafts placed on the sides of buildings. These modern wind turbines are effective in capturing wind in the urban environment while also architecturally designed to flow with the surrounding urban neighborhoods.

HYDROPOWER

In 2013, hydropower represented the renewable energy resource that resulted in the highest percentage of total US power generation at 6.6% and represented 51.5% of renewable power generation (EIA, 2015). Just as wind is an indirect renewable energy resource from the sun, so is hydropower through the **hydrological cycle**. Hydropower is often generated in a dam. Dams have a long history of providing water for domestic use, irrigation, and in controlling flooding. Humans have historically used moving water to turn wheels for lifting water, grinding grain, and a number of other tasks. Today, we have combined the beneficial aspects of dams and waterwheels to create hydroelectric power plants (Nersesian, 2010).

Hydropower is simply power produced from the kinetic energy of moving water. The potential of water as an energy resource is best understood by reviewing the Earth's hydrological cycle (Perlman, 2012). As shown in Figure 9.1.9, we can begin tracking the cycle as warmth from the sun causes water to evaporate, particularly from large bodies of water like the ocean. This warm moist air travels into the atmosphere and is transported towards shore and eventually over land. Once over land, the air begins to condense into clouds and water vapor. Eventually, the air is so heavy that precipitation begins to fall often times in association with mountains as snow or rain. The precipitation falls to the Earth and travels into the ground by infiltration becoming groundwater or travels on the surface of the ground as runoff into streams and rivers. These rivers flow back towards the ocean potentially delayed for a short period of time within inland lakes. Overall, this cycle, driven by the evaporation of water by the sun, is what provides the water that makes rain and snow, fills rivers and lakes, and irrigates crops. This same cycle can be used to produce hydropower.

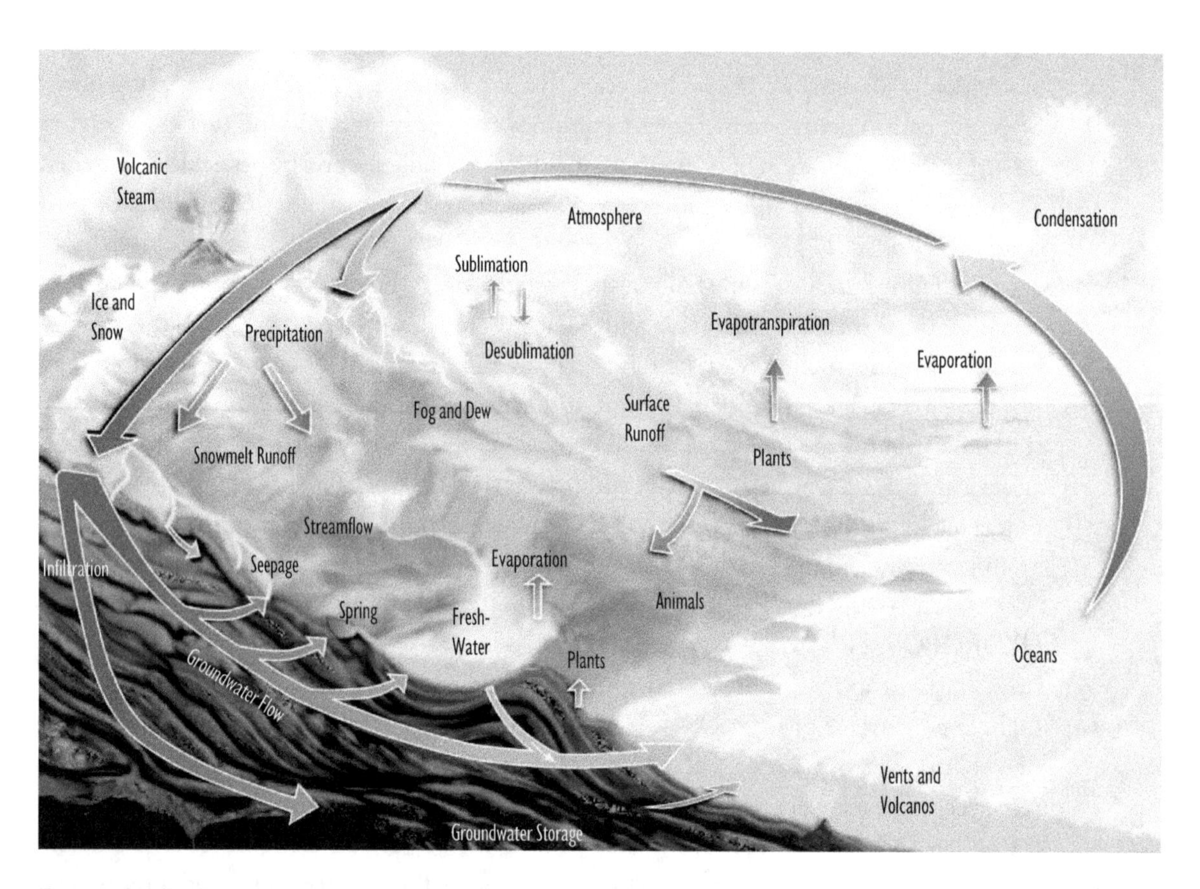

Figure 9.1.9 The water cycle also known as the hydrological cycle diagrams how water is continuously recycled on the Earth. Arbitrarily beginning with the ocean, water is evaporated due to the warmth of the sun. This moist air in the atmosphere travels over land and condenses to form precipitation, usually snow, ice, or rain. This precipitated water then either infiltrates the land and flows as groundwater back toward the ocean or flows as surface water runoff into streams, rivers, and lakes that ultimately lead back to the ocean (image by Evans and Perlman, 2014).

The production of hydropower is only as efficient as the Earth's hydrologic cycle. In most cases, hydropower is generated by blocking a river's flow with a dam. This creates an unnatural lake behind the dam where water can accumulate to a significant depth. This depth and the natural force of gravity are what generate the kinetic energy needed for the generation of hydropower. Figure 9.1.10 shows a basic diagram of how water flowing through a dam can generate potential and kinetic energy to drive the production of hydropower. Within the dam, there is a chute or chutes known as penstocks. On the side of the dam closest to the lake the opening of the penstock is at the top of the dam, but on the downstream side of the dam, the exit of the penstock is located at its bottom.

This engineering sets up a drop in elevation within the dam. As the water flows down the penstock, it builds up energy and before exiting the penstock encounters a turbine. The kinetic energy within the flow of the water spins the turbine that is attached to a generator and produces electricity.

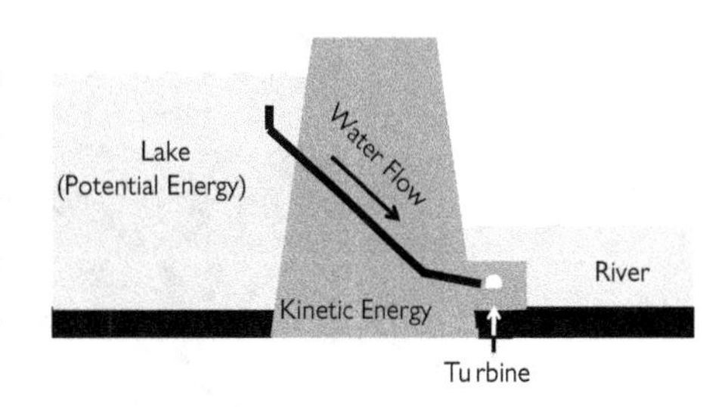

Figure 9.1.10 Basic diagram of a dam showing the buildup of water on one side representing the potential energy of water and the flow of this water through a penstock to create kinetic energy that will spin a turbine at the bottom to generate power.

The largest hydroelectric power station associated with a dam in the united states is grand coulee dam on the Columbia river in Washington state with a total capacity of 6,809 megawatts. Other large power stations that contribute to the total production of hydropower in the united states include the Robert Moses Niagara hydropower station in New York, Bath county Pumped storage station in Virginia, and the chief Joseph dam and the dalles hydropower stations located in Washington and Oregon, respectively. One of the most widely known hydroelectric power stations in the United States is known as the Hoover Dam, shown in Figure 9.1.11. This dam, originally built as the Boulder dam, is over 700 feet tall and over 650 feet wide at its base. The dam is located along the Colorado River where it blocks the flow of the river to create Lake Mead. The Hoover Dam produces 1,039.4 megawatts of electricity, which is provided to the surrounding states of Arizona, Nevada, and California. The dams in the United States are not the largest or most prolific hydropower stations in the world. The largest power station was recently built in China called the Three Gorges Dam. This dam has an installed capacity of 22,500 megawatts. In fact, five of the world's seven largest power plants are hydroelectric power plants, while the other two are nuclear power plants (Global Energy Observatory, 2014).

Hydroelectric power is responsible for an estimated 6.7% of total primary energy production around the world today (British Petroleum, 2014). Figure 9.1.12 shows how hydroelectric power is utilized in different regions of the world. Nearly 60% of all hydroelectric power consumed in the world occurs in the Asia-Pacific and Europe and Eurasia regions, with China representing the single country with the greatest consumption of hydropower due to the use of the Three Gorges Dam (British Petroleum, 2014).

Hydroelectric power plants have a long lifespan and minimal operational costs after the very large capital cost initially invested in building a dam. This low operational cost provides a significant economic advantage for hydropower as a renewable resource for energy production (Casalenuovo, 2011). However, despite this advantage, its production of virtually emissions-free power, and its already important role as a renewable resource for power generation in the United States, it seems unlikely that conventional large-scale

Figure 9.1.11 Photographs of (A) Hoover Dam and the (B) hydroelectric power-generating facility within the dam (images by Adam and Carla Jones, 2011).

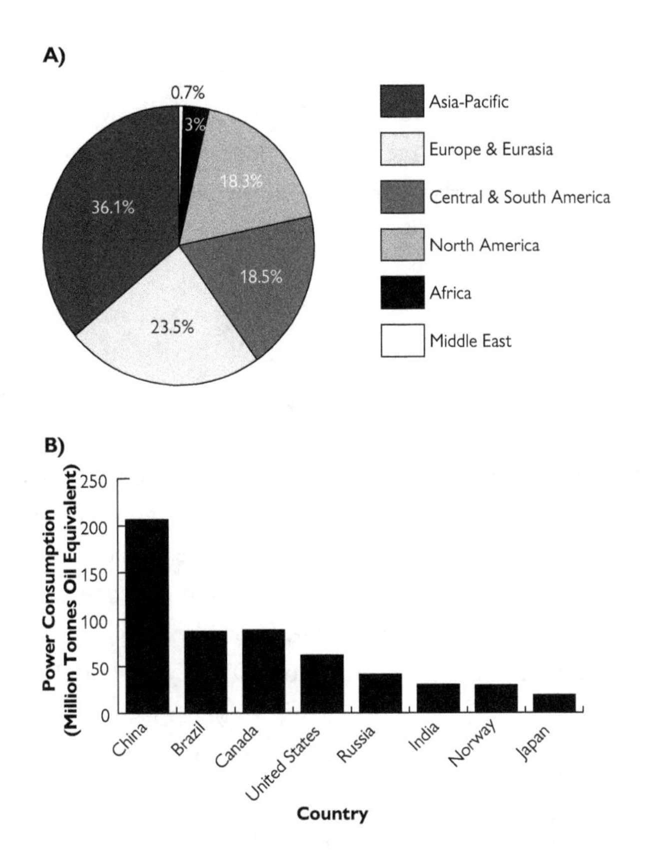

Figure 9.1.12 Hydroelectric power consumption around the world in 2013.

A A graphic comparison of hydroelectric power consumption by region in 2013. The Asia-Pacific and Europe and Eurasia regions consumed 59.6% of all hydroelectric power, while areas such as Africa and the Middle East played a very small role in hydroelectric power.

B In 2013, the single largest consumer of hydroelectric power was China at about 206.3 million tonnes oil equivalent equal to approximately 2.4 billion megawatt-hours. Brazil, Canada, and the United States were the next highest consumers of hydroelectric power.

Data from British Petroleum (2014).

hydroelectric power capacity can be significantly and sustainably expanded in the coming years. One of the largest issues with the expansion of hydroelectric power in the United States is that most of the locations where large dams could be built already contain hydroelectric power stations. Therefore, it may be necessary to take advantage of microscale hydroelectric stations that rely on the flow of natural rivers and streams rather than on the creation of potential energy through the building of a traditional dam. Hydroelectric power stations, particularly the building of dams, also have important environmental repercussions. When a dam is built, it blocks the flow of water to create a large lake, thereby flooding all of the surrounding land and having a severe impact on the ecosystem of that area. Also, within the river itself, the ecosystem suffers due to a change in the flow of the water, the blockage of fish migrations, and/or alterations in local fish populations

(Casalenuovo, 2011). Overall, hydroelectric power is a clean source of energy that could help in replacing electricity generation from coal and natural gas; however, its expansion in the United States will likely depend largely on the development of more small-scale, environmentally sustainable water turbines that are designed to provide electricity for smaller surrounding communities.

OCEAN ENERGY

Seventy one percent of the Earth is covered by water. Of these water sources, 97% are saltwater, mainly oceans, and only 3% are freshwater systems like rivers or lakes (Perlman, 2012). When discussing renewable energy technologies, we generally associate freshwater systems with hydroelectric power; however, this leaves 97% of the planet's water resources unaccounted for in terms of energy including the oceans that are capable of absorbing and transporting large amounts of energy. Therefore, it is necessary to look at the ocean as a source of renewable energy. Currently, research and development are focused on a limited number of potential commercial-scale technologies for ocean energy including **wave energy, ocean thermal energy conversion** *(OTEC)*, and **tidal energy**.

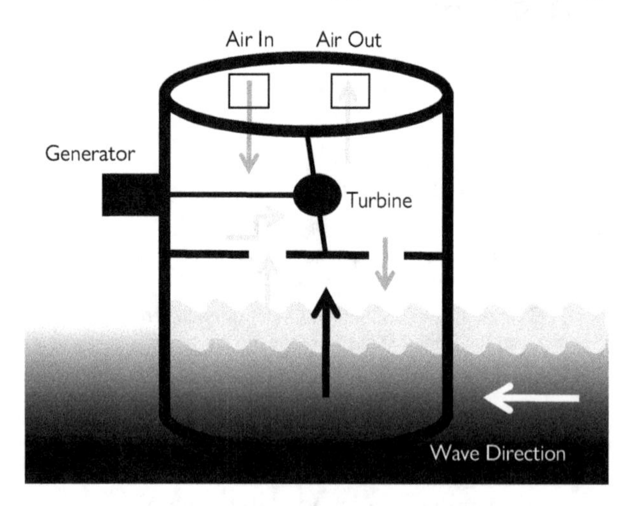

Figure 9.1.13 Diagram of wave power generation within a buoy. The air moving in and out of the buoy from the top would spin a turbine connected to a small generator used to produce power. While one single buoy may only be able to generate a small amount of power, a large collection of these buoys has the potential to produce greater quantities of power (source: California energy commission, 2012).

Wave energy is also derived from the sun as a primary energy source. Waves are generally created from wind, and as was discussed earlier in this chapter, wind is created from the heating of the air by the sun (Nersesian, 2010). Waves are built up as the wind blows along the surface of the water, creating friction. This friction first produces a ripple, building up with time to create much larger waves. Ultimately, the size of a wave depends on the wind speed, the length of time the wind is blowing, and the distance over which the wind pushes the wave.

If you have ever been to the beach and played in the surf, then you have experienced the up and down motion of waves. It is this motion that ultimately generates the kinetic energy that can be used to produce power. This energy can be captured by placing a buoy or other device similar to that shown in Figure 9.1.13 within the path of the wave. When the water moves up and down, it pressurizes the air within the buoy. As the air moves in and out of the buoy, it drives a piston or spins a turbine that can generate power. Almost all devices being developed to generate power from wave energy are designed around the idea of using pressurized air to spin a turbine. In the end, scientists envision creating a farm of these buoys in the ocean where each buoy is connected to a central line that leads to land, carrying the generated electricity into coastal communities (Nersesian, 2010).

The most wave energy is found in coastal areas in Scotland, Canada, Africa, the United States, and Australia. In the United States, the west coast, particularly the southwestern Alaska coast, has the greatest potential for wave power generation. The Electric Power Research Institute estimates that the Alaskan coast could produce 620 terawatt-hours per year of power with wave energy. This is enough power to supply about 58 million homes annually in a state with only about 308,000 housing units (US Census Bureau, 2013; BOEM, 2014). Although wave energy technologies are not commercialized, they are continuing to be developed due to their potential for power generation.

The second renewable energy technology from the ocean being developed but currently not commercialized is ocean thermal energy conversion (OTEC). As was discussed earlier, the ocean takes up a massive percentage of the Earth and basically represents a giant solar energy collector and storage system. The energy absorbed and stored in the ocean can be used to produce power using OTEC.

OTEC is based on the natural formation of thermoclines in the ocean. A thermocline is a transition layer that separates the surface waters from the deep waters of the ocean. In general, the surface waters and deep waters individually maintain fairly constant temperatures; however, the thermocline layer is the transition layer with temperatures changing based on depth. The oceanic thermocline typically forms between 200 and 1,000 meters in depth and separates the warm surface waters from the cold deep waters. OTEC uses this thermal gradient to produce a power cycle. As long as the temperature in the deep ocean water is at least 20 degrees Celsius (36 degrees Fahrenheit) lower than the temperature at the surface, power can be produced. This temperature extreme is generally only found in tropical and subtropical oceanic areas closer to the equator, with the largest extremes seen in the western Pacific Ocean (Burman and Walker, 2009).

A closed OTEC system uses a material with a low boiling point that when exposed to the warm surface temperatures of the ocean will turn into vapor. This vapor is then pushed through a turbine that drives a generator. This vapor is then pushed down the pipes through the thermocline and into the colder, deeper layer of the ocean. The cooler temperatures cause the vapor to condense back into liquid and the cycle will repeat itself. The system can also be designed as an open system working in basically the same manner except that water is used under pressure to create the vapor, and then once the water is condensed by cooler ocean water, it creates desalinated water (Burman and Walker, 2009).

The final ocean energy technology does not directly rely on the energy from the sun as its primary energy source but rather the interaction of the Earth with the moon and, to a small extent, the sun to create tides. Tides form as large bodies of water rise and fall due to the gravitational forces as the Earth rotates. Most places have two high tides and two low tides each day. The timing of tides is predictable and consistent due to the alignment of the sun, the moon, and the Earth (Nersesian, 2010). When the sun and the moon are directly opposite from one another with the Earth in the middle, the positions on the Earth located on this linear trajectory will have the largest tides. The moon is closer to the Earth than the sun, so its gravitational forces are a little stronger and create a slightly higher tide on the side of the Earth closest to the moon. As all of that water moves across the Earth, it contains kinetic energy.

In about 20 places around the world, the ebb and flow of the changing tide is over 16 feet, the minimum difference needed to capture the potential of tidal power (Burman and Walker, 2009). Although tidal energy has been used for many centuries on a smaller scale, scientists are now trying to develop ways to use tidal energy on a more widely available commercial scale. One possible method is to build a tidal barrage or dam. In this scenario, the tide will come in and flood a basin located behind the dam. As the tide flows out, the difference between the height of the flooded basin and the level of the water on the ocean side of the dam can be significant enough to allow the water to flow out via penstocks and generate electricity like at a hydroelectric power plant. Unlike traditional hydroelectric power plants, the potential energy from tides is only available for about 10 hours a day during tidal changes. Thus, power generation is more limited. Another method being considered is a method that would take advantage of the tide coming both in and out where the tidal water would be funneled through channels packed with water turbines. The turbines would be designed to switch directions depending on whether the flow of the tide was going inland or out towards the sea. There are a few tidal plants in existence around the world. The largest is located in La Rance, France, and is capable of producing about 240 megawatts of power from a tidal difference of 26 feet (Nersesian, 2010).

BIOMASS

Up to this point, numerous renewable resources have been discussed that use the sun as their primary energy source, and all of these resources have been developed primarily to assist in the replacement of coal- and natural-gas-generated electricity. While the replacement of this fossil-fuel-generated electricity with renewable energy is essential for the planet, there is also a very real need to create renewable liquid fuels for the transportation sector. Biofuels created from biomass could be used for electricity generation, but could also play a critical role in the production of liquid transportation fuels. Biomass is grown as a result of the absorption of energy from the sun by the process of photosynthesis in plants. Photosynthesis evolved millions of years ago first in cyanobacteria, then in algae, and finally in plants, as a means to harvest energy from the sun and convert it into stored chemical energy. This biological process is also largely responsible for oxygenating the atmosphere and is the most important primary metabolic function on the planet.

For thousands of years, people have used biomass as an energy resource, mostly in the form of burning wood or dung, for heating and cooking. Burning biomass is still a fairly common method for producing heat around the world, but in the United States and Europe burning wood amounts to a very limited part of the total energy utilization (<1%) (EIA, 2015). However, in other parts of the world wood is used extensively to produce heat and light and for cooking. Wood represents a finite supply at any given time in many places in the world, and without careful and sustainable forestry management, the use of wood can result in significant environmental damage from deforestation as well as the release of atmospheric pollutants in smoke.

Burning wood is just one of many sources of energy derived from biomass. Biomass can also be used to produce a variety of different biofuels including bioethanol from sources like corn and sugarcane; biodiesel from soybeans, rapeseed, and algae; biohydrogen from algae; and biogas from biomass waste. The remainder of this book will focus largely on these sources of biofuels and their importance in the future of renewable energy.

RENEWABLE ENERGY UTILIZATION

Renewable energy sources like water, wind, and wood are the foundation from which energy was developed over thousands of years; however, despite the many sources of renewable energy that are available, renewable sources make up a small fraction of energy consumption around the world today. Figure 9.1.14 shows the global utilization of energy by source where fossil fuels make up 86.7% of consumption and non-hydropower-based renewable sources make up only 2.2% (EIA, 2015). With all the developments in renewable energy technologies over the past century and the known environmental

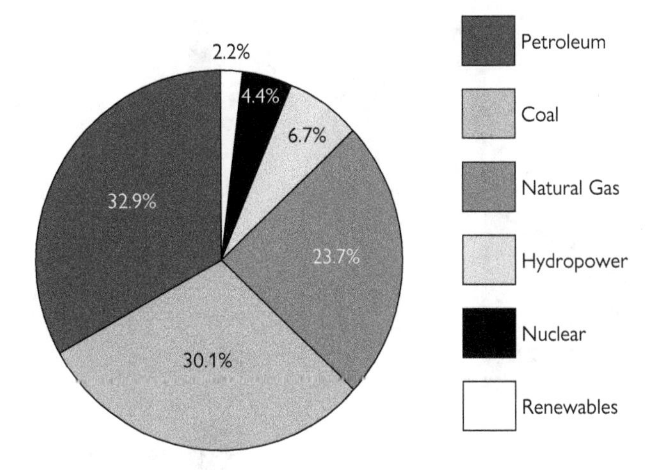

Figure 9.1.14 Global primary energy consumption by source in 2013 showing that the fossil fuels (petroleum, coal, and natural gas) make up 86.7% of global energy consumption, while renewable energy including hydropower makes up only 8.9% (data from EIA, 2015).

damage by fossil fuels, why do these sources not play a more significant role in energy utilization around the world? One of the main reasons these renewable energy technologies have not been able to develop a stronger foothold in energy consumption is their lower power density compared to fossil fuels. Overall, the lower energy density for renewable energy technologies often means that more of the resource must be harvested to generate enough energy to be competitive with fossil fuel resources. This drawback ultimately means that, in most cases, renewable energy technologies are more expensive and not economically competitive with fossil fuels; however, with dwindling fossil fuel supplies and concerns over their environmental impact, the price of fossil fuels may eventually overtake many of these renewable resource technologies and make them competitive in the global energy market.

In the United States, renewable energy (including hydro-power) makes up about 10% of total energy consumption (EIA, 2015). As shown in Figure 9.1.15, water, wood, biofuels and wind were all significant contributors to total renewable energy in the United States in 2013. In thinking about the utilization of these various renewable resources, approximately 78% of them are used primarily for power generation, yet 36% of energy consumption in the United States in 2013 came from petroleum largely used in the creation of transportation fuels (EIA, 2015).

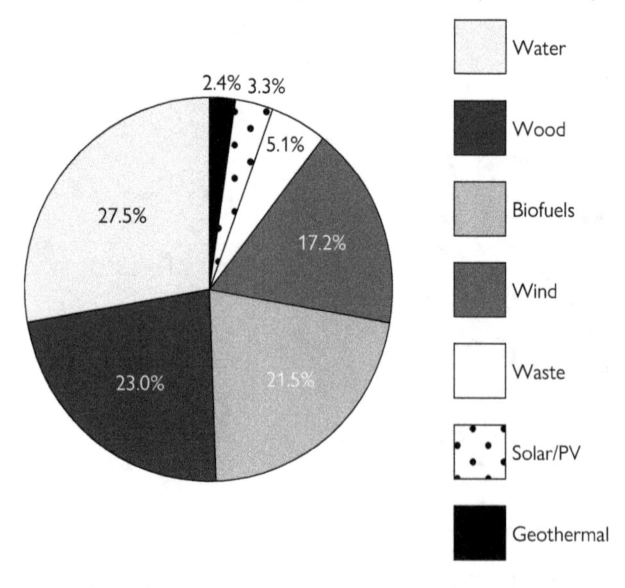

Figure 9.1.15 US renewable energy consumption in 2013 showing that water, wood, biofuels, and wind all contribute significantly to total renewable consumption, while waste, solar including photovoltaics, and geothermal are only minor contributors to us renewable energy (data from EIA, 2015).

Petroleum as an energy resource in the transportation sector is unique not only because it has an extremely high energy density, but also because it is easily transported and stored due to its liquid form. With the transportation sector making up 28% of energy consumption, it is important that a renewable energy technology be developed that can replace this liquid fuel source (EIA, 2015). Most of the renewable energy technologies discussed above may prove to be excellent replacements for coal- and natural-gas-derived power, but they would be unfeasible for the replacement of liquid transportation fuels. However, over the past several decades, it has become increasingly evident that a potential source for the replacement of liquid petroleum fuels may be the original source of those very fossil fuels: plants and algae. Rather than waiting millions of years to allow biomass to be buried to create fossil fuels, biomass energy technologies are now being explored and commercialized in order to use these photosynthetic resources directly for the production of liquid fuels.

The use of biofuels as a source of transportation fuel is certainly not a new concept; in fact, the first combustion engines actually ran off of a biofuel, peanut oil. Today, the most important biofuel in the united states is corn-derived ethanol that is used as an additive in gasoline. This came about in response to the issue of rising petroleum prices, along with concerns about the environment and energy security. To address these issues, the us government developed the renewable fuel standard in 2007 that calls for the replacement of 36 billion gallons of petroleum-based fuels with renewable biofuel sources by 2022. Fourteen billion of those gallons can come from corn ethanol, while the rest must come from non-corn ethanol-based sources (EPA, 2014).

This chapter has given you an overview of the various forms of renewable energy resources available on the planet. The latter parts of this book will focus exclusively on the various biomass sources for the production of biofuels and their commercialization. Because the production of biomass will result from agricultural processes developed over thousands of years, it is important to have a basic understanding of how the use of industrial agricultural knowledge can help both maintain a robust food supply and expand the opportunity to use plants and algae as a source of biofuels. Accordingly, the next chapter will introduce the fundamentals of industrial agriculture.

STUDY QUESTIONS

1. Define renewable and sustainable. Explain why fossil fuels are neither renewable nor sustainable. Is nuclear energy renewable and sustainable? Why or why not? Give some examples of truly renewable and sustainable energy resources.
2. Briefly explain the importance of the design of the nuclear reactor in the use of nuclear fission reactions for the production of electricity.
3. Briefly describe the energy resources that we can utilize from each of the primary energy sources. How can these resources be utilized best in society (electricity, transportation, etc.)?
4. Explain the three main types of solar power generation and how they differ in using the sun's energy to generate power.
5. Briefly discuss how water on the planet can be used to generate energy.
6. Explain why renewable energy technologies do not play a more dominant role in global energy consumption.
7. Explain why biofuels may have a different niche in the renewable energy future than many of the other renewable resources.

REFERENCES

Alsema, E. A., de Wild-Scholten, M. J., and Fthenakis, V. M. (2006) Environmental impacts of PV electricity generation: a critical comparison of energy supply options. *21st European Photovoltaic Solar Energy Conference*, Dresden, Germany.

Barbier, B. (2012) *Cosmicopia*. Astrophysics Science Division, National Aeronautics and Space Administration. Available at helios.gsfc.nasa.gov.

BLM (US Bureau of Land Management) (2012) *Wind Energy Guide*. Wind Energy Development Programmatic EIS. Available at windeis.anl.gov.

Bodansky, D. (2005) *Nuclear Energy: Principles, Practices and Prospects*. Springer, New York.

BOEM (Bureau of Ocean Energy Management) (2014) *Ocean Wave Energy*. Available at www.boem.gov.

British Petroleum (2014) *BP Statistical Review of World Energy 2013*. Available at www.bp.com/statisticalreview.

Burman, K. and Walker, A. (2009) *Ocean Energy Technology Overview*, DOE/GO-102009-2823. US Department of Energy.

California Energy Commission (2012) Ocean energy. Chap. 14 in *The Energy Story*. California Energy Commission, Sacramento. Available at www.energyquest.ca.gov.

Canright, S. (2011) *Earth's Energy Budget*. NASA Education, National Aeronautics and Space Administration. Available at www.nasa.gov.

Casalenuovo, K. (2011) Hydroelectric power. Pp. 242–246. In Mulvaney, D. and Robins, P. (eds): *Green Energy: An A-to-Z Guide*. Sage Publications, Thousand Oaks, CA.

Coimbra, C. (2014) *Our Energy Future: Photovoltaic and Photothermal Energy Production*. University of California, San Diego. Coursera. Available at www.coursera.org/learn/future-of-energy.

EIA (US Energy Information Administration) (2015) *Monthly Energy Review; Electric Power Monthly; Annual Energy Review; Short-Term Energy and Summer Fuels Outlook*. Available at www.eia.gov.

EPA (US Environmental Protection Agency) (2014) *Renewable Fuels: Regulations & Standards*. Renewable Fuel Standard. Available at www.epa.gov.

Evans, J. and Perlman, H. (2014) *The Water Cycle*. US Geological Survey. Available at Water.usgs.gov/edu/watercycle.html.

FWS (US Fish and Wildlife Service) (2002) *Migratory Bird Mortality*. Available at www.fws.gov.

Gabbard, R. T. (2011) Solar energy. Pp. 403–409. In Mulvaney, D. and Robins, P. (eds): *Green Energy: An A-to-Z Guide*. Sage Publications, Thousand Oaks, CA.

Global Energy Observatory (2014) *Current List of Hydro PowerPlants*. Available at globalenergyobservatory.org.

Isherwood, W. (2011) Geothermal energy. Pp. 197–202. In Mulvaney, D. and Robins, P. (eds): *Green Energy: An A-to-Z Guide*. Sage Publications, Thousand Oaks, CA.

Kagel, A., Bates, D., and Gawell, K. (2007) *A Guide to Geothermal Energy and the Environment*. Geothermal Energy Association. Available at www.geo-energy.org.

Knier, G. (2011) How do photovoltaics work? *NASA Science News*, National Aeronautics and Space Administration. Available at science.nasa.gov.

Lewis, N. S. and Nocera, D. G. (2006) Powering the planet: chemical challenges in solar energy utilization. *Proceedings of the National Academy of Sciences* 103:15729–15735.

Mudd, G. M. (2011) Uranium. Pp. 429–435. In Mulvaney, D. and Robins, P. (eds): *Green Energy: An A-to-Z Guide*. Sage Publications, Thousand Oaks, CA.

Nersesian, R. L. (2010) *Energy for the 21st Century*. M. E. Sharpe, New York.

Olanrewaju, A. O. (2011) Wind power. Pp. 444–448. In Mulvaney, D. and Robins, P. (eds): *Green Energy: An A-to-Z Guide*. Sage Publications, Thousand Oaks, CA.

Perlman, H. (2012) *The Water Cycle: Water Science for Schools*. US Geological Survey. Available at ga.water.usgs.gov.

Philibert, C., Frankl, P., and IEA Renewable Energy Division (2010) *Technology Roadmap: Concentrating Solar Power*. International Energy Agency. Available at www.iea.org.

Roberts, B. J. (2009) *Photovoltaic Solar Resources of the United States*. National Renewable Energy Laboratory, US Department of Energy.

Roberts, B. J. (2014) *Geothermal Power Generation*. National Renewable Energy Laboratory, US Department of Energy.

Sevior, M., Okuniewicz, I., Meehan, A., Jones, G., George, D., Flitney, A., and Filewood, G. (2010) *Advanced Nuclear Fission Technology*. University of Melbourne, Parkville, VIC.

Touran, N. (2012) *Energy Densities of Various Fuel Sources*. What is Nuclear? Available at Whatisnuclear.com.

Tynan, G. (2014) *Our Energy Future: The Future of Nuclear Energy*. University of California, San Diego. Coursera. Available at www.coursera.org/learn/future-of-energy.

US Census Bureau (2013) *Alaska QuickFacts*. United States Census Bureau. US Department of Commerce.

WNA (World Nuclear Association) (2014, 2015) *Outline History of Nuclear Energy: Supply of Uranium*. Available at www.world-nuclear.org.

3Tier by Vaisala (2015) *Power and Energy*. Available at www.3tier.com.

CHAPTER TEN

Environmental Law, Policy, and Governance

Rachel Carson's bestseller, *Silent Spring,* represented a significant transition in how we think about the effects of human actions toward the environment. Carson describes a hypothetical town where there is no birdsong. Then throughout the book, Carson explains exactly what was happening to birds and other wildlife that had not happened before. The advances in science that came about because of the two World Wars in the twentieth century led to problems with biomagnification, whereby animals at the top of the food chain, like bald eagles, were being poisoned by chemicals used to kill the tiny mosquito. We have discussed why understanding the underlying science of environmental cycles and processes is crucial to the environmental decision-making process. Thankfully, Carson was able to publish *Silent Spring* and make it clear to the average person why changes in policy were important. Her writing influenced federal government officials and led to changes in our national laws, particularly in the late 1960s and early 1970s. The Clean Air Act, the Clean Water Act, the Endangered Species Act, and the Environmental Protection Agency were all created after Carson's landmark book made it clear such laws were necessary. The selected reading by Janet Browne, "Rachel Carson: Prophet for the Environment" in *Dreamers, Visionaries, and Revolutionaries in the Life Sciences,* describes Carson's life and reviews the ways in which Rachel Carson turned science knowledge into environmental policy.

Having strong laws to protect the environment is only possible due to good science as we read in earlier chapters. In the selected reading, "How Can Good Science Become Good Policy" from *Betrayal of Science and Reason: How Anti-Environmental Rhetoric Threatens Our Future*, Paul R. Ehrlich and Anne H. Ehrlich (1996) reappear in our text to discuss what is necessary for scientists to help make good policy. Environmental studies students need to be able to bridge the gap between science and communication, particularly when it comes to law and policy. Being able to understand varied contexts and cultural differences, as discussed in Chapter 7 concerning environmental justice, makes creating and applying policy decisions possible. In addition, it is critical to have different voices represented within the groups advocating for the environment. Dorceta Taylor also reappears here, with a recommended reading from the "Executive Summary" of her report, *The State of Diversity in Environmental Organizations*. This summary of the state of diversity in environmental organizations demonstrates a need for more and different voices to be represented in protecting the environment. If the same voices are advocating for the same kinds of protections, we leave behind different values of nature and fail to protect the full range of environmental use and knowledge.

RECOMMENDED READING

Carson, R. 1962, "I. A Fable for Tomorrow" and "II. An Obligation to Endure." *Silent Spring*, 1–13. Boston, MA: Houghton Mifflin.

Taylor, D. 2014. "Executive Summary." In *The State of Diversity in Environmental Organizations*. Prepared for Green 2.0. Retrieved from: http://vaipl.org/wp-content/uploads/2014/10/ExecutiveSummary-Diverse-Green.pdf.

READING AND DISCUSSION PROMPTS

1. The US, with about 5% of the world's population, emits well over 20% of the world's greenhouse gases. At the same time, there is a general agreement emerging among nations that a necessary first step in dealing with climate change is to cap (stabilize) world greenhouse emissions at their current levels. What policies do you think might help the US stabilize greenhouse gas emissions?
2. What policy measures do you think would be helpful to support communities that are working to become more resilient to extreme weather events, with consequences like droughts, floods, and fires?
3. Stakeholders are individuals or organizations that have a direct interest in an activity. From the perspective of Ehrlich and Ehrlich, who are the stakeholders for environmental policy?
4. In Chapter 7: Environmental Justice, authors Pezzullo and Sandler describe the Group of Ten. In Chapter 10, Taylor informs us that these environmental agencies have made limited progress incorporating social, racial, and economic justice into their agendas. Why do you think this remains a challenge?

READING 10.1

Rachel Carson

PROPHET FOR THE ENVIRONMENT

By Janet Browne

Rachel Carson speaks most directly to us today through her environmental book *Silent Spring*, published in 1962. She is revered as an exceptional writer and literary naturalist in the tradition of John Muir and Aldo Leopold—a romantic populist, knowledgeable, scientifically accurate, visionary, holistic, and passionate. Her personal "dreaming" was of the pristine seashores and untouched rocky landscapes of Northeast America that she came to love so profoundly. At another level, simultaneously more organic and more transcendent, she dreamed of an interconnected world in which the natural and human were closely interwoven in harmony, an early vision of a balanced living system that helped generate the modern ecological way of thought. Her dismay at the prospect of the destruction of this harmony by thoughtless human interference turned her into an exceptionally focused writer who crystallized existing scientific knowledge and gave powerful new direction to the growing environmental movement. In *Silent Spring* she warned about the ecological devastation that would inevitably appear through the indiscriminate use of pesticides. Carson was suffering from cancer while she wrote the book, and died at age fifty-seven in April 1964, but not before making forceful political interventions relating to the chemical industry in the United States. *Silent Spring* generated a storm of interest and was the foundation for important legislative action regulating the use of chemicals in the environment. Her dream became the dream of many others, and her role in shaping the environmental

Figure 10.1.1 Rachel Carson. Photo courtesy of the National Digital Library of the United States Fish and Wildlife Service.

movement was crucial.

Many scholars have asked how Carson's transformative dream emerged.[1] She was born in Springdale, Pennsylvania, in 1907, and much of her life was dominated by the conflicting demands of a struggle for financial security and strong literary aspirations. She was the third and youngest child of Maria Frazier McLean, a former schoolteacher, and Robert Warden Carson, an insurance salesman and then an employee at West Penn Power. Her father was mostly unable to support the family, and his death in 1935 left them with very limited means. From her young adulthood, Rachel Carson took financial responsibility for her mother, sister, and her sister's children.

Carson was greatly influenced by a succession of exceptional women, of which no doubt her mother was the first. Throughout her life she held a deeply affectionate and nearly exclusive relationship with her mother. Maria Carson kept house, edited and typed Rachel's manuscripts, and encouraged her daughter until her death in 1958. Carson retrospectively credited her mother with instilling in her an early love for nature. Her mother raised her, it could be claimed, in the American "nature studies" movement that fostered active learning outdoors.[2] Her mother also introduced her to the world of literature, and at the age of eleven, she began sending short fiction stories from her home in Pennsylvania to the children's section of *St. Nicholas Magazine*, several of which were published. Carson believed that she gained from her mother an uncompromising Calvinistic morality, in which waste and intellectual laziness were abhorred. She was in early life a devout Christian, a point of view that she abandoned in middle age. Yet even without an obvious religious faith, these personal commitments were refocused into an intense belief in the natural world as the holistic setting for human life, and she adopted a personal credo in which human beings had a moral duty to protect, understand, and appreciate nature in all its forms. This form of secular religion provided Carson with a framework of meaning that was as compelling as any more traditional faith.

Carson was educated at the Pennsylvania College for Women (now Chatham University), where she majored in biology and met Mary Scott Skinner, a biology teacher who became her mentor. She studied marine biology during one summer at Woods Hole Marine Biological Laboratory, graduated in 1929, and joined Johns Hopkins University, aiming for a PhD in zoology. Financial difficulties obliged her to cut short her studies at Johns Hopkins with an MA in 1932. During this time she became an assistant in Raymond Pearl's laboratory, where she worked with rats and *Drosophila* to earn money for tuition. Her own research was on the embryonic development of fish. It is perhaps not sufficiently appreciated that Carson was therefore exceptionally well educated in genetics at a time when it was at the cutting edge of biological science. At the urging of Skinner, with whom she subsequently kept in touch, she took a position with the US Bureau of Fisheries to write radio scripts on biological matters during the Depression and supplemented her income by providing articles on natural history for the *Baltimore Sun*. Her family relocated to Maryland to be with her, and she supported the household. When the opportunity emerged, she sat the civil service exam, outscored all other applicants, and, in 1936, became only the second woman employed professionally at the Bureau of Fisheries. She rose to become editor-in-chief of all publications for the bureau (subsequently the US Fish and Wildlife Service). Her career has, in fact, been a beacon for subsequent women in the sciences and is the topic of a great deal of insightful writing by feminist scholars. Her life marked a turning point in the way women participated in science, and she was instrumental in shifting the prevailing view of women as contributing to science through a variety of supporting roles to one in which women were recognized as engaging in fully active scientific careers.[3]

In these early years, above all else, Carson remembered her first youthful encounter with the sea. This was during the summer of 1928 at Woods Hole Marine Biological Station, in Cape Cod, Massachusetts. For her, the sea held a mystical quality. In an undated letter (c. 1941), she mentioned that she imagined herself under the water "until I could see the whole life of those creatures as they lived them in that sea world."[4] A sense of holism and identification with other, nonhuman, organisms was developing that came to underpin her understanding of ecosystems. These ideas took permanent root during her continuing work in the US Fish and Wildlife Service, where she encountered—and edited—much of the latest oceanographic research. This was how she came across a series of reports on the new pesticide DDT (dichloro-diphenyl-trichloroethane), which would feature so much in her later work. Carson proposed writing a popular account on pesticide research for the *Reader's Digest* but was turned down.

At this point in her life, her family's financial situation was dire. She decided that she could help resolve the crisis by writing a natural-history best seller. In the 1930s, she therefore began to write with great determination and dedication in the hours after her work in the bureau, aiming for a Pulitzer Prize.[5] Her first book was *Under the Sea Wind* (1941). It began as an article on animal migration for the *Atlantic*. Encouraged by an editor from the publishing house of Simon and Schuster, and the author Hendrik Willem Van Loon, she turned it into a book, presenting her material from the perspective of individualized sea and land creatures as they moved through their respective life cycles. It was based on numerous firsthand observations of American fauna, as in the central narrative of a sanderling migrating from Patagonia to Alaska, finding a mate, hatching out chicks, encountering predators, and so forth. Despite the anthropomorphism, the book is full of real nature: tough, ruthless, and subject to chance. She included humans as part of this global ecosystem—for example, describing fishermen netting a shoal of mullet. She already showed deep understanding of the organic cycles of life: "For in the sea, nothing is lost. One dies, another lives, as the precious elements of life are passed on and on in endless chains." This first book was initially well received, and two chapters were reprinted by William Beebe in his influential anthology of America's greatest naturalist writers, published in 1944, but any hope of commercial success was cut off by the beginning of war. It did not sell in any great numbers and was remaindered by the publisher.

Success came ten years later with her widely praised book *The Sea Around Us* (1951). This too was first published in a periodical, in three parts in the *New Yorker*. The book won Carson recognition as a gifted writer and brought her much-needed financial security. She quit her job at the US Fish and Wildlife Service, purchased a two-tone Oldsmobile, and built a small house in Maine, on the coast, near Southport, where she and her family spent their summers for many years. The book received the US National Book Award, although no Pulitzer ever came. In it, her purpose was to give a sense of the sea as an environmental whole, and she divided the book into sections, describing sea life according to depth, the movement of winds and currents, geography of the sea floor, fish stocks and other commercial resources, and the ocean's effect on climate. The intent was larger than this however. She wrote of the eternal rhythms and cycles of life, of the fact that mankind cannot control the sea, about continuities and interrelatedness. There was a biblical tone to the opening pages, although no creative force was cited. All life, she wrote, depends on the oceans. The book was deeply informed by a secular evolutionary understanding of nature, and she spoke in many places about the fierce competitive forces at the heart of biology. She had adopted contemporary Darwinism long before, back at Johns Hopkins, and by the time she published this book, it seems, she was no longer a practicing Christian.

But the moral authority of *Silent Spring* was still a long way off. Her next book was called *The Edge of the Sea* (1955). During this period she became close friends with a Maine neighbor, Dorothy Freeman. Released from the need to continue in a job, she took long nature walks with Dorothy, collected organisms from pools on the tide line, and examined specimens under an expensive new microscope—all of which contributed to the text of the new book. While Carson had other dear friends who gave professional and literary support, she increasingly relied on Dorothy Freeman for emotional nourishment. She also became friends with Bob Hines, who illustrated *The Edge of the Sea*. The structure of the book was more or less geographical, embracing various types of shoreline: sandy, rocky, and subtropical (coralline). This third book was published to great acclaim. Her publishers correspondingly set out to reissue all three books together as a major sea trilogy that explored the whole of ocean life from the shoreline to the oceanic depths.

After this hard-won success, Carson became temporarily adrift in literary terms. Several years beforehand, she had been planning a popular book on evolution—a timely thought with the centenary of Charles Darwin's *Origin of Species* on the horizon in 1959. Yet Julian Huxley forestalled her with his *Evolution in Action* (1953). She tried writing for national television, and delivered an attractive script on clouds that was aired in 1956. It was therefore only in early 1957 that she turned to a project on ecology that she tentatively called *Remembrance of the Earth*. For this project, unlike her others, she did not yet have a sense of her storyline. Here, however, the dreamer in her soul emerged.

She was writing a short article for *Women's Home Companion* called "Help Your Child to Wonder" that featured her grandnephew Roger, who lived with her, and the advice offered to Roger revealed much of her innermost passion for the natural world. Slowly, she began to articulate her subject. It would be life itself, and the relationship of living beings to the physical environment in the modern, atomic age. A shift in her thinking had begun with the wartime bombing of Hiroshima. Now, some twelve years later, in a letter to Dorothy Freeman, she said that she found it difficult to be confident in the capacity of life to withstand such human assaults. She was starting to question the scientific progress that she had formerly taken for granted. Mankind "seems likely to take into his hands … many of the functions of God … . He must do so with humility rather than arrogance."[6]

What pushed her to focus so courageously on pesticides and the agricultural chemical industry? Carson was not the only one expressing concern about chemicals in the environment. Fears about pesticides had been raised as early as 1933 by Arthur Kallett and Frederick Schlink in their book *100,000,000 Guinea Pigs: Dangers in Everyday Foods, Drugs, and Cosmetics*. The one hundred million guinea pigs in the title referred to the size of the human population of the United States at the time. Widely read periodicals such as the *Atlantic Monthly*, *Reader's Digest*, and *Harper's Magazine* occasionally voiced concern. Products used in agriculture containing heavy metals, such as lead, copper, and arsenic, were denounced, especially by Ruth Deforest Lamb, the chief information officer of the US Food and Drug Administration, who wrote about arsenic in spray residue on crops.[7] Even man-made fertilizers were criticized by Rudolf Steiner, the educationalist and organic farmer. The dangers of DDT were described in the *Atlantic Monthly* in 1945 by the

British entomologist Vincent Wigglesworth in an article called "DDT and the Balance of Nature." More expressly, Clarence Cottam, a personal friend of Carson's in the US Fish and Wildlife Service, published a report on DDT in 1946. He became Carson's mentor on the subject of pesticides and conservation. And John Kenneth Terres, a soil biologist and birder, wrote of the possibility of pesticides moving up the food chain. Carson called on the studies of these and other concerned individuals when she began her research.

Carson was not alone, either in evocative or politically pointed environmental thinking. William Vogt, a prominent member of the Conservation Foundation and an advocate for studying the relationship between climate, population, and resources in Latin American countries, published his challenging text, *Road to Survival*, in 1948. The Sierra Club was founded in 1892, the National Audubon Society in 1905, the Conservation Foundation in 1947, and the Nature Conservancy in 1951. She fitted into a well-established American nature-writing trajectory from John Muir and Aldo Leopold to Mary Stoneman Douglas, author of *The Everglades: Rivers of Grass*. These writers saw in each living thing its own particular beauty and place in the natural world.

So it seems likely that it was moral urgency that pushed Carson onward. Judging from the words of *Silent Spring*, her profound secular morality generated the conviction that modern technology was creating in human beings an arrogant hubris that ought to be replaced by a new humility toward nature. The eternal truths of environmental harmony and ecological interrelatedness that she wrote about in her first three books were threatened. The tipping point appears to have been information from an acquaintance, Olga Owens Huckins, who alerted her to the effects of pesticides on wildlife, as seen in a mosquito eradication program near Huckins's home in Duxbury, Massachusetts. The aerial spraying of some unidentified pesticide led to the death of dozens of birds and the disappearance of bees in Huckins's garden. Once Carson knew the extent of disruption caused by poisons, she felt she had to speak out. Inspired by her dreams of an unspoiled nature, reinforced by her childhood memories and all-absorbing fascination for the intricacies of the web of life, Carson thus came to recognize that her existing fame as a popular nature writer and her strong scientific background could be used politically to make a real difference. She committed herself to a crusade, relinquishing her sense of scientific impartiality, and took on the role of a spokeswoman for nature.

Carson immediately began collecting information about pesticides. At first she focused on the United States Department of Agriculture's war against fire ants that was, in Carson's words, "an outstanding example of an ill-conceived, badly executed, and thoroughly detrimental experiment in the mass control of insects." Fire ants had entered the United States from Brazil in the 1920s and spread across the Southwest, building nests as much as five feet high, as strong as concrete. Multiple ant bites could kill a small animal.

Nevertheless, fire ants and farmers managed to coexist. But in the mid-1950s, the USDA initiated an eradication program that called for the spraying by airplane of some twenty to thirty million acres of agricultural land. The department chose a pesticide that included dieldrin and heptachlor, both highly potent chlorinated hydrocarbons (it was later shown that heptachlor causes liver damage, and dieldrin is a neurotoxin). In 1959, the USDA's Agricultural Research Service responded to criticism by Carson and others with a public service film, *Fire Ant on Trial*. Carson concluded that the department had probably never investigated the possible toxicity of these substances or, if it did, had ignored the results. Her conviction deepened in 1959 when US cranberries were found to contain high levels of the herbicide aminotriazole, and the sale of all cranberry products was halted. Carson attended the ensuing Food and Drug Administration hearings on pesticide regulation. According to her letters of the time, she was deeply dejected by the tactics of chemical industry representatives. She reported to Dorothy Freeman after the hearings that the testimony of the agricultural industry's representative, Edward B. Astwood, "can be shot so full of holes as to be absolutely worthless, and the disheartening thing is that he must know this full well."[8]

A second case concerned attempts to control the gypsy moth, another non-native species that was ravaging large areas of forest in the Northeast corridor. Inadequacies of the program became a hot public issue when the properties of wealthy inhabitants of Long Island were sprayed up to fifteen times with DDT in 1957. Residents objected vigorously on a variety of grounds and brought legal action to halt the spraying. Carson engaged with this protest, became politically active by supporting John F. Kennedy in his run for the presidency, and urged Democrats to take up issues of pollution control. She joined the National Resources Committee of the Democratic Advisory Council and then the Women's Committee for New Frontiers. The work of National Cancer Institute scientist, Wilhelm Hueper, who classified many pesticides as carcinogens, was helpful to her at this time, as was the Washington, DC, chapter of the Audubon Society, which actively opposed chemical spraying programs and asked Carson to help publicize the US government's practices. By now, she was sufficiently famous as an environmental writer to be able to recruit nearly everybody she needed. In so doing, she built up a formidable network of allies and colleagues in high places that stood her in good stead when controversy flared after publication of *Silent Spring*.

Pesticides were far grimmer than the celebrations of natural harmony that Carson had previously produced. Her legacy perhaps rests in part on creating a new kind of nature book: one that deals with the gloomy consequences of human actions upon the Earth. Her friend Dorothy Freeman called *Silent Spring* the "poison book." Even so, the title remained undecided until Carson lifted it from her chapter on birds. She prefaced the work with lines from "La Belle Dame sans Merci" (1819) by the English poet John Keats:

The sedge is wither'd from the lake
And no birds sing.

Silent Spring was mostly about DDT. It was first published as three substantial essays in the *New Yorker* in June 1962. Carson struck a fair balance between technical detail and the narrative about chemicals in the environment that she wished to make, but the nature of the subject matter meant that the book was not nearly so lyrical as her former publications. Unlike many modern pesticides, whose effectiveness is limited to destroying one or two types of insects, DDT is capable of killing many different organisms at once, especially water-based animals such as aquatic invertebrates and fish. The insecticidal action of DDT was discovered in 1939 by the Swiss chemist Paul Hermann Müller, who was awarded a Nobel Prize in recognition of the possibility of using DDT to eradicate mosquitoes in the global fight against malaria. The substance was immediately relevant to the US war effort and was used as a spray distributed by airplane during World War II for clearing South Pacific islands of mosquito larvae (these occur in swampy places). It was also used by Allied troops and by some civilian populations to control the ticks and lice that carry typhus. After 1945 it was used extensively in the United States as an agricultural insecticide and in Europe as a domestic fly spray. The proprietary formulation Flit, contained in a popular household spray gun, contained 5% DDT in the late 1940s and early 1950s, before the negative environmental impact of DDT was widely understood.

Carson described how DDT enters the food chain and accumulates in the fatty tissues of animals, including human beings, and can cause some forms of cancer. She thought DDT caused genetic damage (i.e., was mutagenic rather than merely toxic), and had good reason to believe so at that time, but the current evidence is ambiguous on this. Her text nevertheless made clear that DDT accumulates in the food chain. Thus, while DDT might appear only mildly toxic to one organism, if the carrier is eaten by another, the chemical will accumulate and remain active in body tissues. Her scientific case studies often read as miniature narratives about the great interrelatedness of life. One vivid example that she included concerned the spraying policy in Michigan to control beetles that carried Dutch elm disease. Researchers discovered that earthworms living in the forest litter under the sprayed trees were accumulating DDT from their vegetable diet and that the robins eating them were being poisoned. Another study showed that DDT alters a bird's calcium metabolism in a way that results in thin eggshells, sometimes so thin that they break when the female incubates them. These, and other scientific studies, proved to be powerful arguments. A single DDT application on a crop, she wrote, killed insects for months and remained toxic in the environment even after dilution by rainwater. Most of the book is devoted to the effects of pesticides on natural ecosystems, but she allocated space to describing cases of human illnesses attributed to pesticide poisoning. In the final chapter she offered alternatives to the practices she condemned; and ended with the hope that mankind would learn to live in harmony with the environment, "rather than in combat."

Not all her case studies came from the experts. Carson respected the observations of nonprofessionals, a democratic vision of expertise that ran counter to most contemporary ideas about the scientific enterprise at large. The fact that she relied on non-expert witnesses made her book significant in the history of public debate about science: after *Silent Spring*, public confidence in the superiority of scientific expertise could no longer be taken for granted, and environmentalism would develop as a political movement that did not necessarily trust scientists or their scientific results. To write such a book in the politically active 1960s was seen as a direct attack on the edifice of professional science. Yet it is important to remember that Carson was not anti-science. It would be more accurate to say that she believed in expertise without elitism.

Most famously, the book's opening chapter, "A Fable for Tomorrow," is noted as a literary classic. It depicts an imaginary American town where all life—from fish to birds, apple blossoms, and human children—has been "silenced" by the effects of DDT. "It was a spring without voices," she wrote: "It is our alarming misfortune that so primitive a science has armed itself with the most modern and terrible weapons, and that in turning them against the insects it has also turned them against the Earth." On its publication in 1962, *Silent Spring* shocked readers across America and, not surprisingly, brought a howl of indignation from the chemical industry and other interested parties.[9] Agribusinesses and a number of chemical industry bosses went on the attack. Their response can now be seen as consistent with the tactics used by business concerns that deny the findings of science in order to promote economic interests.[10] One prominent adversary was Robert White-Stevens, director of American Cyanamid, a major agricultural chemical company whose activities had been restricted by pesticide regulation after the 1959 cranberry scare. White-Stevens invited the public to imagine the calamity of a world without chemicals or medicines, a position that Carson never advocated. Others, such as William Darby, head of biochemistry at Vanderbilt School of Medicine, dismissed Carson as overexcited. He suggested that if Americans accepted her ideas, they would face hunger and the end of all human progress in the health sciences: "It means disease, epidemics, starvation, misery, and suffering."[11] Ezra Taft Benson, secretary of agriculture to President Eisenhower, belittled her engagement with genetics, asking why "a spinster with no children" should be so concerned about heredity. Economic entomologists understandably also felt themselves under direct attack. It should be said that economic entomologists had grown rapidly in professional status with the development of the pesticide program, and that the discovery and application of DDT was the equivalent for them of the atomic bomb project at Los Alamos National Laboratory, a project that brought public celebrity and national relevance to physicists. Large-scale pesticide projects were doing the same for entomologists. Entomologists, however, believed that DDT posed no threat to humans and minimal danger to wildlife.

In 1962, President John F. Kennedy was quick to assign Jerome Weisner, his science advisor, to set up a panel of the President's Science Advisory Council to investigate Carson's claims. The report concluded that there should be an orderly reduction of pesticide use in the environment. At the same time, public response to the book was high, and letters protesting indiscriminate pesticide usage poured into the political offices of senators and congressmen. Individual states began rapidly to introduce bills to limit pesticide use. The furor over *Silent Spring* ultimately led to the creation of the Environmental Protection Agency, the passage of the Clean Air Act, the Clean Water Act, the Endangered Species Acts, and the banning of a long list of pesticides, including DDT and dieldrin.

Carson's political goal was clear. Yet her years in government also made her pragmatic. She wanted her arguments to bring about improvements but also to be politically feasible. Appearing on a CBS documentary about *Silent Spring* in April 1963, she remarked, "Man's attitude toward nature is today critically important simply because we have now acquired a fateful power to alter and destroy nature. But man is a part of nature, and his war against nature is inevitably a war against himself... . I think we are challenged, as mankind has never been challenged before, to prove our maturity and our mastery, not of nature but of ourselves."[12] Robert White-Stevens also appeared in the documentary, predicting starvation and disease across the globe without agricultural chemicals. Carson's calm and quiet manner stole the show. At the end of May she appeared at a Senate hearing chaired by Abraham Ribicoff, at which she presented the recommendations for policy change that had been in her mind ever since her research into pesticides began. A year later she died in the Cleveland Clinic from the cancer she had been fighting for years.

But her dream did not die. Carson initiated a fundamental shift in the way we regard the environment. The impact of this shift can hardly be overstated. Its influence can be seen in the way that controversies still linger about whether Carson's writing should be regarded as legitimate science, and indeed some commentators from the scientific and business communities define science in a way that relegates her book to the category of "popular science"—a label that deliberately diminishes the power of her evidence and makes it easier to ignore her message. This anti-Carson rhetoric has evolved over the decades, to the point that it has become the object of scholarly analysis in its own right.[13] In early criticisms, Carson's gender was frequently mentioned, often in order to disparage her arguments. The *New York Post* called on Abraham's Lincoln's apocryphal words to Harriet Beecher Stowe: "So you're the little woman who wrote the book that made this great war!" The parallel implied that Carson's abilities were not equal to the outcomes that she initiated. Recent work indicates that a distinguishing feature of Carson's achievement was her reliance on a network of female support that lay outside the normal boundaries of the predominantly masculine science of the day. Something of this female powerbase persists in the recent rise of ecofeminism.[14] In sum, her work generated heated antipathy and equally heated support that continues today.

Carson was an outstanding writer and a powerful inspirational force. Perhaps some of the changes she envisaged might have happened anyway. The environmental movement would probably have emerged without her—she has been wrongly credited with single-handedly launching American environmental politics. Nevertheless, she was the primary catalyst for events waiting to happen and imparted to them a special character. Carson concluded that DDT and other pesticides irrevocably harmed living beings and had contaminated the world's food supply. Subsequent research has established the point beyond any doubt. Due to the persistence of DDT and its metabolites in the environment, very low levels still continue to be detected in foodstuffs, even though it was banned from use in the United States in 1972. Her contribution to the making of the modern world was also much more than an alarming warning about pesticides. Her landmark book had an immediate and lasting impression on the public, and alerted readers of all backgrounds—political, scientific, and literary—that our choices and decisions about the environment, and how we conduct our relationship with nature, genuinely matter.

FURTHER READING

Dunlap, Thomas R. *DDT: Scientists, Citizens, and Public Policy.* Princeton, NJ: Princeton University Press, 1981.

Freeman, Dorothy. *Always, Rachel: The Letters of Rachel Carson and Dorothy Freeman, 1952–1964.* Edited by Martha Freeman. Boston: Beacon Press, 1995.

Gottleib, Robert. *Forcing the Spring: The Transformation of the American Environmental Movement.* Washington, DC: Island Press, 1993.

Lear, Linda J. *Rachel Carson: Witness for Nature.* New York: Henry Holt, 1997.

Lytle, Mark Hamilton. *The Gentle Subversive: Rachel Carson, "Silent Spring," and the Rise of the Environmental Movement.* Oxford: Oxford University Press, 2007.

Murphy, Priscilla Coit. *What a Book Can Do: The Publication and Reception of "Silent Spring."* Amherst: University of Massachusetts Press, 2005.

Pimente, David, and Hugh Lehman, eds. *The Pest Question: Environment, Economics, and Ethics.* London: Chapman & Hall, 1993.

Waddell, Craig, ed. *And No Birds Sing: Rhetorical Analyses of Rachel Carson's "Silent Spring."* Carbondale: Southern Illinois University Press, 2000.

NOTES

1 One of the most authoritative biographies is by Linda J. Lear, *Rachel Carson: Witness for Nature* (New York: Henry Holt, 1997). See also Robert Gottleib, *Forcing the Spring: The Transformation of the American Environmental Movement* (Washington, DC: Island Press, 1993); and Mark

Hamilton Lytle, *The Gentle Subversive: Rachel Carson, Silent Spring, and the Rise of the Environmental Movement* (Oxford: Oxford University Press, 2007).

2 Sally Gregory Kohlstedt, *Teaching Children Science: Hands-On Nature Study in North America, 1890–1930* (Chicago: University of Chicago Press, 2010).

3 Rebecca Raglon, "Rachel Carson and Her Legacy," in *Natural Eloquence: Women Reinscribe Science*, ed. Barbara T. Gates and Ann B. Shteir (Madison: University of Wisconsin Press, 1997), 196–211.

4 Lytle, *Gentle Subversive*, 35.

5 Lytle, *Gentle Subversive*, 56.

6 Dorothy Freeman, *Always, Rachel: The Letters of Rachel Carson and Dorothy Freeman, 1952–1964*, ed. Martha Freeman (Boston: Beacon Press, 1995), 204.

7 Roger Meiners, Pierre Desrochers, and Andrew Morris, eds., *The False Crises of Rachel Carson: Silent Spring at 50* (Washington, DC: Cato Institute, 2012), 42; and Ralph H. Lutts, "Chemical Fallout: Rachel Carson's *Silent Spring*, Radioactive Fallout, and the Environmental Movement," *Environmental Review* 9 (1985): 210–25.

8 Lear, *Rachel Carson*, 342–44, 358–60.

9 Priscilla Coit Murphy, *What a Book Can Do: The Publication and Reception of "Silent Spring"* (Amherst: University of Massachusetts Press, 2005).

10 Naomi Oreskes and Erik M. Conway, *Merchants of Doubt: How a Handful of Scientists Obscured the Truth on Issues from Tobacco Smoke to Global Warming* (New York: Bloomsbury Press, 2010), 216–23, 226–27.

11 Lytle, *Gentle Subversive*, 174.

12 Quoted from Lear, *Rachel Carson*, 450.

13 David K. Hecht, "How to Make a Villain: Rachel Carson and the Politics of Anti-Environmentalism," *Endeavour* 36, no. 4 (2012): 149–55.

14 See Carolyn Merchant, *Radical Ecology: The Search for a Liveable World* (New York: Routledge, 2005), 193–222.

READING 10.2

How Can Good Science Become Good Policy?

By Paul R. Ehrlich and Anne H. Ehrlich

One especially unpalatable consequence of the brownlash's attempts to disseminate erroneous information is the undue influence its rhetoric has on public policy. Brownlashers try to convince not only policy makers but also the public at large that their view is the right one—a moderate, scientifically justified position on environmental matters. But we have seen that much of the propaganda is seriously at variance with informed scientific opinion on many critical issues. How can decision makers and the general public be made more aware of the actual findings of environmental science, and thus of the increasingly grave threats posed by environmental deterioration?

Obviously, public education must play a paramount role in helping disseminate the real conclusions of environmental science (indeed, of science in general). A better understanding of the brownlash, its goals, and its tactics could also help environmental scientists communicate their findings more effectively to the rest of society. We hope this book provides some of that understanding. We also want to offer some suggestions on how to communicate environmental science to the public, based on our own thirty years of experience and that of some colleagues. We divide our suggestions into things we think environmental scientists can and should do and things that concerned citizens, especially environmental activists, can and should do, although the goal in both cases is the same: to push public policy more into line with the realities of environmental science as the turn of the century approaches.

Paul R. Ehrlich and Anne H. Ehrlich, "How Can Good Science Become Good Policy," *Betrayal of Science and Reason: How Anti-Environmental Rhetoric Threatens Our Future*, pp. 203-212, 311-312.

WHAT CAN SCIENTISTS DO?

Simplistic as it sounds, the first thing that environmental scientists—indeed, probably all scientists—should do is get involved. Educating the public should be an integral part of every scientist's career; if something is worth discovering, it is worth communicating. If those of us who are most familiar with the beauty and intricacy of nature, and its essential role in supporting humanity, will not come to nature's—and thus humanity's—defense, who will? How can we complain about the lack of action by politicians or the ignorance of talk show hosts, Sunday morning television pundits, or even brownlash reporters, if we don't help them get the facts straight?

Any scientist who sees a scientific issue being mangled in the media should write a letter to the editor or news director. In addition, the incident could be selected for classroom analysis, included as an example of misinformation in a textbook, or developed into a high school curriculum unit. Why not give a speech on the topic and get out a press release beforehand? Other options include volunteering to give environmental organizations technical advice, calling in to a talk show, discussing the matter with colleagues or administrators, ranting about it to your tennis partner, and waxing eloquent in front of your favorite bartender.

Yet we recognize that scientists are loath to leave their laboratories and get involved in the public arena. We can sympathize somewhat with that view—especially when some political event interrupts our field research! Part of the reason may be a certain reticence among scientists that helps them focus on the details and the frequent tedium of their research. But all too often, public involvement is avoided because it isn't likely to contribute to gathering professional perks: tenure, promotion, salary raises, or intradisciplinary recognition. That's something senior scientists have a special responsibility for changing, particularly in fields like ecology that are so essential to dealing with the human dilemma. The system of professional rewards needs to be changed so that public outreach is counted as an important, positive element of high-caliber professional behavior. At the very least, scientists can support their colleagues, especially junior colleagues, who do first-rate science *and* choose to join the fray. Scientists, like all citizens, should at least "tithe to society" —spend 10 percent of their time trying to make the human endeavor more sustainable.

Many scientists in fields like ecology, Earth sciences, epidemiology, and economics will want to devote much more time than that. They also will want to initiate interdisciplinary work, since virtually all significant problems affecting society fall within the domains of more than one discipline. One of our great pleasures in recent years at Stanford has been participating in interdisciplinary research with economists and attending seminars in which we can discuss the human predicament with agriculturalists, engineers, Earth scientists, professors of business and law, and so on.

Paul has also greatly enjoyed serving on the board of the Royal Swedish Academy of Science's Beijer Institute of Ecological Economics. There he has interacted with some of the world's best economists, as well as a superb group of ecologists. Anne, in her work with organizations like the Sierra Club and the Pugwash Movement, has been impressed by how well scientists, engineers, attorneys, physicians, educators, and other professionals can communicate and work together in a common cause. In our view, the growing unity of scientists from different disciplines who are working to solve environmental problems is one of the most heartening intellectual developments of the past decade.

All scientists who teach, of course, can introduce critical issues wherever they are pertinent to their courses—and can give pertinent courses to as wide a variety of students as possible. On many campuses, there are journalism schools or workshops for working reporters; establishing contact with journalists and participating in programs for them can be especially effective. Among other benefits, such involvement allows journalists to see scientists as approachable and knowledgeable people who—for all the right reasons—care passionately about the issues. The same goes for activities at business schools, which often conduct educational programs for junior executives.

But above all, academic scientists must see to it that college curricula ensure that students have a basic understanding of the workings of science, its principal findings, and how these relate to their own lives. Too many students graduate from college or university knowing next to nothing about the planet they inhabit and how human beings fit into the panoply of life. Some of the key topics we always try to include in courses and workshops at Stanford University and in our public lectures are the following:

1. How the scale of the human enterprise critically affects the environment, that scale being determined by population size, per-capita consumption, and choices of technologies to serve the consumption. This is the material subsumed in the $I = PAT$ identity: a population's impact (I) on the environment is a product of the number of people (P), their per-capita consumption (affluence, A), and a measure of the environmental damage done by the technologies that supply each unit of consumption (T). [1]
2. The nature and importance of ecosystem services.
3. Basic evolutionary theory and its applications to agriculture and public health.
4. The major characteristics and environmental impacts of agricultural ecosystems.
5. How the atmosphere-ocean-climate-weather system operates and how it interacts with the agricultural system.
6. Geologic history, including the history of climate changes.
7. Major features of the epidemiological environment.[2]

8. The central role of energy in environmental affairs and the characteristics of energy systems.
9. An overview of the links between ecology and economics (ecological economics).
10. An overview of social (especially equity) issues as they influence the human dilemma.
11. The influence of environmental change in human history.
12. Problems of scale: the concept that what is safe locally or in the short term may be catastrophic globally or in the long term. For example, chlorofluorocarbons are safe in the kitchen and in the short term, but they represent large-scale disaster in the long term. The depletion of local biodiversity in downtown New York or in Stanford, California, gives no hint of the disastrous consequences of its depletion globally.
13. Risk assessment: how to deal with uncertainty.[3]

Of course, a major challenge for scientists is how to educate the general public and decision makers about these complex issues, especially when the brownlash misinformation campaign has already shaped public opinion. Obviously, improving environmental education from elementary school through university would be a substantial help in the long term, but it is of little help in the short term. A more powerful approach in the short term is to work with the media—especially the electronic media.

But this is not the place for a dissertation on how scientists can be effective on television; there are professionals who can help with that, although relatively few scientists take advantage of them now. For instance, the Safe Energy Communication Council, based in Washington, D.C.,[4] conducts workshops on interviewing effectively, developing media strategies, writing press releases, and so on. And many environmental organizations conduct workshops and distribute advisory literature. Still, a few hints for scientists seem in order:

1. When speaking with the media, one should avoid the standard "introduction, materials and methods, results" format of scientific papers. The camera will be on someone else or the reporter will have gone home before you have reached even the materials and methods. *Conclusions must come first.* After all, a television appearance may consist of only a ten-second "sound bite," and the most important part of one's message needs to get aired.
2. Scientists need to be direct and succinct when dealing with the electronic media. One could talk for hours about the uncertainties associated with global warming. But a statement like "Pumping greenhouse gases into the atmosphere could lead to large-scale food shortages" is entirely accurate scientifically and will catch the public's attention. So would "One of the most environmentally damaging activities of human beings begins in the bedroom."

3. Many excellent scientists are, by disposition or training, not comfortable in dealing with the press. Those who aren't, shouldn't. But those who are willing to "go public" need the support of their colleagues. When Paul first started his campaign of public education using the media, he was afraid he would lose the respect of his colleagues. Instead, the enthusiastic support of the vast majority of them, at Stanford and around the world, has made our lives infinitely more enjoyable. If science is to have the support it needs to help solve the most pressing environmental problems, "popularizer" needs to become a compliment in all disciplines.
4. Anyone who writes for a general audience should avoid scenarios—stories to help people picture the future. Scenarios are attractive because they can help dramatize the potential consequences of society's present trajectory. But, as we have learned,[5] they are almost certain to be misrepresented as "predictions" rather than fictions. No matter how attractive or illustrative, scientists should eschew them.
5. Before going public at all, one's analyses and positions—especially in multidisciplinary areas—should be reviewed by knowledgable colleagues. Peer review is as important in communication as it is in technical work-and even more important when educational efforts span disciplinary boundaries. Mistakes are inevitable in any human endeavor, but scientists are obliged to take extra care to avoid them. We consult with colleagues about questionable publications outside our areas of expertise all the time. We also pester them to review our work, including chapters of this book. For instance, we wanted Susan Solomon to review our chapter on atmospheric issues because we and her other colleagues know that she is a world-class scientist and a stickler for scientific accuracy and that she wouldn't bend a scientific opinion for a friend or a cause. We selected all our scientific reviewers (see the acknowledgments) on the same basis.
6. Practical and optimal policies should be clearly differentiated. Scientists should present what they think is ideal, but then also present what they think is feasible. In that way, citizens have a practical target to work toward in the future. Scientists should make clear, however, that policy advice, though often based on in-depth studies and years of experience, is a value judgment, not a scientific proposition.

Brownlash writers seem to have a great deal of difficulty not only in accurately reporting the views of others but also in separating what would be the *best* policy from what would be a *practical* policy. Consider the following statement from journalist Stephen Budiansky:

> Biologists who have led the fight to save in toto the tropical rain forests and other species-rich habitats of the world have a strange habit of not grasping

> the political implications of their calls to arms in the name of wilderness. In an article in *Science* magazine, overpopulation guru Paul Ehrlich and Harvard biologist Edward O. Wilson, the man who made *biodiversity* a household word, issued a manifesto calling upon mankind to "reduce the scale of human activities" in order to save the planet's biodiversity. The "first step," they said, would be to cease "developing" any more relatively undisturbed land.[6]

Budiansky points to Paul's and Ed's "naïveté" in suggesting that "development can simply be made to cease." He then loftily explains the statistics of population growth as if Paul and Ed were unaware of them. What Paul and Ed actually said was, "Many steps can be taken to preserve biodiversity, *if the political will is generated.* Perhaps the first step, *which would be seen as especially extreme by Americans,* would be to cease 'developing' any more relatively undisturbed land"[7] (our emphasis).

Politically naïve? Of course, Paul and Ed don't expect their personal preferences to be followed, but redeveloping and restoring already badly disturbed areas is clearly one way to preserve both farmland and biodiversity—and thus our civilization. Budiansky obviously confuses what, sadly, is likely to be with what should be.

WHAT CAN CONCERNED CITIZENS DO?

There is simply no substitute for spending time getting acquainted with the issues. Determining the best possible scientific position on an issue can be a non-trivial problem even for scientists in related fields. But clearly the more informed a person is, the better able she or he will be to weigh the issues. For those with some technical background, much can be learned from reputable scientific journals—magazines such as *Science, Nature, BioScience, Chemical and Engineering News, Technology Today, Ambio, Conservation Biology, Climatic Change, Ecological Economics,* and *Ecological Applications.* Many of the articles in these publications are accessible to laypersons as well, especially in the "News and Views" or "Forum" sections, which are often found up front.

Less technical magazines such as *Scientific American, Discover, Natural History, Pacific Discovery, Environment, Science News,* and *New Scientist* often cover environmental issues well. Some magazines published by environmental organizations print informative articles designed for non-specialists, including *The Amicus Journal, Audubon, Sierra, Wilderness,* and *World Watch.*

It is important to recognize that even the scientific literature isn't totally objective; all scientists bring their cultural values to their science. As we discussed at length, what sets science apart from most other ways of finding out about the world are the rather rigid requirements for investigative protocols and testing of hypotheses, backed by an adversarial system in which scientists can advance their careers by showing that well-accepted ideas are false.

Identifying the author of a suspicious environmental story requires access to a substantial library. If the author is labeled a "scientist," is he or she included in *American Men and Women of Science?*[8] Does the individual have recent publications referred to in the *Science Citation Index,*[9] which lists both a scientist's current publications (source indices) and citations of those publications by other scientists (citation indices)? The *Index* can help determine whether the author is a regular contributor to the pertinent scientific literature—and whether those contributions have generally dealt with environmental issues and their relation to the human predicament.

If the item in question is a book authored by a non-scientist, the acknowledgments can often reveal a lot about its credibility. Have a substantial number of scientists been credited with reviewing the contents for accuracy? Are at least some of the reviewers from major universities? There are many fine scientists in four-year colleges and in other non-university positions, but in highly technical areas one would expect to see some reviewing by prominent people at research universities or at leading research institutions or laboratories. There are, of course, a very few scientists at major universities ready to sell out to the highest bidder—but the vast majority are honest scientists to begin with, and all are under considerable peer pressure to give scientifically sound judgments. Like almost everyone else, scientists want the approval of their colleagues. Of course, an author can submit a book to scientific reviewers and then neglect their advice.

Perhaps the simplest way to gain a balanced view of an environmental problem is to consult the national and international assessment literature. Included in this category are reports from the U.S. National Research Council (NRC), the research-conducting arm of the National Academy of Sciences; the Intergovernmental Panel on Climate Change (IPCC); the World Meteorological Organization (WMO); the U.S. Office of Technology Assessment (eliminated, sadly, by Congress in 1995); Australia's Commonwealth Scientific and Industrial Research Organization (CSIRO); the United Nations Environment Programme (UNEP); and so on. Such groups always represent the scientific consensus and provide cautious, conservative evaluations of problems.

All these steps can help you gauge whether someone is trying to get you to believe some anti-science, hut in the end some impromptu analysis may be needed. With highly technical issues such analysis often won't be possible; but in many cases, a little work on a calculator or even some mental arithmetic can supply an answer. Checking a person's conclusions may require looking at relatively unbiased data, which often can be found in statistics from the United Nations, the *World Almanac* or *U.S. Statistical Abstract,* and various government agencies.

The Food and Agriculture Organization of the United Nations (FAO), for example, supplies the estimate that Earth has roughly 3.6 billion acres of arable land (about 0.6 acres per person). Suppose someone claims that human population growth can continue at current rates for 1000 years. That's more than twenty doublings. For mathematical ease, assume there are only 5 billion people now instead of almost 6 billion. Doubling ten times starting with 5 gives you 5 → 10 → 20 → 40 → 80 → 160 → 320 → 640 → 1280 → 2560 → 5120, or roughly 1000 times the current population—some 5 trillion people about five hundred years in the future. Doubling ten more times gives another roughly thousand-fold increase—to *one million times* the current population. Getting out the old calculator, you discover that agricultural production for each of some 5 million billion persons will necessarily come from only 0.7 millionth of an acre—roughly four square inches—per person. Even if we learned to farm all of Earth's surface, land and sea, we'd need to feed each person from a plot of about one square foot (arable land is about one-thirty-sixth of the total surface).

That would be a clever trick—but, of course, a brownlasher will say we'll be farming Mars or planets of other stars. We'll leave you and your calculator to figure out the likelihood of that.[10] Should you be at all mathematically inclined, there is a wonderful book to guide you in making such informative approximations and solving other environmental problems: John Harte's *Consider a Spherical Cow*.[11]

Plain common sense can also help you determine where the dependable views lie in most brownlash debates. Given that the nations of the world were willing to negotiate a treaty banning CFCs, the manufacturers were willing to go along with it, the National Academy of Sciences elected F. Sherwood Rowland and Mario Molina as members, and the very conservative Royal Swedish Academy of Sciences gave them Nobel Prizes, it doesn't take too much discernment to evaluate the credibility of Rush Limbaugh's view that concern over stratospheric ozone is "Poppycock. Balderdash."[12]

Similarly, claims that population isn't a problem simply don't stand up to casual scrutiny. One has only to visit a large city and drive around at rush hour to get some insight into the problems human numbers can create. As to the claim that people can always move to that "empty" space in Iowa or Nevada, ask whether the space is really empty in Iowa and why people are not already living in the open areas in Nevada. Anyone who says that some substance that is carcinogenic in mice "has never given any person cancer," should be asked how anyone could possibly know that. And since scientists agree that adding greenhouse gases to the atmosphere leads to changes in climate, is it sensible to be unconcerned when humanity's activities are releasing large quantities of such gases into the atmosphere and food production is heavily climate dependent?

If there is no world population-food problem, why did Norman Borlaug, "father of the green revolution," state in 1995: "Twenty-five years ago, in my acceptance speech for the 1970 Nobel Prize ... I warned that unless the frightening power of human reproduction was curbed, the success of the green revolution would be only ephemeral"?[13] Why would the newspapers be full of discussions of fishing fleets idled in port for lack of fish to catch?[14]

Anyone who claims that cleared rain forests will "grow back" (as an Australian forester once said to us) should have to explain where the unique animals that inhabited them will live in the meantime.[15]

In short, people should have faith in their own judgment when they've taken the time to examine different views of an issue and taken into account their own predispositions and prejudices. Then they can become activists—devote as much of their time as possible to improving the human condition. The scientific community needs help in replotting humanity's trajectory toward a sustainable future.

NOTES

1 For more details and references, see P. Ehrlich and A. Ehrlich, 1990, *The Population Explosion*, Simon and Schuster, New York, pp. 58–59; and P. Ehrlich and A. Ehrlich, 1991, *Healing the Planet*, Addison-Wesley, Reading, MA, introduction and chapter 2.

2 This is the principal area of environmental deterioration not readily handled under the $I = PAT$ identity (see Ehrlich and Ehrlich, 1990, 1991).

3 Information on risk should include how people respond to voluntarily and involuntarily assumed risks, the importance of "no regrets" strategies, cost-benefit analyses, discounting in time and space, accounting for so-called environmental external costs in the prices of today's goods and services, etc.

4 Telephone 202-483-8491; fax 202-234-9194.

5 Early in our efforts at public education we used scenarios a great deal, but they have come back to haunt us dressed up as "predictions" by the brownlash. The scenarios in *The Population Bomb* were preceded by the following statement: "Scenarios are hypothetical sequences of events used as an aid in thinking about the future … . Remember, these are just possibilities, not predictions. We can be sure that none of them will come true as stated … . " (P. Ehrlich, 1968, *The Population Bomb*, Ballantine, New York, p. 72). Yet over the years, these science fiction pieces from the *Bomb* have repeatedly been cited as failed predictions when the world did not follow the course described.

6 S. Budiansky, 1995, *Nature's Keepers: The New Science of Nature Management*, Free Press, New York, p. 153.

7 P. Ehrlich and E. Wilson, 1991, Biodiversity studies: Science and policy, Science 253:761.

8 *American Men and Women of Science*, 1995–96, (19th ed.), 8 vols., R. R. Bowker, New Providence, NJ.

9 Institute for Scientific Information, 1996, Science Citation Index, Institute for Scientific Information, Philadelphia.

10 To get some hints, you might want to consult J. Fremlin, 1964, How many people can the world support?, *New Scientist*, 29 October, and G. Hardin, 1959, Interstellar migration and the population problem, *Heredity* 50:68–70. Suppose we held Earth's population stationary

by exporting people to other planets (ignoring the small logistical problems of doing so). At current rates, it would take less than a century to populate Venus, Mercury, Mars, the moon, and the moons of Jupiter to the same density as Earth, since the total surface areas of these planets and moons add up to less than three times that of Earth. Going to the stars would require strict population control on the interstellar ships, since it would take many, many generations to reach even the nearest star.

11 J. Harte, 1985, *Consider a Spherical Cow: A Course in Environmental Problem Solving*, William Kaufmann, Los Altos, CA.

12 R. Limbaugh, 1992, *The Way Things Ought to Be*, Pocket Books, New York, p. 154.

13 N. Borlaug, 1995, Food Production, report prepared for Scientific Panels, 1995 Third Annual World Bank Conference on Effectively Financing Environmentally Sustainable Development, Washington, DC, 4 and 9 October.

14 For an overview of the problem, see P. Weber, 1994, Net loss: Fish, jobs, and the marine environment. *Worldwatch Paper 120*, World-watch Institute, Washington, DC.

15 They should also be asked whether the trees really could grow back in the absence of the moist, shady conditions in which the seedlings of many tropical forest trees thrive.

CHAPTER ELEVEN

Environmental Philosophy and Ethics

This chapter looks at how humans find meaning and value in their relationships with the natural world. Environmental philosophy and environmental ethics are disciplines that describe these human-to-nature relationships and values, as well as ideas about animals and animal rights, including the connection between dietary choices, like veganism, to environmental concerns. Environmental ethics asks complex questions about the moral value of nature and notions of good or right ethical actions in the way humans use natural resources.

We begin with a selected reading by Indigenous scholar Robin Wall Kimmerer (Potawatomi), "Restoration and Reciprocity: The Contributions of Traditional Ecological Knowledge" in *Human Dimensions of Ecological Restoration: Integrating Science, Nature, and Culture* (2011). Kimmerer introduces us to the concept of traditional ecological knowledge (TEK), which is the long-term knowledge related to Indigenous peoples' beliefs, practices, and experiences with the environment. The recommended reading on traditional ecological knowledge by Fikret Berkes, Johan Colding, and Carl Folke (2000), "Rediscovery of Traditional Ecological Knowledge as Adaptive Management" in the journal *Ecological Applications*, describes the role and importance of Indigenous worldviews for natural resource management and use. Traditional ecological knowledge is defined by Berkes et al. as "a cumulative body of knowledge, practice and belief, evolving by adaptive processes and handed down through generations by cultural transmission, about the relationship of living beings (including humans) with one another and with their environment."

Indigenous practices have most often been developed by communities of people who have lived many millennia within one ecological area. There is no single version of traditional ecological knowledge as it is based on distinctive ethical and philosophical relationships between people, their culture, and their local environment. TEK is intertwined with the unique worldviews and beliefs of a specific group and is embedded in their language and traditions. It is increasingly recognized that many of the practices of TEK are more environmentally healthy than modern resource use and exploitation. TEK is increasingly considered to have value to sustainability efforts. Kimmerer explains the concepts of reciprocity and gratitude that underlie many different Indigenous paradigms about natural resource use.

The selected reading by Albert Berry Crawford, "Views of Nature" in *Ethics for Environmental Policy*, focuses on the various ways in which humans make meaning of their relationship with the natural world. Crawford describes how we think of nature in a variety of religious, ethical, and aesthetic ways. Crawford asks if we should reconsider our views of nature in order to ensure more sustainable human resource use. We saw in Chapter 2 on sustainability and Chapter 3 on environmental history that humans choose to exploit or conserve natural resources based on different and shifting ideas about what comprises nature and what are the differences between nature and culture. While the Berkes et al. recommended reading goes further into the concept of traditional ecological knowledge, the other readings delve into the ethical debates around diet and food choices. The recommended articles by Michael Fox (1993), "Environmental Ethics and the Ideology of Meat Eating,"and Juliana Sandford (2017), "Reduce, Reuse, Go Vegan," present fascinating and important arguments for and against making dietary choices based on the grounds of moral and environmental care.

RECOMMENDED READING

Berkes, F., Colding, J., and Folke, C. 2000. "Rediscovery of traditional ecological knowledge as adaptive management." *Ecological Applications, 10*(5): 1251–1262.

Fox, M. A. 1993. "Environmental Ethics and the Ideology of Meat Eating." *Between the Species* 9(3): 1–12.

Sandford, J. 2017. "Reduce, Reuse, Go Vegan." *Penn Sustainability Review, 1*(9): 15–22.

READING AND DISCUSSION PROMPTS

1. Describe the difference between a biocentric ethical perspective and an anthropocentric ethical perspective. After you answer the following questions, determine whether your answer shows a more biocentric or anthropocentric perspective:
   a. There are some living things such as cockroaches, mosquitoes, flies, and weedy plants that are sometimes considered not necessary in our society. If those living things are on the verge of extinction/extermination, do we have a duty to protect them?

b. In your opinion, which should we spend more money to protect: a rainforest plant species that can be used for medicine to treat human disease or a rainforest plant that has no known value for humans? Or should they have the same protection?

2. Ethics is about happiness, justice, human rights, and equality. How do you think each of these ideas is important for understanding the human relationship with the environment?
3. Kimmerer's article discusses traditional ecological knowledge and Indigenous worldviews. What is a person's worldview? How does one's worldview affect the daily decisions they make about the environment?

READING 11.1

Restoration and Reciprocity

THE CONTRIBUTIONS OF TRADITIONAL ECOLOGICAL KNOWLEDGE

By Robin Wall Kimmerer

Carol Crowe, an Algonquin ecologist, tells the story of explaining to one of her elders that she was traveling to a conference about sustainable development. The term was not familiar to him, so she explained the notion of managing resources in such a way that future generations would be able to obtain the same ecosystem services that are provided today, without impairment to the land. He was quiet for a time. The idea was hardly new to him. He then asked her to carry a message to the conference. He said, "This idea of sustainability sounds to me like the same old formula by which people simply continue to take from the earth. They just want to keep taking. You can't just take. Tell them, that among our people our concern is not what we can take from the land, but what we can give."

RESTORATION AND RECIPROCITY

The idea of reciprocity with land is fundamental to many indigenous belief systems. Indeed, such beliefs serve as the foundation for what have been described as "cultures of gratitude." In such cultures, people have a responsibility not only to be grateful for the gifts provided by Mother Earth, they are also responsible for playing a positive and active role in the well-being of the land. They are called not to be passive consumers, but to sustain the land that sustains them. Responsibilities to the more-than-human world are simultaneously material and spiritual, and, in fact, the two are inseparable. Ecological restoration can be viewed as an act of reciprocity, where humans exercise their care-giving responsibility for ecosystems (Egan 1988; Oeschlager 1996; Kimmerer 2000; Martinez, Salmon, and Nelson 2008). The traditional ecological knowledge (TEK) of indigenous peoples is rich with prescriptions, both philosophical and pragmatic, for this practice of giving back to the land. This chapter engages TEK as a partner to contemporary restoration science, in a symbiosis based on intellectual pluralism. "We're going to need the enduring knowledge of indigenous science as well as the best of leading edge western science. It's high tech meets high TEK." (Ausubel 2008).

Among my Anishinaabe people, we share a teaching known as "the prophecy of the seventh fire." This teaching relates that, with the coming of strangers to our shores, many changes will befall our people. It is said that the land will become fragmented, plants and animals will be lost, that the people will be scattered and divided from their homelands, and that the language spoken for millennia will nearly disappear. As we know, these things have come to pass. Our peoples live on tiny remnants of their original homelands, and our language and culture face many threats. The prophecy explains that the plants and animals will become diminished, the waters undrinkable, and the air itself changed. This, too, we know has come to pass.

We are also taught that in the time of the seventh fire, there will be a fork in the road. The people remaining on Earth must make a choice either to continue on the path that leads to destruction of life as we know it or to choose a different future—one of renewal. It is said that should the remaining people choose the path toward life, they will turn back along the road from which they have come and begin to pick up the pieces that have been scattered along the road—remnants of language, the old stories and songs, seeds and ragged patches of plants, wandering animals and birds, and together they will begin to put the world back together again. The people will reclaim their responsibilities for taking care of the land, and thus heal the land and the people. The prophecy of the seventh fire speaks, I think, of reciprocal restoration (box 11.1.1).

In the dominant materialistic worldview, humans are understood as standing outside nature, as exogenous forces whose interactions with nature are generally considered negative. Jordan (2003) laments that humans can take from a bountiful landscape, "but we can never give anything back," despite that "our conscience demands it and our imaginations yearn for it." Higgs (2003) likewise ponders, "Are our imaginative capacities diminishing so that we are less and less able to conceive of positive encounters with real nature?" He states that our great challenge is to imagine a "new" relationship between people and nature. What is "new" to Western science often has antecedents in indigenous knowledge, articulated millennia ago. This chapter reveals the contributions of TEK to our thinking about restoration.

BOX 11.1.1: RECIPROCAL RESTORATION

Reciprocal restoration is the mutually reinforcing restoration of land and culture such that repair of ecosystem services contributes to cultural revitalization, and renewal of culture promotes restoration of ecological integrity. Based on the indigenous stewardship principle that "what we do to the land we do to ourselves," restoration of land and culture are inseparable. This approach arises from a creative symbiosis between traditional ecological knowledge (TEK) and restoration science, which honors and uses the distinctive contributions of both intellectual traditions. Reciprocal restoration recognizes that it is not just the land that is broken, but our relationship to it. Reciprocal restoration encompasses repair of both ecosystem and cultural services while fostering renewed relationships of respect, responsibility, and reciprocity. All flourishing is mutual.

Reciprocal restoration is grounded in the positive feedback relationship between cultural revitalization and land restoration. Revitalizing language and culture protects and disseminates TEK, and builds relationships of reciprocity and respect, all of which are good for the land. What's good for the land is good for the people.

The fate of the land and the consequences for culture are much more strongly linked for Native peoples than for those in the dominant culture. Thus, ecological restoration in indigenous communities takes on a special depth and dimension.

EXPANDING THE VISION AND GOALS FOR ECOLOGICAL RESTORATION

Explicit definition of the goal is a fundamental first step in restoration design (Meffee and Carroll 1994). Because indigenous peoples live within the tradition of reciprocity, they may prioritize restoration goals rather differently, with outcomes based on a more broadly imagined vision. Goals manifest in restoration projects undertaken by indigenous peoples span the entire range of recognized restoration practices and motivations (Clewell and Aronson 2006), and often extend well beyond the goal-oriented restoration described by Cairns and Heckman (1996).This expanded vision of restoration encompasses not only repair of ecosystem structure and function, but cultural services as well. Traditional ecological knowledge is valuable to restoration, not only for the wealth of biological information it contains but for the worldview of respect, reciprocity, and responsibility in which it is embedded (Kimmerer 1998; Pierotti and Wildcat 2000). Restoration of reciprocal relationships with land is central to the indigenous vision of restoration, which may also include the following:

- Restoration of subsistence-use activities
- Focus on cultural keystone species
- Restoration of traditional indigenous diets
- Revitalization of TEK, language, and culture
- Exercise of spiritual responsibility
- Development of place-based, sustainable economies
- Restoration of traditional land management for the benefit of nonhuman relatives (i.e., biodiversity)

What these expanded goals have in common is the priority given to restoration of relationships to place that may be manifest in subsistence activities, spiritual responsibility, language revitalization, and other cultural practices. These goals are more inclusive than the science- and conservation-oriented goal of creating a self-sustaining ecosystem, free of human intervention. Nonetheless, the indigenous ethic of participatory responsibility does not preclude the goal of maintaining landscape areas free of human use. For example, the Klamath forest restoration plan (Wolf 2004) identifies resource utilization areas as well as those set aside as reserves substantially unaltered by human activity. Likewise, the Salish-Kootenai tribes in Montana protect tribally designated wilderness areas. A guiding principle that emerges from numerous tribal restoration projects is that the well-being of the land is inextricably tied to the well-being of the community and the individual.

Restoration of Subsistence-Use Activities

For many indigenous groups, restoration goals may include regenerating the capacity of the landscape to support traditional subsistence activities—hunting, fishing, gathering. The ethic of reciprocity embodies the idea that the land provides for the people and the people, in turn, must care for the land. A landscape is seen as whole and healthy when it can provide enough to share with the people. The goal of restoring subsistence raises the standards for ecological integrity. It is not sufficient to restore a fish population and then issue an advisory against eating those fish due to contamination. In the restoration of Onondaga Lake, one of the most chemically polluted lakes in the country, the Onondaga Nation's vision statement states that restoration is not complete until people can once again eat the fish (Onondaga Nation 2010). This goal actively resists the slide of baseline expectations for ecosystem integrity and places additional, higher expectations on a restored landscape.

Indigenous-led restoration projects all over the world call for a return to subsistence-capable landscapes with viable populations of plants and animals. Such projects include salmon restoration in the Pacific Northwest, restoration and protection of walleye fisheries by the Red Lake Ojibwe (Dokken 2010), the return of traditional berrying grounds, and the restoration of basket-making resources and hunting grounds, as well as places for gathering nontimber forest products (see chap. 19, this volume, for a discussion of cultural severance).

Restoration of subsistence is tied to restoration of indigenous cultural identity, language, health, and also to the vitality of the restored "resource" itself. Appropriate harvest is understood as a benefit to the land. There is considerable evidence for human subsistence activity providing the disturbance regime and stimulus for regenerating many culturally significant plants. For example, ethnobotanist Kat Anderson has documented that the indigenous harvesting of root food plants in California grasslands maintains the vigor of the population through a suite of practices she calls "tending" (Anderson 1996; Anderson and Rowney 1999). Traditional harvest and tending practices have been shown to maintain the productivity and diversity of subsistence plant communities, including camas meadows, basketry plants, acorns, and others (Turner 2005). In experimental restorations of the culturally significant sweetgrass (*Wingaashk*, *Hierochloe odorata*), we observed that plots harvested according to traditional practices exhibited a significantly higher rate of recruitment and lowered mortality than the unharvested controls, which actually declined in vigor (Reid 2005; Shebitz and Kimmerer 2005). In this case and others, subsistence practices actually stimulated the success of the plant species. These experiments uphold the indigenous principle that, "If we use a plant respectfully, it will stay with us and flourish. If we ignore it, it will go away." These findings suggest that in order to successfully restore some keystone species, one must also restore the mutually beneficial subsistence relationship with them.

In the indigenous view, an authentic landscape incorporates human participation in ecological flourishing. A beautiful meadow of blue camas (*Qém'es*, *Pa-siko*, *Camassia quamash*) is not an authentic landscape until people engage in reciprocity with that meadow by harvesting and feasting with that traditional food. Higgs (2005) describes the restoration of neglected camas meadows that began when the Lekwungen First Nation, in British Columbia, reinstituted traditional harvesting practices. The care-giving practices of weeding, dividing, and sowing that accompany harvest, coupled with selective burning, promote the regeneration of camas as well as regeneration of the reciprocal relationship.

Focus on Cultural Keystone Species

In addition to biodiversity as a whole, indigenous restoration projects may focus on restoration of desired species that are understood as "cultural keystone species" (Garibaldi and Turner 2004) because of their vital roles in both material and nonmaterial aspects of a culture (i.e., they provide food, medicine, and materials for spiritual and ceremonial practice).

Of course, many species that indigenous peoples seek to restore play overlapping roles as cultural and biological keystone species. Examples include the marsh reeds and water buffalo of the Marsh Arabs, red cedar (*Q!we'le*, *Lata'wi*, *Thuja plicata*) in the Pacific Northwest (Garibaldi and Turner 2004), and salmon (*Oncorhynchus* spp.) along the Pacific Coast of California (House 2000). Stumpff (2003) describes the important leadership role American Indian nations are playing in the restoration of such keystone species as the wolf (*mahigan*, *Canis lupus*) and bison (*Tatanka*, *Bison bison*). Her findings indicate that these restoration programs were implemented using contemporary science, but were guided by TEK, for cultural goals. Likewise, Garibaldi and Turner (2004) argue that by prioritizing restoration of cultural keystone species, indigenous peoples address the linked goals of social and ecological well-being.

It has often been articulated that indigenous peoples view their fates as linked to that of their nonhuman relatives. For example, the wolf and bison of North America have shared a common trajectory with the continent's indigenous people—people with whom they share a landscape, a history, and kinship. Like the native peoples who depend upon them, all were dispossessed from their homelands, driven nearly to extinction, and yet have had the resilience to persist and now rebound in the face of great ecological and cultural change. The renewal of these animals and other cultural keystone species inspires, and is inextricably connected to, the revitalization of indigenous communities. Their restoration is regarded as a human responsibility that is simultaneously material and spiritual. These species are understood as elders, teachers, and sources of knowledge.

Restoration of Traditional Indigenous Diets

Landscape restoration may also be motivated by issues of public health, including a suite of illnesses associated with dietary dislocation from traditional, land-based diets to store-bought, commodity foods. For example, the epidemic of diabetes in indigenous populations has been linked to replacement of traditional foods with high sugar and fat-laden diets of mainstream society (LaDuke 2005). Restoration of traditional diets demands a landscape that supports the plant and animal species with which a culture coevolved. Among the best-known initiatives to restore native foods is the widespread effort to revitalize the harvesting and consumption of wild rice (*Manoomin*, *Zizania aquatica*) among the Anishinaabe of the Great Lakes (LaDuke 1993). Restoration of this cultural keystone species simultaneously benefits human health, ecosystem integrity, water quality, and wildlife. It also aids economic development and language revitalization—an exemplar of the way that consideration of indigenous perspectives can significantly transform the way we understand the scope and power of restoration.

Revitalization of Language and Culture

Many indigenous restoration projects are holistic in nature by integrating land, language, ethics, and religion into the restoration of relationship with a cultural landscape. In a worldview where everything is connected, restoration of language is vital to land restoration, as the intact cultural landscape is the matrix in which language resides (Battiste 2000). Language revitalization and land restoration provide a powerful example of reciprocal restoration. A case in point is the White Mountain Apache word "*ni*," which is their word for "land" *and* for "mind" (Bray 1999). Relationship to land and the teachings contained there are held in the language (Abrams 1996).

The links between restoration of land and restoration of language may be very direct. For example, indigenous place names are often descriptive of ecological features and encode information as to the nature of potential reference ecosystems (Davidson-Hunt and Berkes 2001; Nabhan 1997). Anthropologist Keith Basso eloquently documents how Apache place names reference stories and events that have teaching value and may be prescriptive of right relationship (Basso 1996). Likewise, indigenous taxonomies are often rich in biological insights. Plant names are frequently derived from observed relationships between species. Gary Nabhan details numerous examples of plant names among southwestern indigenous peoples that describe pollination and dispersal interactions, habitat preferences, and human uses (Nabhan 2000). He recounts how Tohono O'odham plant names proved valuable to conservation biologists when defining critical habitat for the endangered desert tortoise (*komik'c-ed*, *Gopherus agassizii*). In collaboration with indigenous linguists, they identified a tortoise reserve area rich in a plant species known in the Tohono O'odham language as "desert tortoise eats it."

Other connections between land and language restoration are less direct but no less valuable. The structure of language, indeed its very grammar, reflects the underlying set of assumptions regarding relationships to the natural world. For example, in my Anishinaabe language, the complex verb forms are rooted in what I refer to as "the grammar of animacy" (Kimmerer 2011). In English, where all beings in the nonhuman realm are referred to with the pronoun "it," personhood is reserved for human beings. Everything else is an object; a thing. English dramatically constrains how we think about other species. But in Anisuinaabemowin, we refer to trees and birds and water with the same pronouns we use for human beings. There is no "it" in the living world, everyone is a "subject," a person, and, thus, deserving of the same respect and compassion that we extend to the human family.

This grammar reflects a fundamentally different orientation to the natural world, which would be lost forever if endangered languages, like endangered species, become extinct. Revitalization of language allows us to imagine and potentially implement different visions of sustainability.

Exercise of Spiritual Responsibility

The cosmologies of many indigenous peoples include what are called Original Instructions or guidance about how to live in the world. In return for the gift of life on a generous earth, humans are called to a covenant of spiritual and material reciprocity, to care for the land and water that care for them. This moral responsibility is manifest in religion and ceremony as well as in material lifeways, such as subsistence activities and land management (DeLoria 1992). Ecological restoration provides an opportunity for indigenous people to exercise their spiritual responsibility of caregiving and reciprocity toward the land and the more-than-human world. A statement from Dennis Martinez (1992a) captures this added dimension to restoration, which is absent from the strictly materialist views of restoration science:

> Cultural survival depends on healthy land and a healthy, responsible relationship between humans and the land. The traditional care-giving responsibilities which maintained healthy land need to be expanded to include ecological restoration. Ecological restoration is inseparable from cultural and spiritual restoration, and is inseparable from the spiritual responsibilities of care-giving and world-renewal. Collectively and individually, these indigenous spiritual values must be central to the vision of community ecological restoration. Western science and technology, is a limited conceptual and methodological tool—the "head and hands" of restoration implementation. Native spirituality is the "heart" that guides the head and hands.

Ceremony is a powerful means to articulate moral responsibility, enter into spiritual reciprocity, and promote group cohesion and reinforce shared values. In the watershed restoration work described by Dennis Martinez (1992b) for the Sinkyone Intertribal Project, the restoration began not with shovels in the ground, but with the restoration of an ancient ceremony to welcome the salmon back home. In the lands called the "sacred ecosystem," healing of the spiritual relationship with the salmon came before engineering of the hydrology and set the stage for the work to follow.

In the indigenous paradigm, it is said that we don't understand a thing until we understand it with all dimensions of a human person—mind, body, emotion, and spirit (Cajete 1994); Western scientific education gives privileged status to objective information only and specifically excludes emotional and spiritual dimensions. Traditional ecological knowledge recognizes the different strengths of these multiple understandings and explicitly incorporates the cultural experience of the observer into interpretation of the natural world. Traditional ecological knowledge is highly rational, empirical, and pragmatic, while simultaneously integrating cultural values and moral perspectives. With its worldview of respect, responsibility, and reciprocity with nature, TEK does not compete with science nor detract from its power, but extends its scope into additional human interactions with the natural world (box 11.1.2).

DEVELOPMENT OF PLACE-BASED, SUSTAINABLE ECONOMIES

The interdependence of ecosystem services and cultural services means that restoration may also serve the goal of development of sustainable, place-based economies. Such economies are characterized by a reliance on local resources and short commodity chains in which the labor, value-added, and economic benefits remain largely in the local economy. Emery (1994) suggests that these human ecological systems are regulated by four elements: resource availability, access to resources, knowledge of resources, and economic demand. Ecological restoration and TEK may enhance the critical factor of resource availability, while biocultural restoration augments elements of demand, access, and knowledge of the resource and its use.

Restoration of sustainable, place-based economies can also serve to stem the outflow of young people from an indigenous community to seek employment. Such migration can pose a significant risk to cultural integrity because opportunities for intergenerational knowledge transfer, language fluency, and other cultural ties are weakened. Sustainable economies encourage caretakers of the land to continue their stewardship practices. Thus, restoration that encompasses revitalization of both ecosystem and cultural services becomes a priority.

The White Earth Land Recovery Project of the White Earth Ojibwe provides an outstanding example of reciprocal restoration of a place-based economy in practice. Concomitant with the recovery of tribal lands lost in illegal land takings of the past century, the White Earth community has worked to create a sustainable, local economy tied to simultaneous restoration of land and culture. Recovery of title to a portion of the historic land base has enabled restoration of access to ecological resources. The TEK of the community has been engaged to develop the local economy through harvest and processing of local nontimber forest products—maple products, preserves from wild-gathered fruits, wild rice, and traditional agriculture—for local consumption and for sale. These activities simultaneously promote ecological well-being of the landscape through traditional caregiving practices, community health through restoration of the traditional diet, and revitalization of TEK and language.

Restoration of the "Remembered Forest" of the Klamath peoples similarly represents the goal of reciprocal restoration of a forest-based economy (Wolf 2004). The Klamath people of southern Oregon were made landless by disastrous federal policies of Termination in 1954 (Hood 1972), followed by intensive forest exploitation as the lands they had tended sustainably for centuries were overharvested by the U.S. Forest Service. Even without title to their own ancestral lands, the Klamath Tribe developed a forest restoration plan designed to regain a tribal homeland and subsistence base where forest management was driven by tribal values of permanence, collaboration, sense of place, ecological health, balance, and healing. The restoration plan includes restoration of ecosystem structure and function as well as subsistence income and enhancement of spiritual and cultural values (Wolf 2004).

BOX 11.1.2: WHAT IS TRADITIONAL ECOLOGICAL KNOWLEDGE?

Traditional ecological knowledge (TEK) refers to the knowledge, practices, and beliefs about the relationship of living beings to one another and to the physical environment that are held by peoples in relatively nontechnological societies with a direct dependence on local resources (Berkes 1993). Traditional ecological knowledge exists around the world, independent of ethnicity. It is born of long intimacy and attentiveness to a homeland and can arise wherever people are materially and spiritually integrated with their landscape (Kimmerer 2000). Traditional ecological knowledge is a form of rational and reliable information developed through generations of intimate contact by Native peoples with their lands (Mauro and Hardison 2000). The United Nations Environment Programme (1998) has recognized TEK as having equal status with scientific knowledge, and Vine DeLoria Jr. (1995) termed TEK the "intellectual twin to science." This long intellectual tradition exists in parallel to Western science's scientific ecological knowledge (SEK), yet it has been historically marginalized by the scientific community (Salmon 1996).

Traditional ecological knowledge has much in common with SEK, which is not surprising since both traditions derive from the same source—systematic observations of nature. Both knowledge systems yield detailed empirical information about natural phenomena and relationships among ecosystem components. Both SEK and TEK have predictive power, and in both intellectual traditions, observations are interpreted within a particular cultural context.

Traditional ecological knowledge encompasses a wide range of biological information and has significant overlap with the content of a mainstream course in ecology or conservation biology. The scope of TEK documented by scientists includes detailed empirical knowledge of population biology, resource assessment and monitoring, successional dynamics, patterns of fluctuation in climate and resources, species interactions, ethnotaxonomy, sustainable harvesting, adaptive management, and manipulation of disturbance regimes (Berkes 2008). Case histories of the utility of TEK in conservation biology span a range of biomes from the tundra to the tropical rainforest (Williams and Baines 1993; Berkes, Folke, and Gadgil 1995; Fernandez-Gimenez 2000; Gadgil, Seshagiri Rao, Utkarsh, Pramod, and Chhatre 2000).

However, TEK differs from SEK in a number of important ways. Traditional ecological knowledge observations tend to be qualitative, and create a diachronic database (i.e., a record of observations from a single locale over a long time period). In TEK, the observers tend to be the resource users themselves (e.g., hunters, fishers, and gatherers) whose harvesting success is inextricably linked to the quality and reliability of their ecological observations. In contrast, scientific observations made by a small group of professionals tend to be quantitative and often represent synchronic data or simultaneous observations from a wide range of sites and frequently lack the long-term perspective of TEK. Additional differences between SEK and TEK are described in Berkes (1993).

Moreover, SEK is conducted in an academic culture where nature is viewed objectively, and the data collected are "value-free." In this aspect, TEK diverges significantly from SEK (Pierotti and Wildcat 2000) because TEK is much more than collecting and analyzing the empirical information concerning ecological relationships. Indeed, TEK is woven into and inseparable from the social and spiritual context of the culture. Traditional ecological knowledge includes the ethic of reciprocal respect and obligations between humans and the nonhuman world that I discuss throughout this chapter. In TEK science, nature is subject, not object. Such holistic ways of understanding the environment offer alternatives to the dominant consumptive values of Western societies (Hunn 1999; Berkes 2008). Embraced as an equal partner to the power of SEK, TEK offers not only important biological insights but a cultural framework for environmental problem solving that incorporates human values.

As Gadgil and colleagues (1993) write, "Modern scientific knowledge, with its accompanying worldview of human beings apart from and above the natural world, has been extraordinarily successful in furthering human understanding and manipulation of simpler systems. However, neither this worldview nor scientific knowledge has been particularly successful when confronted with complex ecological systems. ... It is in this context that traditional ecological knowledge is of significance."

In terms of ecological restoration, TEK is useful when defining reference ecosystems because Native languages and artifacts of material culture are a living library of species composition (Alcoze and Hurteau 2001). Ethnographic data including linguistic analysis, material culture, and the oral tradition can provide detailed compositional data for the reference state. Unfortunately, few ecological scientists are trained to access these valuable data sources.

Traditional ecological knowledge can also provide an alternative way of approaching the restoration process. The dominant metaphor in this approach is not nature as machine with humans in control, but nature as a living community, populated with nonhuman persons, all contributing to the integrity of the system. Just as healing an individual relies on the resilience and vitality of the patient, who is an active participant in his or her own recovery, healing of the land is understood as offering support to its return to health in which humans play a subsidiary role. Because the process is understood as directed by nature, the practitioners adaptively change the plan as the land responds to treatments. The stated goal of the restoration is to help a site evolve through cyclical changes, rather than establishing a linear trajectory (Long, Tecle, and Burnette 2003). A similar framework formed the basis of the Karuk tribal forest restoration model (Martinez 1992b, 1995), which also conceived of restoration as a partnership with natural processes rather than an imposed formula.

Consistent with a call to incorporate TEK into ecological restoration is the recognition that this integration should be inseparable from a serious discussion about protection of traditional knowledge from exploitation. Traditional ecological knowledge represents the collective intellectual contributions of indigenous people, accumulated and systematized over millennia. The identity of the practitioners, informants, and the community should always be fully referenced and acknowledged with the same diligence that scientists apply to the contributions of their academic colleagues.

The ability of indigenous peoples to exercise their stewardship roles with the land is central to the principle of reciprocal restoration, and also inextricably linked to legal title to the land. However, land title is a serious problem for many aboriginal peoples, like the White Earth Ojibwe, the Klamath, and countless others. Such is the case for the Onondaga Nation of upstate New York. Their homelands include the sacred site of Onondaga Lake where the Iroquois Confederacy was founded and now, unfortunately, thirteen Superfund sites. The Onondaga Nation has filed a historic land rights action to regain aboriginal title, not with the intent to seize property, but to regain the ability to exercise their responsibilities for the watershed and to restore both land and people. Their "Vision for a Clean Onondaga Lake" articulates the synergy between restoring a landscape and cultural restoration (Onondaga Nation 2010).

Restoration of Traditional Land Management for Biodiversity

Especially in the Americas and Australia, the notion of the presettlement state is problematic because it is frequently tied to the "myth of the pristine" (Denevan 1992), which supposes that the landscape encountered at the time of European settlement was in a "state of nature" and free from human disturbance. In the Americas, this perspective ignores at least twelve thousand years of human history of land management and an even longer period in Australia. There is now abundant evidence that the pre-European settlement landscape was the product of indigenous natural resource management, such as prescribed fire (Kimmerer and Lake 2001). Therefore, it may not be possible to restore the presettlement landscape without also restoring the traditional land management practices.

Traditional resource management methods share several goals with contemporary restoration efforts, including manipulating the patterns and processes of ecological succession to produce the desired species composition and structure. Indigenous management practices were effective in creating and maintaining species assemblages that produced a sustained yield of food and subsistence materials for humans, while also generating shifting mosaics of high productivity and biodiversity. The ethnographic literature is rich with descriptions of highly site-specific land care practices designed to produce a given vegetation composition (Mann 2005; Berkes 2008). These may be of significant value to restoration ecologists.

Kat Anderson (1996, 2001, 2006) provides an excellent review of the wide array of indigenous land management practices in California that ensured a sustainable harvest of culturally significant plant materials. Such practices mirror the definition of ecological restoration offered by Allen and Hoekstra (1992) as "gardening with wild species in a natural mosaic."

It is beyond the scope of this chapter to review the myriad ecosystem management practices employed by indigenous peoples. However, if, as Robinson and Handel (2000) suggest, ecological restoration is essentially facilitated succession, then it is important to recognize that TEK is rich with examples in which indigenous peoples modified the successional trajectory to produce distinctive ecological communities that meet cultural goals.

Restoration of Kincentric Relationships

Why restore relationship? Relationship is key to the sustainability, authenticity, and longevity of restored ecosystems. It likewise provides important cultural feedback about dynamic restoration outcomes. Relationship between humans and place can be the most enduring connection of all (Martinez, Salmon, and Nelson 2008), surviving and deepening even as ecosystems evolve and change. This is particularly true in the face of climate change. The structure and function of "Nature" becomes a moving target, while long-term relationships to nature represent a long-term resource for resiliency and adaptation. Second, we all know that socioeconomic and political pressures along with complementary resource shortfalls undermine the success of restoration projects. An engaged public, committed to the success and stewardship of a restored ecosystem, can generate the political will and economic pressure to support restoration policy and implementation. Regeneration of healthy relationships with land is a key component of landscape authenticity. Perhaps most important, restoration of relationship offers the opportunity for cultivation of a "moral center" called for by Higgs (1997)—an idea that is beyond the scope of purely science-driven restoration. Traditional indigenous viewpoints recognize that we live in a moral landscape governed by relationships of mutual responsibility, which are simultaneously material and spiritual. A focus on restoration of relationship guided by TEK moves us away from an anthropocentric relationship to land, into the realm of a "kincentric" relationship (Salmon 2000) in which our moral responsibility extends to all of our nonhuman relatives.

A focus on kincentric relationships underpins a wide range of tribal restoration projects. For example, the Seminole Nation has undertaken a restoration of Everglade habitats of the Florida panther (*kowechobe*, *Puma concolor*), through removal of invasive species and return of water flows. Nonhuman species are the prime beneficiaries of the restoration; what conservationists call "biodiversity," traditional peoples call "kin."

Another key element of reciprocal restoration and building kincentric relationship with the land is the importance of intergenerational knowledge sharing and education (part 6, this volume). Youth camps that involve environmental education on the land and in school are focal components of the restoration process. The Kaibab Environmental Education Network in northern Arizona is an excellent example of a restoration model for indigenous communities because it links tribal students and educators in projects that incorporate traditional and contemporary restoration strategies (Thom Alcoze, pers. comm.).

The Role of TEK in Defining the Reference Ecosystem

Traditional ecological knowledge is useful when defining reference ecosystems because Native languages and material culture are a living library of species composition (Alcoze and Hurteau 2001). Ethnographic data including linguistic analysis, material culture, and the oral tradition can provide detailed compositional data for the reference state. Unfortunately, few ecological scientists are trained to access these valuable data sources.

Martinez (1995) reports that presettlement plant inventories can be derived from the plant names in the indigenous languages of the region. Likewise, species composition of lands with uninterrupted indigenous management regimes can provide invaluable information as to the composition of the presettlement vegetation. For example, the tallgrass prairies of Walpole Island First Nation in eastern Canada are regarded as among the most species rich on the continent. These intact ecosystems are regarded as exemplars of the presettlement state, in large part because the "natural" disturbance regime that generated these prairies is also intact. The high ecological integrity of these grasslands stems in part from an uninterrupted history of prescribed burning by the Potawatomi, Ojibwe, and Ottawa peoples responsible for these ancestral lands. Thus the ideal of "Nature" as a state free of cultural influences is called into question, when we recognize some of our most cherished landscapes as artifacts of indigenous management. It may not be possible to restore "presettlement" landscapes without consideration of TEK and, indeed, without restoration of the cultural practices by which indigenous peoples sustained them.

The Role of TEK in the Restoration Process

Traditional ecological knowledge can also provide an alternative way of approaching the restoration process. The dominant metaphor in this approach is not nature as machine with humans in control, but nature as a living community, peopled with human and nonhuman persons, all contributing to the integrity of the system. This process of restoration stands in sharp contrast to the mechanistic view of restoration "as an attempt to force transitions toward the desired state" (Hobbs and Norton 1996). In indigenous land management, humans play a subsidiary role. As one elder advises, "Go slowly. Listen to the land, it will tell you what to do." Because the process is understood as directed by nature, the practitioners adaptively change the plan as the land responds to treatments. The stated goal of the restoration is to help a site evolve through cyclical changes, rather than establishing a linear trajectory (Long, Tecle, and Burnette 2003). A similar framework formed the basis of the Karuk tribal forest restoration model (Martinez 1995), which also conceived of restoration as a partnership with natural processes rather than an imposed formula. It was understood that plants that arrived as volunteers did not need to be removed to correspond to the end design. Rather they were carefully observed and understood as bringing something of value needed by the developing community. The practitioners were receptive to the potential contributions of unintended species, consistent with the worldview of plants as carriers of knowledge. The restoration team looked for feedback of mutual learning between the land and the people.

Likewise, the experience of the White Mountain Apache Nation tribe demonstrates how cultural traditions and TEK can act as guiding forces for restoration. Their lands in eastern Arizona had been degraded by federal mismanagement. Compensatory funds were devoted to watershed restoration to repair the damage. The tribal strategy is to "take care of the land so that the land can, once again take better care of the people" (Welch and Riley 2001). Their approach to the restoration process is grounded in the wisdom of their creation stories and powerful cultural metaphors that remind people to safeguard the life processes that link the human and nonhuman communities. Elders and knowledge holders were vital participants in the design and implementation of restoration plans. The techniques used in riparian zone restoration were derived from traditional land caregiving methods practiced by the people for millennia, including methods for streambank erosion control methods, selective burning, and transplanting vegetation (Long, Tecle, and Burnette 2003).

FROM FUNCTION TO FIDELITY OR EVOLVING DEFINITIONS OF ECOLOGICAL RESTORATION

Until recently, the many definitions of ecological restoration in the literature were mostly limited to considerations of ecosystem structure and function in a fairly narrow, materialistic sense—reflecting the scientific paradigm (National Research Council 1992). The U.S. Forest Service (2010) definition is broadly representative of this perspective: "Ecological restoration is the process of assisting the recovery of resilience and adaptive capacity of ecosystems that have been degraded, damaged or destroyed. Restoration focuses on establishing the composition, structure, pattern and ecological processes necessary to make terrestrial and aquatic ecosystems sustainable, resilient and healthy under current and future conditions." This is mirrored in the basic definition of ecological restoration provided by the Society for Ecological Restoration. "Ecological restoration is the process of assisting the recovery of an ecosystem that has been degraded, damaged or destroyed" (SER Primer 2004).

It is noteworthy that these definitions fail to incorporate human relationship or cultural resources into restoration goals or practices. Restoration, although a profoundly human endeavor, is conceptualized within a worldview that places human beings outside of natural systems and prioritizes repair of structure and function above restoration of relationship. However, a broken relationship with land is at the root of the ecological degradation that restoration seeks to repair. Restoration of relationship to land would, therefore, seem to require equivalence, if not a priority focus, as a restoration goal.

Coincident with the formulation of the functional definitions of ecological restoration, a definition of restoration was also being formulated from the indigenous worldview, in which nature is viewed not as a collection of objects but as a community of subjects that includes human beings as members of the democracy of species. Within this paradigm, colleagues in the Indigenous Environmental Network conceptualized ecological restoration as *inseparable from cultural and spiritual restoration.*

In the past few years, the terms used to define the boundaries of ecological restoration have subtly shifted from a focus primarily on structure and function of ecosystems to a broader consideration that includes concepts of human relationship to place. Indeed, the Society for Ecological Restoration has broadened its definition to include human interactions in those ecosystems they define as cultural by saying, "The restoration of such [cultural] ecosystems normally includes the concomitant recovery of indigenous ecological management practices, including support for the cultural survival of indigenous peoples and their languages as living libraries of traditional ecological knowledge" (SER Primer 2004). While this is an important recognition of indigenous cultures within the context of restoration, it fails to address how the mainstream society might use ecological restoration practices to reengage with nature and move beyond the idea of nature as other and into the worldview of reciprocal restoration.

A Gradient of Terminology

Terminology is important in the way it frames the discourse, and several terms have been used to express varying levels of integration between cultures and land restoration. Here I discuss and compare three terms that have been used to describe this relationship—"biocultural restoration," "eco-cultural restoration," and "reciprocal restoration." The term "biocultural restoration" was first used by Dan Janzen to describe his initiatives to involve local cultures as allies in the restoration at Guanacaste National Park in Costa Rica (1988). Cairns (2000) uses the term to categorize restoration projects that have a significant input and support from citizen groups and take place in a cultural landscape. In a number of cases, the approach to integrating culture and restoration has been decidedly top-down, and cultural participation appears limited to restorationists cultivating social support for their projects. Biocultural restoration has become associated with this important, but potentially superficial, approach to cultural engagement.

Some authors have replaced "biocultural" with "eco-cultural" (Higgs 2003; Martinez 2003). In examining the pattern of use of this term, it seems to be applied to restoration projects that are substantially guided and informed by the cultural goals and knowledge of the inhabitants of a cultural landscape, where the humans are active participants in the restoration. Eco-cultural restoration represents a much deeper level of cultural engagement of an indigenous culture, as in the case of the Sinkyone Intertribal Wilderness Project (Martinez 1992).

If we use the indigenous worldview to frame the relationship of restoration, what language might we use? Among the primary tenets of indigenous environmental philosophy is reciprocity. Thus I propose that we need a new term to describe that to which we might aspire; a new term wherein we recognize and act from the essential interconnectedness of land and people, where all flourishing is mutual. That new/old term is "reciprocal restoration" (see box 11.1.1).

BECOMING INDIGENOUS TO PLACE

In addition to its significance for indigenous cultures, reciprocal restoration has the potential to occur within mainstream society by reengaging people with land, renewing the human–place connection, and enabling people to reclaim their responsibility for sustaining the land that sustains them. Higgs (2005) notes that "restoration is successful only to the extent that the life of the human community is changed to reflect the health of the restored ecosystem." Traditional ecological knowledge is vital to support this new direction in restoration ecology, as a model for restoration of relationship grounded in the worldview of humans participating in the well-being of land.

Reciprocal restoration also offers the opportunity for an immigrant culture to start becoming "indigenous to place" by healing relationships with land and history. This does not mean appropriating the culture of indigenous people, but generating an authentic new relationship. It means throwing off the mindset of the immigrant, including the frontier mindset of "take what you can get and move on." It means becoming involved with the "language" and dynamics of the place you live—learning its landforms, weather patterns, animals, plants, waterways, and seasons. Being indigenous to place means to live as if we'll be here for the long haul, as if our children's future mattered. It means taking care of the land as if our lives, both spiritual and material, depended on it. It involves entering into a covenant of reciprocity with the land, which includes restoration. That's what it means to become indigenous to place. This can be done in a variety of ways (e.g., eco-cultural restoration, the restoration of traditional practices and cultural landscapes, ecological art).

CONCLUSION

- It is not the land that is broken, but our relationship with it. Thus, the work of ecological restoration must be to restore human–land relationship.

- Traditional ecological knowledge can contribute to both the philosophy and the practice of ecological restoration by expanding our vision of what restoration can entail to include eco-cultural and reciprocal restoration.
- Traditional resource management practices provide insight into tools for restoration through manipulation of disturbance regimes.
- Indigenous concepts of right relationship include respect, reciprocity, responsibility, and relatedness.
- Relationship can include active participation in the well-being of land.

REFERENCES

Abrams, D. 1996. *The Spell of the Sensuous: Perception and Language in a More-than-Human World.* New York: Pantheon Books.

Alcoze, T., and M. Hurteau. 2001. "Implementing the Archaeo-environmental Reconstruction Technique: Rediscovering the Historic Ground Layer of Three Plant Communities in the Greater Grand Canyon Region." In *The Historical Ecology Handbook: A Restorationist's Guide to Reference Ecosystems*, edited by D. Egan and E. A. Howell, 413–24. Washington DC: Island Press.

Allen, W. H. 1988. "Biocultural Restoration of a Tropical Forest." *BioScience* 38 (3): 156–61.

Allen, T., and T. Hoekstra. 1992. *Toward a Unified Ecology.* New York: Columbia University Press.

Anderson, M. K. 1996. "Tending the Wilderness." *Restoration & Management Notes* 14 (2): 154–66.

———. 2001. "The Contribution of Ethnobiology to the Reconstruction and Restoration of Historic Ecosystems." In *Historical Ecology Handbook*, edited by D. Egan and E. A. How-ell, 55–72. Washington, DC: Island Press.

———. 2006. *Tending the Wild: Native American Knowledge and the Management of California's Natural Resources.* Berkeley: University of California Press.

Anderson, M. K., and D. L. Rowney. 1999. "The Edible Plant *Dichelostemma capitata*: Its Vegetative Reproduction in Response to Different Indigenous Harvesting Regimes in California." *Restoration Ecology* 7 (3): 231–40.

Ausubel, K. 2008. "Remembering the Original Instructions." In *Original Instructions: Indigenous Teachings for a Sustainable Future*, edited by M. K. Nelson, xxi–xxv. Rochester, VT: Bear and Company.

Basso, K. 1996. *Wisdom Sits in Places.* Albuquerque: University of New Mexico Press.

Battiste, M., ed. 2000. *Reclaiming Indigenous Voice and Vision.* Vancouver: University of British Columbia Press.

Berkes, F. 1993. "Traditional Ecological Knowledge in Perspective." In *Traditional Ecological Knowledge: Concepts and Cases*, edited by J. T. Inglis, 1–9. Ottawa: International Program on Traditional Ecological Knowledge and International Development Research Centre.

———. 2008. *Sacred Ecology: Traditional Ecological Knowledge and Resource Management.* 2nd ed. Philadelphia: Taylor and Francis.

Berkes, F., C. Folke, and M. Gadgil. 1995. "Traditional Ecological Knowledge, Biodiversity, Resilience and Sustainability." In *Biodiversity Conservation*, edited by C. Perrings, K.-G. Maler, C. Folke, C. S. Holling, and B.-O. Jansson, 269–87. Dordrecht, Netherlands: Kluwer Academic.

Bray, D., ed. 1999. *Western Apache-English Dictionary.* Tempe, AZ: Bilingual Review Press. Cairns Jr., J. 2000. "Setting Ecological Restoration Goals for Technical Feasibility and Scientific Validity." *Ecological Engineering* 15: 171–80.

Cairns Jr., J., and J. R. Heckman. 1996. "Restoration Ecology: The State of an Emerging Field." *Annual Review of Energy and Environment* 21: 167–89.

Cajete, G. C. 1994. *Look to the Mountain: An Ecology of Indigenous Education.* Skyland, NC: Kivali Press.

Clewell, A., and J. Aronson. 2006. "Motivations for the Restoration of Ecosystems." *Conservation Biology* 20 (2): 420–28.

Davidson-Hunt, I., and F. Berkes. 2001. "Changing Resource Management Paradigms, Traditional Ecological Knowledge, and Non-timber Forest Products." In *Forest Communities in the Third Millennium*, edited by I. Davidson-Hunt, L. C. Duchesne, and J. C. Zasada, 78–92. U.S. Forest Service North Central Research Station General Technical Report NC-217. St. Paul, MN: USDA Forest Service.

———. 2003. "Learning as You Journey: Anishinaabe Perception of Social-Ecological Environments and Adaptive Learning." *Conservation Ecology* 8 (1): 5. http://www.consecol.org/vol8/iss1/art5/.

DeLoria, V. 1992. "Spiritual Management: Prospects for Restoration on Tribal Lands." *Restoration & Management Notes* 10 (1): 48–50.

———. 1995. *Red Earth, White Lies.* New York: Harper and Row.

Denevan, W. M. 1992. "The Pristine Myth: The Landscape of the Americas in 1492." *Annals of the Association of American Geographers* 82 (3): 369–85.

Dokken, B. 2010. *A Tale of Two Lakes.* St. Paul: Minnesota Department of Natural Resources. http://www.dnr.state.mn.us/volunteer/marapr00/red_lake.html.

Egan, D. 1988. "Our Heritage of Landscaping with Native Plants. A Hermeneutical Study of Texts from 1919–1929." Master's thesis, Landscape Architecture Department, University of Wisconsin–Madison.

Emery, M. 1994. "The Search Conference: State of the Art." Unpublished paper, Center for Continuing Education. Australian National University.

Fernandez-Gimenez, M. E. 2000. "The Role of Nomadic Mongolian Pastoralists' Ecological Knowledge in Rangeland Management." *Ecological Applications* 10: 1318–26.

Gadgil, M., F. Berkes, and C. Folke. 1993. "Indigenous Knowledge for Biodiversity Conservation." *Ambio* 22: 151–56.

Gadgil, M., P. R. Seshagiri Rao, G. Utkarsh, P. Pramod, and A. Chhatre. 2000. "New Meanings for Old Knowledge: The Peoples Biodiversity Registers Program." *Ecological Applications* 10: 1307–17.

Garibaldi, A., and N. Turner. 2004. "Cultural Keystone Species: Implications for Ecological Conservation and Restoration." *Ecology and Society* 9 (3): 1. http://www.ecologyandsociety.org/vol9/iss3/art1/.

Higgs, E. S. 1997. "What Is Good Ecological Restoration?" *Conservation Biology* 11 (2): 338–48.

———. 2003. *Nature by Design: People, Natural Process and Ecological Restoration*. Cam-bridge, MA: MIT Press.

———. 2005. "The Two-Culture Problem: Ecological Restoration and the Integration of Knowledge." *Restoration Ecology* 13 (1): 159–64.

Hobbs, R., and J. Norton. 1996. "Towards a Conceptual Framework for Restoration Ecology." *Restoration Ecology* 4: 93–100.

Hood, S. "Termination of the Klamath Tribe in Oregon." *Ethnohistory* 19 (4): 379–92.

House, F. 2000. *Totem Salmon: Life Lessons from Another Species*. Boston: Beacon Press.

Hunn, E. 1999. "The Value of Subsistence for the Future of the World." In *Ethnoecology: Situated Knowledge/Located Lives*, edited by V. D. Nazarea, 23–36. Tucson: Arizona University Press.

Janzen, D. H. 1988. "Tropical Ecological and Biocultural Restoration." *Science* 239: 243–44.

Jordan III, W. R. 2003. *The Sunflower Forest: Ecological Restoration and the New Communion with Nature*. Berkeley: University of California Press.

Kimmerer, R. W. 1998. "Intellectual Diversity: Bringing the Native Perspective into Natural Resources Education." *Winds of Change* Summer, 14–18.

———. 2000. "Native Knowledge for Native Ecosystems." *Journal of Forestry* 98 (8): 4–9.

———. 2011. "Learning the Grammar of Animacy." In *The Colors of Nature: Culture, Identity, and Natural World*, edited by A. H. Deming and L. E. Savoy, 167–77. Minneapolis, MN: Milkweed Editions.

Kimmerer, R. W., and F. K. Lake. 2001. "Maintaining the Mosaic: The Role of Indigenous Burning in Land Management." *Journal of Forestry* 99: 36–41.

LaDuke, W. 1993. "Voices from White Earth Gaia—Waabaabiganikaag." Thirteenth Annual Schumacher Lecture, Yale University, New Haven, CT.

———. 2005. *Recovering the Sacred: The Power of Naming and Claiming*. New York: South End Press.

Long, J., A. Tecle, and B. Burnette. 2003. "Cultural Foundations for Ecological Restoration on the White Mountain Apache Reservation." *Ecology and Society* 8 (1): 4; http://www.consecol.org/vol8/iss1/art4.

Mann, C. 2005. *1491: New Revelations of the Americas before Columbus*. New York: Knopf.

Martinez, D. 1992a. Presentation at the Indigenous Environmental Network "Protecting Mother Earth" Conference, Celilo Falls, Oregon, USA.

———. 1992b. "Northwestern Coastal Forests: The Sinkyone Intertribal Park Project." *Restoration & Management Notes* 10 (1): 64–69.

———. 1995. "Karuk Tribal Module of Mainstem Salmon Watershed Restoration: Karuk Ancestral Lands and People as Reference Ecosystem for Eco-cultural Restoration in Collaborative Ecosystem Management." Unpublished report. On file with U.S. Department of Agriculture, Forest Service, Klamath National Forest, 1312 Fairlane Rd, Yreka, CA 96097.

———. 2003. "Protected Areas, Indigenous Peoples, and the Western Idea of Nature." *Ecological Restoration* 21 (4): 247–50.

Martinez, D., E. Salmon, and M. K. Nelson. 2008. "Restoring Indigenous History and Culture to Nature." In *Original Instructions: Indigenous Teachings for a Sustainable Future*, edited by M. K. Nelson. 88–105. Rochester, VT: Bear and Company. 88–105

Mauro, F., and P. D. Hardison. 2000. "Traditional Knowledge of Indigenous and Local Communities: International Debate and Policy Initiatives." *Ecological Applications* 10: 1263–69.

Meffee, G., and C. Carroll. 1994. *Principles of Conservation Biology.* Sunderland, MA: Sinauer Associates.

Nabhan, G. P. 1997. *Cultures of Habitat: On Nature, Culture, and Story.* Washington, DC: Counterpoint Press.

———. 2000. "Interspecific Relationships Affecting Endangered Species Recognized by O'Odham and Comcaac Cultures." *Ecological Applications* 10: 1288–95.

National Research Council. 1992. *Restoration of Aquatic Ecosystems: Science, Technology and Public Policy.* Washington, DC: National Academy Press.

Oeschlager, M. 1996. *Caring for Creation: An Ecumenical Approach to the Environmental Crisis.* New Haven, CT: Yale University Press.

Onondaga Nation. 2010. "The Onondaga Nation's Vision for a Clean Onondaga Lake." http://www.onondaganation.org/lake_vision.html.

Pierotti, R., and D. Wildcat. 2000. "Traditional Ecological Knowledge: The Third Alternative." *Ecological Applications* 10 (5): 1333–40.

Reid, L. 2005. "The Effects of Traditional Harvesting Practices on Restored Sweetgrass Populations." MS thesis, State University of New York College of Environmental Science and Forestry, Syracuse, New York.

Robbins, J. 1997. "The Return of the Wolf." *Wildlife Conservation* 100: 44–48.

Robinson, G., and S. Handel. 2000. "Directing Spatial Patterns of Recruitment During an Experimental Urban Woodland Reclamation." *Ecological Applications* 10 (1): 174–88.

Salmon, E. 1996. "Decolonizing Our Voices." *Winds of Change* Summer, 70–72.

———. 2000. "Kincentric Ecology: Indigenous Perception of the Human–Nature Relationship." *Ecological Applications* 1 (5): 1327–32.

Shebitz, D., and R. Kimmerer. 2005. "Re-establishing Roots of a Mohawk Community and a Culturally Significant Plant: Sweetgrass." *Restoration Ecology* 13(2): 257–64.

Simpson, L. 2002. "Indigenous Environmental Education for Cultural Survival." *Canadian Journal of Environmental Education* 7 (1): 13–25.

Society for Ecological Restoration (SER) Science and Policy Working Group. 2004. *Society for Ecological Restoration International Primer on Ecological Restoration.* Washington, DC: Society for Ecological Restoration.

Stumpff, L. 2003. "Protecting Restorative Relationships and Traditional Values: American Indian Tribes, Wildlife and Wild Lands." In *Science and Stewardship to Protect and Sustain Wilderness Values: 7th World Wilderness Congress Symposium*, compiled by A. Watson and J. Sproull, 63–71. USDA Forest Service Proceedings RMRS-P-27. Ogden, UT: U.S. Department of Agriculture, Forest Service, Rocky Mountain Research Station.

Turner, N. J. 2005. *The Earth's Blanket: Traditional Teachings for Sustainable Living.* Seattle: University of Washington Press.

United Nations Environment Programme (UNEP). 1998. *Report of the Fourth Meeting of the Parties to the Convention on Biodiversity.* Nairobi, Kenya: United Nations Environment Programme.

U.S. Forest Service. 2010. *Forest Service Manual 2000 National Forest Resource Management, Chapter 2020 Ecological Restoration and Resilience.* Washington, DC: U.S. Forest Service National Headquarters.

Welch, J. R., and R. Riley. 2001. "Reclaiming Land and Spirit in the Western Apache Homeland." *American Indian Quarterly* 25 (1): 5–12.

Williams, N. M., and G. Baines, eds. 1993. *Traditional Ecological Knowledge: Wisdom for Sustainable Development.* Canberra: Australian National University, Centre for Resource and Environmental Studies.

Wolf, E. 2004. *Klamath Heartlands: A Guide to the Klamath Reservation Forest Plan.* Portland, OR: Ecotrust.

READING 11.2

Views of Nature

By Albert Berry Crawford

Nature has been conceived in many ways: as a world in which spirits animate plants and animals and the places they inhabit; as a world created by God, an abode where humans are able to work on individual salvation; as an interconnected and constantly changing network of opposing yin-yang forces naturally tending toward balance and harmony; as a material order governed by physical laws and shaped over vast periods of time by evolutionary processes; as untamed wilderness that impedes civilization and must be brought under control; as a storehouse of raw materials for the production of goods that make human life more secure and enjoyable; as pristine wilderness, where harried urban dwellers are able to retreat for recreation, contemplation, and aesthetic enjoyment; as a world of things-in-themselves that cannot be apprehended save through mind-imposed (or culture-conditioned) forms of perception and understanding; and what life was like when the human imprint was far less pervasive. These are some of the images that have been entertained by people living in different cultures at various times in human history.

Many contemporary urbanites view nature as the storehouse of resources from which the necessities of life are derived: land, food, water, energy, recreational resources, etc. Science and technology are relied upon to keep nature at bay and to increase margins of safety, convenience, and comfort within human-themed environments. Excursions into the wild are enjoyed by some, but generally in small doses and in controlled circumstances. Some see "things human" and "things nonhuman" as constituting different orders of reality, in which the human order is regarded as superior to the natural order, and the natural order is regarded as having value to the extent it serves, or is made to serve, human ends.

Some see human superiority as divinely ordained, while others see humankind as standing at the top of the evolutionary ladder, as life's crowning achievement.

The following takes a closer look at how nature has been conceived in a number of these traditions, including the following: nature as divine creation, as the antithesis of mind and civilization, as evolutionary product and process, as human artifact, as cultural construct, and as wilderness.

The final section (titled "the concept of nature revisited") frames a more ecological-oriented concept of nature and discusses how reconceptualization of nature shapes work in conservation biology to protect, preserve, and conserve natural resources.

NATURE AS DIVINE CREATION

Diverse views of nature are found in the Judeo-Christian tradition. Beliefs and doctrines that cast nature in a less than positive light include the view that nature is an abode over which humans have been given mastery and dominion,[1] efforts by Israelite prophets to rid religious thinking of nature gods to ensure that undivided allegiance is given to the one true God,[2] accounts that see nature as the domain of hostile energies in which the faith and fortitude of the faithful are put to test,[3] and the belief that divine creation is hierarchically ordered, with humans above animals, animals above plants, and plants above inanimate matter.

---

1 In Genesis 1:26–29, God said, "Let us make man in our image, after our likeness; and let them have dominion over the fish of the sea, and over the birds of the air, and over the cattle, and over all the earth." In Genesis 9:1–3, God blessed Noah and his sons, and said to them, "Be fruitful and multiply, and fill the earth. The fear of you and the dread of you shall be upon every beast of the earth, and upon every bird of the air, upon everything that creeps on the ground and all the fish of the sea; into your hand they are delivered. ... I give you everything."

2 The early Semites worshipped nature gods, chief among them Baal, variously characterized as the god of fertility, the protector of crops and livestock, the god of the thunderstorm, and a mighty warrior god. The Old Testament prophets saw Baal as the enemy of the God of the Israelites, and, in their attempts to extirpate these false gods, played a role in desacralizing nature.

3 For the Neoplatonist theologian, Origen, "The world of flesh is the world of demons ... and gross matter the domain of Satan." For Saint Bonaventure, the created world is not wretched, but a place in which flesh and desire fetter humans and must be overcome and transcended. For Martin Luther, nature is a symbol of God's wrath and certainly not anything to admire or commune with. It is, Luther wrote, the "domain of hostile energies ... which motivate the despairing soul to seek out and cling to 'the right hand of God.'" "And what of thorns, thistles, water, fire, caterpillars, flies, fleas, and bedbugs?" he asked. "Collectively and individually, are not all of them messengers who preach to us concerning sin and God's wrath?"

The idea that nature is hierarchically ordered is prominent in the theology of Saint Thomas Aquinas. Based on the belief that God's creation is populated by beings variously distant from God's perfection, with humans (only humans) created in the image of God, Saint Thomas gave this summation: "We conclude, then, that lifeless beings exist for living beings, plants for animals, and the latter for man. The whole of material nature exists for man, inasmuch as he is a rational animal."[4]

If nature is cast in a negative light in these ways, one also finds positive images throughout Judeo-Christian scripture and the teachings of Catholic saints. Genesis 1:22 tells that "God saw that it [God's creation] was good." Psalms 19:1 tells how the heavens and firmament proclaim God's glory, as does Isaiah 6:3: "Holy, holy, holy is the Lord of hosts; the whole earth is full of his glory."

In Matthew 25:14–3 of the New Testament, mankind's stewardship responsibility is made explicit and emphasized: "We who are entrusted with God's property are expected to care for God's property and to distribute God's bounty justly; we will be held accountable for these stewardship responsibilities."

Saint Augustine extols values found in nature itself: "They [people who disdain nature] do not consider how admirable these things are in their own places, how excellent in their own natures, how beautifully adjusted to the rest of creation, and how much grace they contribute to the universe by their own contributions, as to a commonwealth."

Saint Francis of Assisi marveled at nature's beauty and order and expressed gratitude and respect for fellow animals and plants, all members of God's creation. In his *Canticle of the Sun*, Saint Francis proclaimed, "Be praised, my Lord, with all your creatures. … Be praised, my Lord, for our Sister Mother Earth, Who nourishes and governs us, and produces various fruits with many-colored flowers and herbs … Praise and bless the Lord, and give thanks and serve him with great humility."

In the 2015 *Encyclical on the Environment* ("*Laudito Si*"), Pope Francis emphasizes the mandate of responsible stewardship pronounced in the gospel of Saint Matthew and the teachings of Saint Augustine and Saint Francis of Assisi (Pope Francis's namesake). As stated in the encyclical, "Saint Francis of Assisi reminds us that our common home is like a sister with whom we share our life and a beautiful mother who opens her arms to embrace us," adding that "This sister now cries out to us because of the harm we have inflicted on her by our irresponsible use and abuse of the goods with which God has endowed her." Also: "If we approach nature without Saint Francis' sense of awe and

4 The Aristotelian influence is unmistakable. Rationality ("rational soul") is the defining form, the essence, of human beings and is higher in the order of being to plants, which have only the power of growth ("nutritive soul") and to animals, which have, in addition, the powers of locomotion, sensation, and feeling ("sensitive soul").

wonder, our demeanor will be that of master, consumers, and exploiters, unable to set limits." In another section, the encyclical states that "It is not enough to think of species merely as potential resources to be exploited, while overlooking that they have value in themselves." In regard to climate change, the 2015 encyclical makes this statement: "The problem is that we lack the vision and courage needed to confront climate change with concern for all and without prejudice toward coming generations."

Elements of these various conceptions have echoed and reechoed through the ages, and play a role in shaping the views of many people today.

NATURE AS ANTITHESIS OF MIND AND CIVILIZATION

The "modern view" is also shaped by Enlightenment ideology, articulated in its fundamentals by René Descartes and Francis Bacon. Descartes maintained that there are two fundamentally different kinds of reality: mind (*res cogitans*) and matter (*res extensa*). Bacon formulated the rudiments of the scientific method and saw the new science as an indispensable tool for controlling wild nature for the benefit of mankind. From Descartes, nature came to be seen by people living in Western societies as the dumb and machine-like "other." From Bacon, nature came to be seen as inimical to civilization and needing to be harnessed and brought under human control through scientific understanding. As these ideas were assimilated and augmented by advances in Newtonian science, nature was viewed as a machine whose operations are causally determined and capable of being fully understood—a view epitomized in this famous statement by Pierre-Simon Laplace: "An intellect, which at a certain moment would know all forces that nature set in motion, and all positions of all items of which nature is composed, … would embrace in a single formula the movements of the greatest bodies of the universe and those of the tiniest atom; for such an intellect, nothing would be uncertain and the future just like the past would be present before its eyes."[5]

Darwinian images of nature as "red in tooth and claw" (Tennyson's phrase) were later introduced to the public mind, reinforcing the Baconian view of nature as menacing, dangerous, and the antithesis of culture.

The juxtaposition of nature with what was proclaimed to be the nobility of the human mind and human culture had the effect of further desacralizing nature. Viewed as the antithesis of "things human," nature's value was reduced to its use-value for humans, and emerging science was given the mandate to control disease, droughts, dangerous

5 Pierre-Simon Laplace, *A Philosophical Essay on Probabilities* (New York: 1902), p. 4. Using a more recent idiom, Laplace's statement has been rendered as follows: If one knew the position, mass, and velocity of every atom in nature, one could, in principle, predict the entire future of the universe.

animals, and whatever else there is about nature that was seen to seen to be threatening and menacing to human life and impediments to the progress of civilization.

These themes echoed in the new America with the mandate to push back the frontier, cut down the forests for crops and pasture, build railroads and towns, and overcome the resistance of savages.

NATURE AS EVOLUTIONARY PRODUCT

Charles Darwin's *Origin of the Species*, exuberantly described by Darwin's contemporary Thomas Huxley "as the most powerful and the most comprehensive idea that has ever risen on earth," offered a new understanding of human origins. Darwin's seminal idea, grounded in his painstaking research conducted in a five-year voyage on the *Beagle* around coastlines in Africa, Asia, the South Seas, and the Galapagos of South America, challenged the idea that nature is the product of divine creation.

Darwin's hypothesis was revolutionary: all species of life have descended over time from common ancestry as the result of an ongoing process of natural selection. In his introduction to *Origin of the Species*, Darwin gave this summary account:

> As many more individuals of each species are born than can possibly survive; and, as, consequently, there is a frequently recurring struggle for existence, it follows that any being, if it varies however slightly in any manner profitable to itself, under the complex and sometimes varying conditions of life, will have a better chance of surviving, and thus, be naturally selected. From the strong principle of inheritance,[6] any selected variety will tend to propagate its new and modified form.

Darwin's theory of natural selection has since gained broad scientific acceptance and applied in many contexts. Controversial offshoots of the theory of natural selection have been advanced, notably the practice of eugenics to purify human gene pools and in schools of thought labeled as "social Darwinism." While such applications are today widely seen as aberrations of Darwin's central scientific accepts, the principle of natural selection, supplemented by advances in genetics made possible through molecular biology, finds widespread application in virtually all fields of science.

NATURE AS HUMAN ARTIFACT

The modification of landscapes, ecosystems, and geophysical systems has been occurring for tens of thousands of years as a result of human activities such as gathering, hunting, burning, cutting, grazing, planting, damming, mining, excavating, and building. Since the ramp-up of the Industrial Revolution a scant three centuries ago, human modification of nature has accelerated with mind-numbing speed. In *The End of Nature*, Bill McKibben discusses how humans have transformed not only the land and its communities of life, but also geophysical processes, including the composition of the earth's atmosphere.

Industrial and transportation technologies have wrought extensive changes on a macroscale, and genetic engineering and nanotechnology are bringing changes of comparable scope on a microscale. Other technologies are revolutionizing the manufacturing of products for use in industry, medicine, and households, including advances in robotics and 3-D printing. These developments have led to the claim made by some commentators that nature is fast becoming a human artifact. In the most extreme formulation of the nature-as-artifact thesis, wild nature is said to have become a remade artifact engineered to satisfy human needs and enable human aspirations. Science and technology have given humans the "upper hand," including the prospect of controlling the trajectory of life on the planet through widespread application of gene-editing (CRISPR) technology. Humans are in control, and little of what was once wild nature remains.

The extreme version of the nature-as-artifact thesis is surely overstated. Human activities have extensively modified the physical environment, but there are still lands relatively undisturbed by humans, including the tundra of North America, northern Europe, and Asia, the coniferous forests south of the tundra, the Amazonian rain forest, the Tibetan Plateau, the Australian Outback, the Sahara and Gobi deserts, and the depths of the world's oceans. The International Union for the Conservation of Nature (IUCN) estimates that 45 percent of the planet's surface are "wildlands," defined as lands retaining 70 percent of their original vegetation and having a human population of less than five people per kilometer. Of the world's landmass thus classified as wildlands, approximately 15 percent is legally protected.

Clearly, also, many disturbed places have the capacity to recover from human intervention, just as life in general has the capacity to adapt to perturbations and to continue to evolve as it has for billions of years. And while technology has extended the ability of humans to protect themselves against nonhuman agents and events, nature lets us know, sometimes catastrophically, that human control is limited and tenuous. Volcanoes, earthquakes, hurricanes, and other of nature's "reality checks" temper hubris and tell us what we intuitively know anyhow—that the greater natural order establishes the boundary conditions of human thought, action, and safety.

NATURE AS CULTURAL CONSTRUCT

Rather than seeing nature as a product of human making, postmodernists emphasize that nature is a cultural construct. While this contention has numerous variations, the core assertion is that nature is how it is perceived and understood to be within a particular cultural milieu. Enlightenment thinkers saw nature as the "other": as machine-like, deterministic, inimical to civilization, and utterly devoid of intrinsic value.

Romantic writers articulated very different conceptions, seeing nature as reflecting the artistry of God, as having intrinsic value, and as a sanctuary for spiritual renewal. But however nature is represented to be, the postmodernist contention is that nature is just that: a representation. Any representation is the product of cultural ways of seeing and conceiving; there is no privileged standpoint, no objective truth, no viewpoint that transcends cultural context.

Postmodernists take up the task of "deconstructing" projects and views with the objective of revealing underlying assumptions and presuppositions, hidden motives, and bias. Along these lines, postmodernists contend that ideologies are propagated by and reflect the interests of powerful elites within a culture, and that institutions and nations with relatively greater economic and political power have historically imposed their agendas on the less powerful. It is argued in this vein that the view of wilderness enshrined in the Wilderness Act of 1964—"places untrammeled by man without permanent improvement and human habitation, where man himself is a visitor who does not remain"—is one among many conceptions of nature that governments in the United States and other Western countries have sought to impose on undeveloped countries, urging them to preserve natural resources and forgo the kinds of development that have enabled the already-industrialized nations of the West and North to achieve high standards of living. Not surprisingly, critiques of this kind are also voiced by critics within the underdeveloped world.[7]

Writers in the ecofeminist tradition have joined postmodernists in rejecting ethnocentric bias in how nature is conceived, focusing more narrowly on male-oriented (androcentric) biases in inherited ideology and their perpetuation in contemporary society. Bacon's characterization of nature as female in character (as wild, dangerous, and reluctant to give up her secrets) and scientific investigation as a fundamentally male enterprise (as requiring an objective, rational, and nonemotional mind-set) have been roundly denounced by ecofeminists. Ecofeminist writers have also targeted dualisms associated with the "modern view"—mind/body, reason/emotion, objective/subjective, abstraction/embodiment, culture/nature—together with the tendency to associate superiority with male attributes (reason, objective, etc.) and inferiority with their female counterparts (body, emotion, etc.). Karen Warren characterizes such dualisms as aberrations of "value-hierarchical thinking" and the "logic of domination."[8]

---

7 A widely read commentary on Anglo-American environmentalism is Ramachandra Gua's "Radical Environmentalism and Wilderness Preservation: A Third World Critique." This widely reprinted article first appeared in *Environmental Ethics*, Vol.1, Spring 1989.

8 Karen Warren, "The Power and Promise of Ecofeminism," in *Environmental Philosophy: From Animal Rights to Radical Ecology*, Michael E. Zimmerman et al., eds., (Pearson Prentice Hall, 2005).

Acknowledging that events, conditions, and processes in the world are disclosed to us through our perceptions of them, and that without such perceptual disclosures humans would have nothing to understand, various writers reject the conclusion that perception and understanding isolate humans utterly and completely from the world they perceive and seek to understand. Without resorting to a "naïve realism"—the view that cognition exactly and precisely discloses an independently existing world as it "really is"—Holmes Rolston articulates a "critical realism" to combat not only naïve realism but also the view that nature is, inescapably, a mental or cultural construct. With reference to scrupulously conducted scientific investigations in evolutionary biology, molecular biology, ecology, and cosmology—investigations in which explanatory hypotheses are developed and tested by observations and in which experiments are designed to confirm or deny those hypotheses—Rolston argues that, over time, we get "nature for real," not merely the cultural construction of nature. What is discovered is bound up with theoretical constructs, but the basic test of truth for scientific knowledge is exacting: a hypothesis stands only as long as its predicted results are corroborated by repeated experimentation, while non-corroborating evidence quickly discredits that hypothesis. Unlike naïve realism, critical realism recognizes the conceptual contribution of the knowing subject in the formation of theories and acknowledges the incomplete, selective, and perspectival character of scientific theories. Although no perfect correspondence exists between scientific hypotheses and reality "out there," the critical realist nevertheless maintains that rigorous science yields, or progressively yields, an accurate and reliable map of physical reality.[9]

It is misleading to erect a sharp distinction between subject and object, perceiver and perceived, culture and nature, and then to construct a reductive explanation of one in terms of the other. It is as meaningful to speak of a "natural" order as it is to speak of a "cultural" order. In some places (e.g., a university or a library), cultural products and processes predominate; in others (e.g., a rainforest or a coral reef), natural products and processes predominate. Moreover, in maintaining that nature is only a cultural construct while at the same time insisting that all conceptual constructs are relative to particular cultural contexts, postmodernism is said by some writers to trap itself in a contradiction; it inconsistently privileges its own conception of nature as nonrelativist truth. As Charlene Spretnak put it, "'Postmodern' is '*most*modern' because its proponents have been socialized and educated in the scientific-humanist world view, which is dedicated to the denial of the power and presence of nature."[10]

---

9 See Rolston's "Nature for Real: Is Nature a Social Construct?" in *The Philosophy of the Environment*, D. J. Chappell, ed. (Edinburgh University Press, 1997), pp. 38–64.

10 Charlene Spretnak, *The Resurgence of the Real: Body, Nature, and Place in a Hypermodern World* (Addison-Wesley, 1997), p. 66.

NATURE AS WILDERNESS

The idea of nature as wilderness gained popular appeal in Europe through the writings of the European Romanticists Percy Bysse Shelley, John Keats, and Jean Jacques Rousseau, and in America through the works of the American transcendentalists Ralph Waldo Emerson, Henry David Thoreau, Walt Whitman, and John Muir—and through grand landscape paintings, photographs of nature's many moods, and the inspiring descriptions of wild places by nature writers. Nature came to be seen as magnificent places where dispirited humans living in controlled urban environments could find escape, liberation, tranquility, and inspiration. The visions and sentiments expressed in these works played a key role in changing popular attitudes toward nature as hostile and dangerous and in creating a political climate for the establishment of national parks and wilderness areas in the US and elsewhere.

While negative attitudes toward wild places have waned in contemporary western cultures, various writers have sought to debunk what they call the "wilderness myth." Critics point out that there are few places on Earth today that meet the definition of wilderness given in the Wilderness Act—that indigenous peoples occupied and modified the lands that are now designated as wilderness areas in the US and elsewhere, that attempts to set aside wilderness areas and to preserve wilderness conditions require intensive and continuous human management of those areas, and that it dilutes responsibility for protecting areas that are less pristine. Critics have also argued that wilderness preservation as conceived in the Wilderness Act is ethnocentric and flies in the face of the basic fact that change and adaptability to change are basic dynamics in evolving ecosystems, not constancy and uniformity.[11]

There is merit in these critiques, but they, too, run the risk of blurring important distinctions and distorting facts. There are important differences, Holmes Rolston reminds us, between human-inhabited and human-uninhabited regions, between nature and culture, between the generally slow pace of biological change and the increasingly fast pace of social and technological change, and between the modifications made by indigenous peoples of the lands they occupied and those wrought by industrialized societies with bulldozers, large populations, and economics that are remarkably efficient in satisfying the voracious wants and desires of growing populations.[12]

---

11 Arguments for and against the "wilderness concept" are presented by the editors and contributing authors to *The Great New Wilderness Debate*, J. Baird Callicott and Michael P. Nelson, eds., (Athens, GA.: University of Georgia Press, 1998).

12 Holmes Rolston, "The Wilderness Idea Reaffirmed," in *The Environment Professional* 13 (1991), pp. 370–77.

THE CONCEPT OF NATURE RECONSIDERED

The natural world *has* been transformed to a large extent by ubiquitous human presence and by ever-expanding technological capability to exploit nature's products and processes to serve human ends, but certainly not completely so. Individual and societal views of nature *are* shaped by the beliefs, values, and institutions of the culture in which one lives, but this does not mean that "nature for real" cannot be understood through rigorous and continuing scientific inquiry, or that cultural constructs of nature that disadvantage women, people living in Third World countries, and others are immune from moral criticism and reform, or that insidious dualisms should not go unchallenged. Humans and other life *have* evolved by processes of natural selection, but the capacity of systems throughout nature to self-organize, adapt, and create novelty is also part of the story of life's evolution. Religious beliefs *do* give meaning and hope in many people's lives, but religious accounts that reject *ex cathedra* evolutionary and other accounts of the relationship of humans to the broader natural order limit and distort an understanding of the human condition. None of the various conceptions of nature briefly sketched previously are adequate by themselves—or for a world in which rapidly growing human populations are transforming landscapes and consuming resources at accelerating rates, nature's regenerative capacities are being diminished, resource shortages are recurring on a global scale with ominous potential for widespread conflict and warfare, human-caused species extinctions are occurring on a scale rivaling the mass extinctions of the distant geological past, and climate change is occurring as a result of rapidly increasing concentrations of greenhouse gases in the atmosphere.

Nature is not only a product, but a vast biosphere in which life-creating and life-sustaining processes occur and have occurred for more than three billion years. The ongoing saga of life is about the capacity of many lives to adapt, survive, and thrive in their environments. It's also about the adaptive and information-based capacity of genomes (the concrete embodiment of species-kinds) to orchestrate structure and function at the cellular level, and about the capacity of ecosystems to enable a great diversity of existing kinds to coexist, coadapt, and coevolve in relations of mutual benefit and to generate new kinds of increasing diversity and complexity. Manifestations of these capacities constitute the most basic processes that occur in the planet's biosphere, and themselves are processes through which pro-life tendencies are selected in the natural order.

The wilderness concept goes awry when nature is seen as an end product that needs to preserved in a fixed, unchanging state. If the term "wild" is used to refer to processes in the natural world whose operations and products predate human life and whose continuation, while influenced by human activity, are not dependent on human life, the challenge is to preserve wildness, not wilderness. An organism, ecosystem, or bioregion is wild to the extent that its functioning is not disturbed or controlled by human beings, or to the extent that it is capable of recovering from human interference. Clearly there are relatively wild places left on Earth, and clearly many disturbed places have the capacity to recover and operate on their own.

In his essay "Walking," Thoreau said: "In wildness is the preservation of the world." The term "wildness" in this statement is sometimes interpreted as "wilderness," but Jack Turner insists that this is a misrepresentation of what Thoreau meant. Turner points out that Thoreau noted in his *Fact Book* that "wild" is the past participle of "to will" and that wildness is "self-willed land."[13] By identifying wildness with fixed conditions in nature rather than self-organizing processes that produce and sustain those conditions, we get a flawed concept of wildness. We also get, according to Turner, wilderness areas that are too small, too accommodating of human recreational interests, too controlled and regulated, and too tamed. In Turner's words: "Thus diminished, wilderness becomes a special unit of property, treated like a historic relic or ruin—a valuable remnant."[14]

In what follows, then, the term "wild" is used to refer to life and life systems whose existence is not dependent on human life and that would continue to function and adapt without human life. The concept of nature-as-wildness legislates against statements such as "Nature is what it is conceived to be" (nature as cultural construct) or "Nature is what humans make of it" (nature as human artifact), or as wilderness set-asides to be maintained in fixed states (nature as wilderness). It also mitigates against the statement that "Everything is natural." At the same time, however, it accommodates basic facts: that humans are part of nature; that culture is situated within and depends on wider natural systems; that wildness can be found in gardens and urban parks as well as set-aside wilderness areas; and that neither culture nor conditions in wild nature refer to unchanging conditions. Similar to culture, nature is both product and process and constantly undergoes change. Furthermore, it does not presuppose that nature and human culture are inevitably and irreconcilably opposed, or that the human influence on other life is necessarily good or bad. Arguments for the preservation of wilderness and wildlife are examined in subsequent chapters, but the present point is that such arguments should not be settled in advance by flawed or overly restrictive definitions of the terms "wildness," "wilderness," and "nature."

13 Jack Turner, *The Abstract Wild* (Tucson: University of Arizona Press, 1996), p. 111.

14 Ibid., pp. 84–86.

CHAPTER TWELVE

Environmental Futures

This final chapter brings together the different environmental studies topics we have discussed to look forward to what our future may hold. As you have learned in this text, climate change is the most critical environmental challenge we currently face. How we manage climate change (or fail to) has implications for our environmental, social, and economic futures. The selected reading by Marcia Angell (2016), "Our Beleaguered Planet" from *The American Prospect,* reviews how the issue of climate change has been debated and managed over the past half century. We remember from readings about climate change in Chapter 5 and about population growth in Chapter 8, that one of the primary drivers of climate change is increasing human population since more people produce more emissions. However, we also understand that the source of these emissions and the areas where population growth is highest are not necessarily the same. The connection between human population growth and climate change is complex. Angell's reading gives us some direction on untangling that complexity and moving forward.

In addition, the far-reaching effects of a changing climate on our planet are only beginning to be understood. Angell discusses the Zika virus outbreak in 2015, a situation that is similar to the novel corona virus pandemic, COVID-19, in 2020. Because humans are continuing to increase our populations with few limits and little planning, we have invaded wild animal habitats. Bringing these animals into constant close contact with humans has created a situation in which global pandemics from zoonotic diseases, those that originate in a nonhuman species, are only going to increase. Pulling together the interdisciplinary strands of environmental studies will be required to deal with this complex and uncertain future and to ensure that our planet, all of it, remains healthy.

One of the ways that our current society measures success is by the growth of the economy. However, at this point simply assessing the size of an economy does not measure the health of its people or the health of the natural world. Mark Sagoff's selected reading, "Do We Consume Too Much?" from *Philosophy, Technology, and the Environment*, edited by David Kaplan (2017), discusses how over consumption reflects our underlying values as a society. If we only measure success based on the size of the economy, as we saw in Chapter 2 with "The Story of Stuff," we must then constantly consume more to make the economy grow. If we choose to measure health and success by other metrics, this will require rethinking much of what we value as individuals, communities, and all of society. Sagoff describes several different aspects of our natural world that will need to be valued differently to reflect our desire to change to a more sustainable world from food to forests and oceans.

Hopefully we can see more clearly that decisions about how to manage common natural resources require not only scientific and practical considerations but also ethical and philosophical deliberations. We are called to make moral decisions based on our values as a society, about how to use and manage shared resources. Moving toward a sustainable, just, and equitable world will not be easy, but hopefully the interdisciplinary lessons from this environmental studies text will help you participate in creating this new world.

RECOMMENDED READING

Keimowitz, A. 2018. "I Felt Despair About Climate Change—Until a Brush with Death Changed My Mind." *Science*, March 9. Retrieved from: https://slate.com/technology/2018/03/an-environmental-professor-on-learning-to-cope-with-climate-change.html.

READING AND DISCUSSION PROMPTS

1. Marcia Angell's article was published in 2016 when the current public health scare was Zika virus. Compare Angell's description of the origins and spread of Zika virus, SARS, MERS, and bird flu with the 2020 COVID-19 pandemic. What similar environmental and social conditions drove the origin and spread of these diseases? How can we better manage the environment to prevent zoonotic diseases in the future?
2. In the Angell article, what key policy change does she point to as being a critical tool in the fight to stabilize, and eventually reduce, human population growth? Why do you think this policy might work?
3. In the Sagoff article, what is the author's view of the mainstream environmentalism idea that consumption is a "zero-sum game." In other words, there are

limited resources on earth, and what feeds one person is taken from another. Does he agree with this idea? Why or why not?

4. At the beginning of the text, you read about consumption and reflected on your personal consumption patterns. Now that you have worked through the text, repeat this exercise: Do you think you personally consume too much or not? How do your own patterns of consumption affect your happiness, your relationships with other people, and the way you feel about nature?

READING 12.1

Our Beleaguered Planet

By Marcia Angell

Zika, the mosquito-borne virus that is spreading rapidly in South America and heading north toward the U.S. as summer comes, shows how a previously isolated and sporadic illness can suddenly become a frightening pandemic because of the combined effects of global warming and overpopulation. Carried by the *Aedes aegypti* mosquito, Zika apparently arose in Uganda in the 1940s and occurred only episodically until 2015, when it began to spread explosively in Brazil, mainly in densely crowded urban areas.

Like other mosquitoes, which are vectors for many diseases, *Aedes aegypti* thrives in a warm climate, and, as nearly all experts now agree, the world's climate is steadily growing warmer because of human activity. In addition, this particular mosquito has evolved to live in dose proximity to humans, and breeds in small amounts of water in human trash, such as bottle caps and plastic containers. The transmission of the virus occurs in both directions—from mosquitoes to people and from infected people back to mosquitoes. The more densely packed the population, the more easily Zika spreads, and that is particularly so in slums where there are few screens or air conditioners, and even mosquito repellent is rare—and where trash collection is even rarer. Thus, Zika is the poster child of a pandemic resulting from both climate change and overpopulation.

Nearly everyone now acknowledges that global warming is real and caused by human activity. There are very few "deniers" left, except among paid consultants to oil companies and on the Republican side of the aisle in Congress. Since the Industrial Revolution,

Marcia Angell, "Our Beleaguered Planet," *The American Prospect*, vol. 27, no. 2, pp. 91-94.

carbon emissions have grown right along with population and the use of fossil fuels. The resultant increase in greenhouse gases, which trap heat in the atmosphere, causes the climate to warm, and sea levels to rise as glaciers melt. Atmospheric carbon dioxide, the most important of the greenhouse gases, reached a record 398 parts per million (ppm) in 2015, up from 285 ppm in 1850. Much of the carbon dioxide is absorbed by the oceans, which causes them to become more acidic and threatens the marine food chain on which we all depend. Droughts are more frequent and deserts are expanding. Floods and severe storms are also more frequent as the atmosphere warms.

But the cause of global warming is not just our "carbon footprint"—that is, the amount of greenhouse gases emitted per capita—but the number of humans contributing to it. The world population is now more than 7.3 billion, compared with 2.5 billion in 1950, when I was growing up, and 1.3 billion in 1850 during the Industrial Revolution. It will reach about 9.5 billion in 2050. Yet, while there is much discussion of climate change, very little is said these days about population growth. It seems almost to have been ruled off the table as a legitimate topic, even though it is an essential part of the equation.

How many people can the planet support? The carrying capacity for any species is defined as the maximum number that can be sustained indefinitely, and in the case of humans is usually said to be about ten billion, albeit with a wide range of estimates. But humans are not just any species; we are increasingly divided into rich and poor, both within and across countries, and the effects of overpopulation are seen unevenly, and well before any theoretical carrying capacity is reached. For nearly all of human history, the risk has instead been under-population—the lack of communities large enough to foster human progress, and even at times, the threat of extinction. We didn't reach the first billion until about 1800. But with better sanitation and living standards, especially since the Industrial Revolution, global population grew rapidly, with shorter and shorter doubling times. In addition to fossil fuels, we are now exhausting other natural resources, as well as despoiling the environment in trying to extract them. And we have created what is known, somewhat misleadingly, as the "great Pacific garbage patch" by dumping into the oceans vast amounts of discarded plastic containers, which tend to break into small particles that remain suspended in certain regions just beneath the water's surface.

IN 1798, THOMAS MALTHUS famously predicted that population growth would soon lead to mass starvation. After he was shown to be stunningly wrong, not much public attention was given to the subject until 1968, when Paul R. Ehrlich published his best-selling book, *The Population Bomb*—at a time when the global population was a mere 3.6 billion. Like Malthus, Ehrlich predicted imminent mass starvation, and argued for stringent population control. But in the last half of the 20th century, remarkable technological improvements in agriculture—the "green revolution"—greatly increased food supply, and Ehrlich's predictions, like those of Malthus, were off the mark.

The fact that dire predictions had proved wrong may have been one reason that overpopulation largely disappeared from public discourse in the 1980s. The decade saw a renewed confidence in technology to solve nearly any problem. And with growing economic inequality, it was easy for wealthy populations to conclude that they were immune to the effects of overpopulation. There was also an element of "political correctness," in that the problems of overpopulation were mainly the problems of poor people in poor regions of the world, and many in the developed world felt that family size is a private matter and it was unseemly to suggest that disadvantaged populations should have fewer children. (No one had anything good to say about China's one-child policy, quite apart from the methods used to achieve it.)

Moreover, the 1980s was the decade when climate change first became widely recognized, not only by scientists, but increasingly by the larger public, and that concern supplanted concern about overpopulation. In 1988, James E. Hansen, Director of NASA's Goddard Institute for Space Studies, testified before Congress on the dangers of global warming, and about the same time, the World Meteorological Organization established the Intergovernmental Panel on Climate Change. The focus shifted from population to carbon emissions, even though they were, and are, related. It was as though if we could all cut down on the use of fossil fuels and be better stewards of the environment, the total number of people wouldn't matter. But it does matter, of course. There is a limit, even though one can argue what that is, and how much suffering people on the fringes should endure before we recognize it.

Areas with the fastest population growth are those with the smallest per capita carbon footprint. But that will change as consumption of resources increases.

The threats, then, are twofold and interrelated: First, the number of people, and second, the way we live. However, there is an inverse and paradoxical relationship. In general, areas of the world with the fastest population growth are those with the smallest per capita carbon footprint and consumption of resources. But poorer regions are hardly going to be satisfied to remain that way. Underdeveloped regions of the world aspire to the life of affluent regions, which means that even as their birthrates decline, which they inevitably do with economic development, their environmental footprint will grow. With poverty still widespread, their populations will also continue to grow. Even if we stabilized the population at its current level, it is likely that consumption per capita would continue to increase because of rapid, often uncontrolled, development—exactly as happened in China and is happening in India.

A grave effect of overpopulation and climate change is the scarcity of clean water, either to drink or for sanitation. Much of the available water is used for irrigation, and as conditions become warmer and more arid, more water is required for crops. The scarcity is particularly acute in North Africa and the Middle East, but we can see it also in the American Southwest and southern California. For example, the Colorado River, the source of much of the water there, is depleted before it can reach its original outlet to the Sea of Cortez. The rivers and aquifers of Africa are similarly becoming exhausted. The larger the population, the worse the problem.

One result is mass migration in search of water and arable land, and this probably underlies some of the unrest in North Africa and the Middle East. Migrants are especially vulnerable to starvation and violence of all kinds, in addition to disruption of education, childhood immunizations, and other health care. Even while much of the earth is growing more arid, some places are now experiencing disastrous floods. But that water is of little use, because of contamination with sewage. The rainfall in the growing megacities is also largely wasted, since it doesn't reach the soil and is quickly contaminated.

These effects are bad enough, but what may be most threatening is epidemic disease. The slums of the new, rapidly growing megacities are breeding grounds for disease. In Lagos, Nigeria, for example, a city of some 21 million people, about two-thirds of the inhabitants live in slums. Contamination from sewage causes cholera, but there is also the likelihood of the spread of other infectious diseases that have previously been contained in small geographic areas or by seasonal cool weather. For example, for many years Ebola outbreaks have occurred sporadically in isolated villages, but did not reach epidemic proportions until there were large and mobile populations.

Before Zika, several other pandemics—defined as worldwide epidemics—have appeared in recent years. They arose in one part of the world, but because of crowding and easy travel, they were able to spread widely. A new disease (or new to the broader world) called SARS (severe acute respiratory syndrome) arose in southern China in 2002 and was carried to some two dozen countries by infected travelers. Another apparently new disease called MERS (Middle East respiratory syndrome) arose in Saudi Arabia in 2012, but spread to many countries, including the United States, and to South Korea, where it is still causing serious, sometimes fatal, illness.

FERNANDO ILANO / AP IMAGES

So far, we have not had a pandemic on the scale of the 1918 flu pandemic or the bubonic plague of the 14th century. But conditions are

Makoko slum in Lagos, Nigeria

HANNIBAL HANSCHAE / DPA / AP IMAGES

ripe for it. Probably the most likely cause would be an influenza virus, transmitted to humans from birds or other animals. Ina recent op-ed about Zika in *The New York Times,* Michael T. Osterholm, the director of the Center for Infectious Disease Research and Policy at the University of Minnesota, wrote, "Even more than these viruses, we should be afraid of a planet-wide catastrophe caused by influenza." Flu viruses mutate often, and can shift in both their host targets and their virulence. Bird flu, which is often fatal, is not readily transmissible between humans, but that could change. Moreover, because transmissible flu viruses are airborne, they spread easily and quickly from person to person. Most important, people can spread the virus before they have symptoms, unlike the case with other diseases such as Ebola. Thus, someone can get on a plane feeling quite well, but still spread the virus to everyone around him by talking or coughing.

The 2011 film *Contagion* illustrated the dangers very well: A flu-like virus causes a deadly pandemic, starting with a young Minneapolis woman (Gwyneth Paltrow) who had just returned from a trip to Hong Kong. At the end of the film, we learn that she was probably infected by shaking hands with the chef at a restaurant. His hands were contaminated with the blood of a pig that had been infected by a bat that dropped a piece of banana into the pig pen. Parts of the film were unrealistic, but this idea of the origin of a flu epidemic was not. The ability to monitor or contain such outbreaks is limited, particularly in sub-Saharan Africa. As Keiji Fukuda, then the assistant director-general for health security at the World Health Organization (WHO), said in 2013, "The world is not ready for a large, severe outbreak."

TO DEAL WITH THE TWIN threats of overpopulation and climate change, we will need to get busy. Small, incremental efforts will not be enough. Much is made of the fact that as living standards and urbanization increase, and as women in particular become better educated, fertility rates drop. In fact, in some countries, including Japan, Russia, much of Eastern Europe, Germany, Italy, and Spain, population is either static or declining. But population growth is not evenly distributed. These small declines in the wealthy countries will be more than offset by continued growth in other parts of the world. The population in Africa, for example, is expected to double by 2050—from about 1.2 billion to 2.5 billion. Although the rate of growth worldwide has slowed in recent years, it has not reached zero, so the population will inexorably grow, albeit more slowly. The United Nations Department of Economic and Social Affairs predicts continued growth for the remainder of this century, with a projected population of about 11 billion in 2100.

What can be done? There are two non-coercive and constructive ways to bring the rate of population growth to zero or less. First, we need to provide enough economic security to families in developing countries to reduce the incentive to have large numbers of children. It is often assumed that providing better birth control is the answer, and that may be partially true. But it is likely that many families want a large number of children because they need them for farm labor or to contribute otherwise to family income, and also to provide for their parents when they reach old age. Unlike families in the developed world, these families see children as a "profit center," not a "cost center." People need to be protected against illness, extreme poverty, and the infirmities of old age to be willing to have fewer children. They need a minimum social safety net.

Second, we need to make stronger efforts to ensure that girls are educated. The evidence is overwhelming that maternal education, regardless of income, correlates with smaller family size. It is essential, then, to focus on the education of girls and more generally the status of women, for moral reasons as well as population control.

In 1994, when the global population was 5.6 billion, the International Conference on Population and Development met in Cairo and issued a lengthy Programme of Action that was widely heralded and adopted by a special session of the U.N. General Assembly in 1999. It was notable for its strong, and I believe warranted, emphasis on human welfare and the status of women. In fact, it was a veritable Christmas list of all the things that make life worth living, even including a fulfilling sex life within an egalitarian marriage. But it said little about the harms of overpopulation, nor how to bring about, and pay for, the undeniably better world it called for. And it included this in its opening statement: "The implementation of the recommendations contained in the Programme of Action is the sovereign right of each country, consistent with national laws and development priorities, with full respect for the various religious and ethical values and cultural backgrounds of its people, and in conformity with universally recognized international human rights." Anyone who has read Katherine Zoepf's January 11 *New Yorker* article "Sisters in Law," about the legal status of women in Saudi Arabia, or the February 5 *New York Times* article by Pam Belluck and Joe Cochrane about female genital cutting in Indonesia, where it is performed on nearly half of Indonesian girls, will see the problem with the deference to sovereign rights, religious and ethical values, and cultural backgrounds.

Even though bringing population growth under control is crucial, global warming and the wanton consumption of natural resources are still primarily caused by the way we in the developed world live. It is still our carbon footprint that is doing most of the damage. Three years ago, *New York Times* reporter Elisabeth Rosenthal wrote an article titled "Your Biggest Carbon Sin May Be Air Travel." It concerned the industry-inspired U.S. law that forbids American airlines from participating in the European Union Emissions Trading System, which charges airlines for excess carbon emissions generated by flights in or out of European airports. She pointed out that for many Americans, air travel is probably the largest contributor to their individual carbon footprint. And she added: "It is for me. And for people like A1 Gore or Richard Branson who crisscross the world, often by private jet, proclaiming their devotion to the environment." It is for me, too. Air travel emissions account for about 5 percent of global warming, according to Rosenthal, but that fraction is projected to rise. Unless there are required changes in our habits that apply to everyone, analogous to the rationing of gasoline for cars during World War II, A1 Gore and I will probably continue to live pretty much the way we have, with only small changes at the margins. People will embrace restrictions in the way they live only if they are shared.

Just as the notion of the supreme nationstate needs modification, so does our devotion to unfettered capitalism and the grail of GDP growth.

To tackle the problem seriously means to tackle it at the national level, and paradoxically to do so by modifying our allegiance to nationhood. We all breathe the same air, and depend on the same oceans. Because we have no international body with sufficient authority, we will have to rely on nation-states to join together to modify their behavior for the good of the planet, and that means blunting the super-patriotism that afflicts most countries. Just as the formation of the U.S. required the 13 colonies to modify their sense of sovereignty for the greater good, so must the countries of the world do that for the sake of the planet. Yet, some European countries are now actually arguing for *increasing* population growth, because they see the aging and decline of their population as a national threat. They would like to create more young people to support the old ones, and generally to grow their way out of their problems. For similar reasons, China has announced an end to its one-child policy. But no country is alone on the planet. Not only would these countries add to the global problems, but even within their own borders, the policy simply delays the effects of an aging population for another generation.

To provide enough security to families in developing countries to reduce their incentive to have large numbers of children will take money, not only from the governments of these countries, but even more from developed countries. The concept of a subsidy for basic needs is not new. Some European countries are currently considering providing a small income to all their residents for that reason. A similar scheme could be set up by which wealthy nations contribute to a global fund to ensure basic needs for impoverished regions of the world. Contributions could be based on a small percentage of GDP. A portion might be earmarked to support education for girls.

Developed countries also need to subject themselves to the same constraints we ask of developing regions. Large families could become socially unacceptable in the same way that cigarette smoking gradually became less acceptable in the U.S. But the real job for affluent countries is to rein in overconsumption, profligate waste, and the use of fossil fuels. This requires a transition that is far beyond anything now being seriously discussed in mainstream politics or global diplomacy. The much-celebrated U.N. Climate Change Conference, held in Paris late last year, merely pledged participating countries to work toward a goal and revisit the subject in five years. Proposals to accomplish a serious transition to a sustainable economy are invariably countered by massive lobbying by business elites and more general objections that this will cost jobs and limit economic growth. We need a shift that radically reconceives prosperity and how we define it. To survive as well-functioning, civilized communities in a static global population, there will inevitably have to be some redistribution of wealth, both within countries and across them. We might have to make do with less—certainly with less as traditionally understood—and distribute it more equitably. Just as the notion of the supreme nation-state needs modification, so, too, does our devotion to unfettered capitalism and the grail of GDP growth. While politically, my solutions are a nonstarter, that could change. They are certainly more palatable than pandemics, starvation, and wars as a means of population control and resource allocation, and we could come to that realization fairly suddenly.

I am very much aware that I have not laid out a political road map—that is, a route to building a mass movement and the leadership to deal adequately with the problems. I simply don't know how that is to be done, and I'm pessimistic that it will be. After all, our Congress can't pass even the simplest, most uncontroversial legislation, and much of the rest of the world is not only ungovernable, but committed to tribal warfare of one sort or another. But I do know that we cannot continue as we are now, and that small efforts at the margins are not enough. My purpose is to convey a sense of urgency and the reasons for it.

The first step is to begin talking candidly about the issues. Overpopulation cannot continue to be the problem that dares not speak its name. Humans are not just fouling their nest, but crowding it beyond its capacity. Only when both problems are taken seriously and become part of respectable discourse will we be able to move ahead on the steps necessary to deal with the self-destructive way we are treating our planet.

READING 12.2

Do We Consume Too Much?

By Mark Sagoff

A Roz Chast cartoon in a 2011 issue of *The New Yorker* depicts two robed monks, each carrying a sign. One sign reads "The end of the world is at hand for religious reasons." The other declares "The end of the world is at hand for ecological reasons." Which will it be? Some conservation biologists believe that it might not matter. According to David Orr (2005), there is "an interesting convergence of views between conservation biologists and religious fundamentalists," because "both agree that things are going to hell in the proverbial handbasket." Conservation biologists, Orr notes, often argue that "whether by climate change, biotic impoverishment, catastrophic pollution, resource wars, emergent diseases, or a combination of several, the end is in sight, although we can quibble about the details and the schedule."

Many environmentalists who believe that the world is enjoying its final days subscribe to the Malthusian theory that resources inevitably diminish and become exhausted as population and consumption increase. For many decades, such environmentalists have warned that "human demand is outstripping what nature can supply—even though the great majority of human beings have not even approached the extraordinary American level of resource consumption." They deplore the "human overshoot of the Earth's carrying capacity" (Ehrlich and Ehrlich 2004, 69).

OVERCONSUMPTION—ETHICS, OR ECONOMICS?

Do we consume too much? To some, the answer is self-evident. If there is only so much food, timber, petroleum, and other material to go around, the more we consume, the less must be available for others. The global economy cannot grow indefinitely on a finite planet. As populations increase and economies expand, natural resources must be depleted; prices will rise, and humanity—especially the poor and future generations at all income levels—will suffer.

Other reasons to suppose we consume too much are less often stated though also widely believed. Of these reasons the simplest—a lesson we learn from our parents and from literature since the Old Testament—may be the best: Although we must satisfy basic needs, a good life is not one devoted to amassing material possessions. What we own comes to own us, keeping us from fulfilling commitments that give meaning to life, such as those to family, friends, and faith. The appreciation of nature also deepens our lives. As we consume more, however, we are more likely to transform the natural world, so that less of it will remain for us to learn from, communicate with, and appreciate.

During the nineteenth century, preservationists forthrightly gave ethical and spiritual reasons for protecting the natural world. John Muir condemned the "temple destroyers, devotees of ravaging commercialism" who "instead of lifting their eyes to the God of the mountains, lift them to the Almighty dollar" (1912, 256). This was not a call for better cost–benefit analysis: Muir described nature not as a commodity but as a companion. Nature is sacred, Muir held, whether or not resources are scarce.

Emerson and Thoreau thought of nature as full of divinity. Walt Whitman celebrated a leaf of grass as no less than the journeywork of the stars: "After you have exhausted what there is in business, politics, conviviality, love, and so on," he wrote in *Specimen Days*, and "found that none of these finally satisfy, or permanently wear—what remains? Nature remains" (1971, 61). These writers thought of nature as a refuge from economic activity, not as a resource for it.

Today many scientists say we are running out of resources or threatening the services ecosystems provide. Predictions of resource scarcity and ecological collapse appear objective and value-free, whereas pronouncements that nature is sacred or has intrinsic value can appear embarrassing in a secular society. One might suppose, moreover, that prudential and economic arguments may succeed better than moral or spiritual ones in swaying public policy. This is especially true if the warnings of resource depletion, global warming, and plummeting standards of living are dire enough—and if a consensus of scientists vouch for them.

Predictions of resource depletion, food scarcity, and falling standards of living, however, may work against our moral intuitions. Consider the responsibility many of us feel to improve the lot of those less fortunate than we. By declaring consumption a zero-sum game, by insisting that what feeds one person is taken from another, environmentalists offer a counsel of despair. Must we abandon the hope that the poor can enjoy better standards of living? The Malthusian proposition that Earth's population already overwhelms its carrying capacity—an idea associated for fifty years with mainstream environmentalist thought—may make us feel guilty but strangely relieves us of responsibility. If there are too many people, some must go.

A different approach, which is consistent with our spiritual commitment to preserve nature and with our moral responsibility to help one another, rejects the apocalyptic narrative of environmentalism. The alternative approach suggests not so much that we consume less as that we invest more. Environmentalists could push for investment in technologies that will increase productivity per unit energy, get more economic output from less material input, provide new sources of power, increase crop yields by engineering better seeds, and move from an industrial economy to a service economy. A really good battery for an electric car could make the petroleum industry nearly obsolete because an electric car could run on a charge that costs pennies per mile. Technological advances of these kinds account for the remarkable improvements in living conditions most people in the world have experienced in the past 40 years, the period over which environmentalists had predicted the steepest declines. They also account for the preservation of nature—for example, the remarkable reforestation of the eastern United States.

What should we environmentalists do? Should we insist, with many conservation biologists and other scientists, that the Earth has reached its limits and the end is in sight, although we can quibble about the details and the schedule? Should we instead leave the End Days to the saints and work with the kinds of knowledge-based high-tech industries that seek to engineer solutions for (or, if necessary, ways to adapt to) the local and global challenges of preserving nature while promoting prosperity?

The idea that increased consumption will inevitably lead to depletion and scarcity, as often as it is repeated, is mistaken both in principle and in fact. It is based on four misconceptions. The first is that we are running out of non-renewable resources, such as minerals. The second is that the world will run out of renewable resources, such as food. The third is that energy resources will soon run out. The fourth misconception argues from the "doubling time" of world population to the conclusion that human bodies cover every inch of the Earth. These misconceptions could turn into self-fulfilling prophecies if we believed them, and if we therefore failed to make the kinds of investments and reforms that have improved standards of living in most of the world.

ARE WE RUNNING OUT OF NON-RENEWABLE RESOURCES?

Although commodity markets are volatile (with the markets for petroleum especially sensitive to political conditions), the prices of minerals have declined since the 1980s. The prices of resource-based commodities have declined, and the reserves of most raw materials have increased. The reserves have increased because technologies have greatly improved exploration and extraction (for example, the use of bacteria to leach metals from low-grade ores). Reserves of resources "are actually functions of technology," one analyst has written. "The more advanced the technology, the more reserves become known and recoverable." (Lee 1989, 116) For this reason, among others, as the World Bank reiterated in 2009, although commodity prices are volatile, "over the long run, demand for commodities is not expected to outstrip supply" (World Bank 2009, xi).

One reason for the persistent decline in the costs of minerals and metals is that plentiful resources are quickly substituted for those that become scarce. As technologies that use more abundant resources do the work of technologies dependent on less-abundant resources (for example, ceramics in place of tungsten, fiber optics in place of copper wire, and aluminum cans in place of tin ones), the demand for and the price of scarce resources decline. One can easily find earlier instances of substitution. Early in the nineteenth century, whale oil was the preferred fuel for household illumination. A dwindling supply prompted innovations in the lighting industry, including the invention of gas and kerosene lamps and Edison's carbon-filament electric bulb. Whale oil has substitutes, such as electricity and petroleum-based lubricants. From an economic point of view, technology can easily find substitutes for whale products. From an aesthetic, ethical, and spiritual point of view, in contrast, whales are irreplaceable.

The more we learn about materials, the more efficiently we use them. The progress from whale oil to candles to carbon-filament incandescent lamps to tungsten incandescent lamps, for example, decreased the energy required for and the cost of a unit of household lighting by many times. On perfecting the electric bulb, which made lighting inexpensive, Thomas Edison is widely quoted as saying that "only the rich will burn candles." Compact fluorescent lights are four times as efficient as today's incandescent bulbs and last ten to twenty times as long. Comparable energy savings are available in other appliances; for example, refrigerators sold today are more efficient than those sold in 1990, saving consumers billions of dollars on their electric bills. If the future is like the past, the productivity of natural resources will continue to rise along with the productivity of labor, and we will require fewer resources per unit of production.

Modern economies depend more on the progress of technology than on the exploitation of nature. Although raw materials will always be necessary, knowledge has become the essential factor in the production of goods and services. Technological advance, which seems to be exponential insofar as each discovery prompts others, promises to improve standards of living while lightening the human footprint on the natural world. Of course, no one believes that economic development (or technological and scientific progress) will automatically lead to environmental improvement. It only provides the means; we must gather the moral, cultural, and political will to pursue the end. We can always obtain other resources. The limits to knowledge are the limits to growth.

WILL THERE BE ENOUGH FOOD?

"People today," a prominent agricultural economist wrote in 2000, "have more adequate nutrition than ever before and acquire that nutrition at the lowest cost in all human history, while the world has more people than ever before—not by a little but by a lot." (Johnson 2000, 1) This happened, Johnson argued, because "we have found low-cost and abundant substitutes for natural resources important in the production process" (ibid., 2). By around 2000, the price of food and feed grains, in real dollars (adjusted for inflation), had declined by half from what it had been 50 years earlier in international markets.

From 1961 to 2009, global production of food doubled (FAO 2009). The world produces enough cereals and oilseeds to feed a healthful vegetarian diet adequate in protein and calories to 10 billion people—a billion more than the number at which demographers predict world population will peak later this century. If, however, the idea is to feed 10 billion people not healthful vegetarian diets but the kind of meat-laden, artery-clogging, obesity-causing gluttonous meals that many Americans eat, the production of grains and oilseeds may have to triple—primarily to feed livestock (Matson and Vitousek 2006, 709). Conceivably, if everyone had the money to pay for food at current prices, with technological advances occurring particularly in bioengineering, the world could produce enough beef and donuts to fatten everyone for the slaughter of diabetes, cirrhosis, and heart disease.

Farmers worldwide could double the acreage in production, but this should not be necessary. Increasing productivity will flow from the agricultural revolution driven by biotechnology—a field that includes advanced genetics and genomics, bioinformatics, genetically modified plants, and tissue culture. According to Lester Brown (1989), "there are vast opportunities for increasing water efficiency" in arid regions, ranging from installing better water-delivery systems to planting drought-resistant crops," and "scientists can help push back the physical frontiers of cropping by developing varieties that are more drought resistant, salt tolerant, and early maturing. The payoff on the first two could be particularly high." Biotechnology introduces an entirely new stage in humankind's attempts to produce more crops and plants. The Gene Revolution takes over where the Green Revolution left off.

Before one heads to the nearest steak house to tuck into a T-bone, one should acknowledge three problems for this optimistic account. First, the essential input onto agriculture is money. Money is not spread evenly over the Earth; it is concentrated in the wealthier nations. According to the Millennium Ecosystem Assessment (2005), "despite rising food production and falling food prices, more than 850 million people still suffer today from chronic undernourishment." Many of the poorest countries, such as Chad and Congo, possess more than enough excellent agricultural land but lack social organization and investment. Institutional reform—responsible government, peace, the functioning of markets, the provision of educational and health services (in other words, development)—is the appropriate response to poverty and therefore the appropriate response to malnutrition. Second, according to the Millennium Ecosystem Assessment, "among industrial countries, and increasingly among developing ones, diet-related risks, mainly associated with overnutrition, in combination with physical inactivity now account for one third of the burden of disease"; by comparison, "worldwide, undernutrition accounted for nearly 10% of the global burden of disease." Third, to make 9 billion people obese, biotech-based agriculture would have to convert the Earth to a feedlot for human beings. Farmers can now provide a healthful diet for that many people on less acreage than they use today, thus sparing land for nature. In other words, we can spare nature by sparing ourselves.

By locking themselves into the Malthusian rhetoric by predicting impending worldwide starvation and using the plight of the very poor as evidence of it, environmentalists ignore and even alienate groups who emphasize the quality and safety rather than the abundance of food and who understand that under-nutrition represents a local not a global problem. The discussion has moved from the question whether the Earth sets limits to the question of how to get wealthy people to eat less and poor people to eat more. Advocates of animal rights deplore horrific the feedlot operations and the related factory-farm methods required to overfeed people. Environmentalists have obvious allies in advocates of human development, public health, and animal rights. To have any credibility, however, environmentalists must abandon the apocalyptic narrative.

ARE WE RUNNING OUT OF ENERGY?

Predictions that the world would by now have run out of petroleum, or will do so shortly, are an industry. Among the titles of books published in the early 2000s were *Beyond Oil: The View from Hubbert's Peak*, *The End of Oil: On the Edge of a Perilous New World*, *Out of Gas: The End of the Age of Oil*, and *The Party's Over: Oil, War and the Fate of Industrial Societies* (Deffeyes 2005; Roberts 2005; Goodstein 2004; Heinberg 2003). The most persistent worries about resource scarcity concern energy. "The supply of fuels and other natural resources is becoming the limiting factor constraining the rate of economic growth," a group of experts proclaimed in 1996 (Gever et al. 1996, 9). They predicted the exhaustion of domestic oil and gas supplies by 2020 and, within a few decades, "major energy shortages as well as food shortages in the world."

In stark contrast with the dire jeremiads of the 1990s, the US Department of Energy 2012 projections "show natural gas and renewables gaining an increasing share of US electric power generation, domestic crude oil and natural gas production growing, reliance on imported oil decreasing, US natural gas production exceeding consumption, and energy-related carbon dioxide emissions remaining below their 2005 level through 2035" (US Energy Information Administration 2012). According to the Department of Energy, oil production had not peaked in the US, and that "domestic crude oil production is expected to grow by more than 20 percent over the coming decade" (ibid.). They projected that increased oil, natural gas and renewable energy production and energy efficiency improvements would significantly reduce the United States' reliance on imported energy.

The most abundant fossil or carbon-based fuel is coal, and some of the largest reserves of it are found in the United States. They will last more than 100 years. In this respect, no global shortages of hydrocarbon fuels are in sight. There is no immediate danger of the entire world's running out of energy. That is not what the energy problem is all about. Yet for decades environmental Cassandras have reiterated that we are running out of energy, thus directing attention to sources rather than sinks. Thankfully there is a growing consensus that the real energy problems are global climatic instability and global political instability. Reasonable minds can disagree about which problem is worse; but both require that the world move away from its dependence on fossil fuels and toward reliance on cleaner and smarter kinds of energy and toward more efficient use of energy.

First, the burning of hydrocarbon fuels contributes to global warming and climate change. In 1958, the concentration of carbon dioxide (CO_2) stood at 315 parts per million (ppm). Today, it has reached 394 ppm, about one third higher than the historical norm over 400,000 years. Levels of CO_2 are increasing so fast that in 40 or 50 years concentrations may be twice the historic levels (www.climate.nasa.gov/climate_resources). Since the planetary climate may already be changing in response to current CO_2 loadings, scientists consider the situation urgent. The global energy problem has less to do with depleting resources than with controlling emissions.

The second problem has to do with geopolitical stability. Thomas Friedman (2006) observes that oil-rich states tend to be the least democratic, and that the wealthier the ruling class gets, the more tyrannical, truculent, obstructive, and dangerous it becomes. The "petrocracies" destabilize global balances of power while holding oil-dependent states hostage. Although the food problem is best understood as local (giving the very poor access to nutrition), the energy problem is global. The principal concern is not the supply of energy but the effects of its use on geopolitics and climate.

Although leading environmentalists have focused on scarcity, they have also joined nearly everyone else in deploring the effects of the consumption of carbon-based fuels on the political and the atmospheric climate. To provide leadership and direction rather than simply reiterate their apocalyptic projections, environmentalists should advocate investment in some mix of power-producing and climate-sparing technologies. There is a smorgasbord of suggestions. These include hybrid, plug-in hybrid, and electric vehicles; greater energy efficiency in housing and appliances; and the production of liquid fuels from renewable sources, some produced by genetically engineered or synthesized microorganisms capable of creating biomass cheaply or even directly splitting the carbon dioxide molecule. Other approaches include the expansion of nuclear power generation (including smaller distributed and sealed units), the development of geothermal and wind energy, and basic and applied research in battery technology, fuel-cell technology, tidal power, and other forms of power. Efforts are underway to construct a smarter and more efficient electric energy transmission grid.

In the American Reinvestment and Recovery Act of 2009, the Obama administration threw a staggering amount of money at clean energy technologies. It is impossible at this time to pick winners among the scores of innovations. Some of this money will stick. Commercially available technologies can support present or greatly expanded worldwide economic activity while stabilizing global climate—and can save money. Even very large expansions in population and industrial activity need not be energy-constrained.

If many opportunities exist for saving energy and curtailing pollution, why have we not seized them? One reason is that low fossil-fuel prices remove incentives for fuel efficiency and for moving to other energy sources. If energy supplies were scarce, prices would have risen to levels that would force the kinds of innovations and transitions we now need the political will to make. Environmentalists might have more credibility in supporting novel forms of energy production if they were not weighed down by decades of doomsaying. The major obstacles standing in the way of a clean-energy economy are not technical in nature but concern the regulations, incentives, public attitudes, and other factors that make up the energy market.

ARE THERE TOO MANY PEOPLE?

In the 1970s, the population crisis was easy to define and dramatize. The Malthusian logic of exponential growth or "doubling times," forcefully presented in books such as *The Population Bomb* and *The Population Explosion*, argued that the "battle to feed all of humanity is over" and analogized the spread of population with cancer: "A cancer is an uncontrolled multiplication of cells; the population explosion is an uncontrolled multiplication of people. ... The [surgical] operation will demand many apparently brutal and heartless decisions. The pain may be intense. But the disease is so far advanced that only with radical surgery does the patient have a chance of survival." (Ehrlich 1971, 152)

By emphasizing the exponential mathematics of population growth—as if people were cancerous cells whose reproductive freedom had to be controlled by radical surgery—environmentalists made four mistakes.

First, they missed the opportunity to endorse the belief that people should have all—but only—the children they want. The goal of assisting parents worldwide to plan for their children might appeal to family values and thus to social conservatives in a way that concerns about too many people did not. Efforts to improve the status of women may enjoy more political support and may be more effective than conventional fertility-control policies.

Second, by inveighing against economic growth (by demanding a small economy for a small Earth), environmentalists alienated potential allies in the development community. Leading environmentalists explicitly rejected the hope that development can greatly increase the size of the economic pie and pull many more people out of poverty. This hope, Paul and Anne Ehrlich wrote, expresses a "basically a humane idea … made insane by the constraints nature places on human activity" (1990, 269).

Development economists replied that a no-economic-growth approach in the developing world would deprive entire populations of access to better living conditions and lead to even more deforestation and land degradation. Amartya Sen, among other scholars, pointed out that insistence on the Malthusian belief that nature puts narrow constraints on human activity diverts attention from the real causes of malnutrition, namely poverty and political powerlessness. The Malthusian approach, Sen argued, leads to complacent optimism because food production at the global level is more than adequate. With such "misleading variables as food output per unit of population, the Malthusian approach profoundly misspecifies the problems facing the poor of the world," which have to do with local conditions not with global constraints, and "it is often overlooked that what may be called 'Malthusian optimism' has actually killed millions of people" (Sen 1989).

Third, by invoking "doubling times" as if that concept could be as meaningfully applied to people as to tumors, environmentalists ignored science and reason—that is, everything demographers knew about the transition then underway to a stable global population. As people move to cities, where children are not needed to do agricultural labor, as they are assured that their children will survive (so they can have fewer children), and as the status of women improves, families become smaller. World population growth, which resulted from lower mortality not higher fertility, had been decelerating since the 1950s and dramatically after the 1970s. In 2008, the United Nations projected the global population "to reach 7 billion in late 2011, up from the current 6.8 billion, and surpass 9 billion people by 2050," when it would stabilize and probably decline (UN Department of

Economic and Social Affairs, Population Division, 2009, vii). Most demographers believe that population will stop increasing during this century and then decline slowly to perhaps 8.4 billion in 2100 (ibid., vii).

Today, most people live in countries or regions in which fertility is below the level of long-run replacement. According to a United Nations press release published in 2011, "42 percent of the world's population lives in low-fertility countries, that is, countries where women are not having enough children to ensure that, on average, each woman is replaced by a daughter who survives to the age of procreation." Another 40 percent live in nations approaching that level (UN Press Release 2011). Of course, population will increase inexorably as lifespans increase. According to UN projections, "globally, life expectancy is projected to increase from 68 years in 2005–2010 to 81 in 2095–2100" (ibid.).

Fourth, the environmental community has yet to respond to the principal moral problem that confronts population policy—one that involves longevity not fertility. The oldest segments of the population increase the fastest as science and technology extend the length of life. A UN report observes that in developed regions of the world "the population aged 60 or over is increasing at the fastest pace ever (growing at 2.0 percent annually) and is expected to increase by more than 50 per cent over the next four decades, rising from 264 million in 2009 to 416 million in 2050," and that developing world is aging even more rapidly: "Over the next two decades, the population aged 60 or over in the developing world is projected to increase at rates far surpassing 3 per cent per year, and its numbers are expected to rise from 473 million in 2009 to 1.6 billion in 2050" (ibid., viii).

Anyone interested in doubling times or exponential growth should consider the following statistics: In industrialized countries the number of centenarians has doubled every decade since 1950. In many countries, people aged 80 or over constitute the fastest-growing segment of the population. In 1900, 374,000 people in the United States had attained the age of 80;. Today, 10 million Americans are elderly; by 2030, that number is expected nearly to double, making huge demands on younger workers, whose labor may be needed and whose incomes will be taxed to pay for their care.

The problem is no longer Malthus, it's Methuselah. What do environmentalists say about this? As long as environmental leaders argue forever that there are too many people without suggesting how long a life should last, they seem self-serving. These environmentalists appear to comprise a vast and growing gerontocracy outraged that younger people whom they may need to take care of them presume to care for their own children.

WHAT IS WRONG WITH CONSUMPTION?

Many of us who grew up with the attitudes of the 1960s and the 1970s took pride in how little we owned. We celebrated our freedom when we could fit all our possessions into the back of a car. As we grow older, we tend to accumulate an appalling amount of stuff. Piled high with gas grills, lawn mowers, excess furniture, bicycles, children's toys, garden implements, ladders, lawn and leaf bags stuffed with memorabilia, and boxes yet to be unpacked from the last move, the two-car garages beside our suburban homes are too full to accommodate our SUVs. The quantity of resources (particularly energy) we waste and the quantity of trash we throw away add to our worries.

We are distressed by the suffering of others, the erosion of the ties of community, and the loss of the beauty and spontaneity of the natural world. These concerns express the most traditional and fundamental of American religious and cultural values. Even if predictions of resource depletion and ecological collapse are mistaken, it seems that they ought to be true, to punish us for our success and our sins.

Perhaps a feeling of guilt impels environmentalists to adopt their vision of impending Apocalypse, in the form of imminent resource depletion, starvation, and ecological Armageddon. In contrast, religious communities, especially mainstream Evangelical and other Christian groups, emphasize stewardship of the Earth for the very long run. In fact, more than sixty faith-based groups today pursue missions they describe as "environmental conservation" or "caring for creation" (www.webofcreation.org). In 1990, the National Association of Evangelicals issued a policy document that urged greater concern for the environment that included this statement:

> We urge Christians to shape their personal lives in creation-friendly ways: practicing effective recycling, conserving resources, and experiencing the joy of contact with nature. We urge government to encourage fuel efficiency, reduce pollution, encourage sustainable use of natural resources, and provide for the proper care of wildlife and their natural habitats. (National Association of Evangelicals 1990)

If the environmental community were to join with mainstream religious groups in preaching a narrative of hope rather than one of futility and imminent demise, the environmental movement would find itself in a better position to work with charitable organizations to relieve the lot of the poorest of the poor. There is a lot of misery worldwide to relieve.

However, imposing a market economy on traditional cultures in the name of development—the idea that everyone can and should always produce and consume more—is not always the solution. It creates problems as well as opportunities. A market economy may dissolve the ties to family, land, community, and place on which indigenous peoples traditionally rely for their security. Thus, projects intended to relieve the poverty of indigenous peoples may, by causing the loss of cultural identity, engender the very powerlessness they aim to remedy. Pope Paul VI, in the encyclical Populorum Progressio (1967), described the dilemma confronting indigenous peoples: "either to preserve traditional beliefs and structures and reject social progress; or to embrace foreign technology and foreign culture, and reject ancestral traditions with their wealth of humanism." A similar dilemma confronts wealthy societies. No one has written a better critique of the assault that commerce makes on the quality of our lives than Thoreau provides in *Walden*. We are always in a rush—a "Saint Vitus' dance" (Thoreau 1995, 174). Idleness is suspect. Americans today spend less time with their families, neighbors, and friends than they did in the 1950s. We are almost literally working ourselves to death. That money does not make us happier, once our basic needs are met, is a commonplace overwhelmingly confirmed by sociological evidence. Paul Wachtel, who teaches social psychology at the City University of New York, has concluded that bigger incomes "do not yield an increase in feelings of satisfaction or well-being, at least for populations who are above a poverty or subsistence level" (Wachtel 1994, 5). This cannot be explained simply by the fact that people have to work harder to earn more money. Even those who win large sums of money in lotteries often report that their lives are not substantially happier as a result (Argyle 1986). Well-being depends upon health, membership in a community in which one feels secure, friends, faith, family, love, and virtues that money cannot buy.

Economists in earlier times predicted that wealth would not matter to people once they attained a comfortable standard of living. "In ease of body and peace of mind, all the different ranks of life are nearly upon a level," wrote Adam Smith, the eighteenth-century English advocate of the free market (1976, 185). In the 1930s the British economist John Maynard Keynes argued that after a period of expansion accumulation of wealth would no longer improve personal well being (Keynes 1963). Subsequent economists, however, found that, even after much of the industrial world had attained the levels of wealth Keynes thought were sufficient, people still wanted more. From this they inferred that wants are insatiable (Nelson 1991). Perhaps this is true. But the insatiability of wants poses a difficulty for standard economic theory, which posits that humanity's single goal is to increase or maximize wealth. If wants increase as fast as income grows, what purpose can wealth serve?

Whether or not economic growth is sustainable, there is little reason to think that continued growth is desirable once people attain a decent standard of living. It is no longer possible for most people to believe that economic progress will solve all the problems of mankind, spiritual as well as material. Environmentalists will not make convincing arguments as long as they frame the debate over sustainability in terms of the physical limits to growth rather than the moral purpose of it. Even if technology overcomes the physical limits nature sets on the amount we can produce and consume, however, there are moral, spiritual, and cultural limits to growth. Environmentalists defeat themselves by denying the power of technological progress. If the debate were couched not in economic terms but in moral or social terms—if it were to center on the values we seek to serve rather than the resources we may exhaust—environmentalists might more easily win the argument.

MAKING A PLACE FOR NATURE

According to Thoreau, "a man's relation to Nature must come very near to a personal one" (1949, 252). For environmentalists in the tradition of Thoreau and Muir, stewardship is a form of fellowship. Although we must use nature, we do not value it primarily for the economic purposes it serves. We take our bearings from the natural world—our sense of time from its days and seasons, and our sense of place from the character of a landscape and the particular plants and animals native to it. An intimacy with nature ends our isolation in the world. We know where we belong, and we can find the way home.

In defending old-growth forests, wetlands, or species, we environmentalists make our best arguments when we think of nature chiefly in aesthetic and moral terms. Rather than having the courage of our moral and cultural convictions, however, we too often rely on economic arguments for protecting nature, in the process attributing to natural objects more instrumental value than they have. By imputing to an endangered species an economic value or a price much greater than it fetches in a market, we "save the phenomena" for economic theory but do little for the environment. When we make the prices come out "right" by imputing market demand to aspects of nature, which in fact have moral, spiritual, or aesthetic value, we confuse ourselves and fail to convince others.

There is no credible argument that all or even most of the species we are concerned to protect have any economic significance or that they are essential to the functioning of the ecological systems on which we depend. If whales were to become extinct, for example, the seas would not fill up with krill. David Ehrenfeld, a biologist at Rutgers University, points out that the species most likely to be endangered are those the biosphere is least likely to miss: "Many of these species were never common or ecologically influential; by no stretch of the imagination can we make them out to be vital cogs in the ecological machine." (Ehrenfeld 1988, 215)

Species may be profoundly important for cultural and spiritual reasons, however. Consider the example of the wild salmon, whose habitat is being destroyed by hydroelectric dams along the Columbia River. Although this loss is not important to the economy overall (there is no shortage of farmed salmon), it is of great cultural significance to the Amerindian tribes that have traditionally subsisted on wild salmon, and to the region as a whole. By viewing local flora and fauna as a sacred heritage—by recognizing their intrinsic value—we discover who we are rather than what we want. On moral and cultural grounds society might be justified in making economic sacrifices—removing dams, for example—to protect remnant populations of the Snake River sockeye, even if, as critics complain, hundreds or thousands of dollars are spent for every fish.

Even those plants and animals that do not define places possess enormous intrinsic value and are worth preserving for their own sake. What gives these creatures value lies in their histories, wonderful in themselves, rather than in any use to which they can be put. The biologist E. O. Wilson elegantly takes up this theme: "Every kind of organism has reached this moment in time by threading one needle after another, throwing up brilliant artifices to survive and reproduce against nearly impossible odds." (1992, 345. Every plant or animal evokes not just sympathy but also reverence and wonder in those who know its place, properties, and history.

In *Earth in the Balance*, Al Gore wrote "We have become so successful at controlling nature that we have lost our connection to it" (1992, 225). It is all too easy, Gore wrote, "to regard the earth as a collection of 'resources,' having an intrinsic value no larger than their usefulness at the moment" (ibid., 1). The question before us is not whether we are going to run out of resources. It is whether the theory of welfare economics is the appropriate context for thinking about environmental policy.

Even John Stuart Mill, one of the principal authors of utilitarian philosophy, recognized that the natural world has great intrinsic and not just instrumental value. More than 100 years ago, as England lost its last wild places, Mill condemned a world "with nothing left to the spontaneous activity of nature; with every rood of land brought into cultivation, which is capable of growing food for human beings; every flowery waste or natural pasture ploughed up; all quadrupeds or birds which are not domesticated for man's use exterminated as his rivals for food, every hedgerow or superfluous tree rooted out, and scarcely a place left where a wild shrub or flower could grow without being eradicated as a weed in the name of improved agriculture" (1987, 750).

The world has the wealth and the resources to provide everyone the opportunity for a decent life. We consume too much when market relationships displace the bonds of community, compassion, culture, and place. We consume too much when consumption becomes an end in itself and makes us lose affection and reverence for the natural world.

REFERENCES

Argyle, Michael. 1986. *The Psychology of Happiness.* Methuen.

Brown, Lester. 1989. The grain drain. *Futurist* 23 (4): 17–18.

Deffeyes, Kenneth S. 2005. *Beyond Oil: The View from Hubbert's Peak.* Farrar, Straus and Giroux.

Ehrenfeld, David. 1988. Why put a value on biodiversity? In *Biodiversity*, ed. E. O. Wilson. National Academy Press.

Ehrlich, Paul. 1971. *The Population Bomb.* Ballantine Books.

Ehrlich, Paul R., and Anne H. Ehrlich. 1990. *The Population Explosion.* Simon and Schuster.

Ehrlich, Paul R., and Anne H. Ehrlich. 2004. *One with Nineveh: Politics, Consumption, and the Human Future*. Island.

FAO (UN Food and Agriculture Organization). 2009. Global food supply gradually steadying. Press release, June 4 (http://www.fao.org/news/story/en/item/20351/icode/).

Friedman, Thomas L. 2006. "As energy prices rise, it's all downhill for democracy." *New York Times*, May 5.

Goodstein, David. 2004. *Out of Gas: The End of the Age of Oil*. Norton.

Gever, John. Robert Kaufmann, David Skole, and Charles Vorosmarty. 1996. *Beyond Oil: The Threat to Food and Fuel in the Coming Decades*. Ballinger.

Gore, Al. 1992. *Earth in the Balance: Ecology and the Human Spirit*. Houghton Mifflin.

Heinberg, Richard. 2003. *The Party's Over: Oil, War and the Fate of Industrial Societies*. New Society Publishers.

Johnson, Gale D. 2000. Population, food, and knowledge. *American Economic Review* 90 (1): 1–14.

Keynes, John Maynard. 1963. Economic possibilities for our grandchildren. In Keynes, *Essays in Persuasion*. Norton.

Lee, Thomas H. 1989. Advanced fossil fuel systems and beyond. In *Technology and Environment*, ed. Jesse H. Ausubel and Hedy E. Sladovich. National Academy Press.

Matson, Pamela, and Peter Vitousek. 2006. Agricultural intensification: Will land spared from farming be land spared for nature? *Conservation Biology* 20 (3): 709–710.

Mill, John Stuart. 1987. *Principles of Political Economy with some of their Applications to Social Philosophy*. Kelley.

Assessment, Millennium Ecosystem. Ecosystems and Human Well-being: Current State and Trends. 2005. http://www.millenniumassessments.org/.

Muir, John. 1912. *The Yosemite*. Century.

National Association of Evangelicals. 1990. *Stewardship*. nae.net

Nelson, Robert H. 1991. *Reaching for Heaven on Earth: The Theological Meaning of Economics*. Rowman and Littlefield.

Orr, W. David. 2005. Armageddon versus extinction. *Conservation Biology* 19 (2): 290–292.

Pope Paul VI. 1967. "Populorum Progressio," Encyclical of Pope Paul VI on the Development of Peoples, March 26, 1967. In *The Papal Encyclicals 1958–1981*, ed. Claudia C. Ihm. Pierian Press.

Roberts, Paul. 2005. *The End of Oil: On the Edge of a Perilous New World*. Houghton Mifflin.

Sen, Amartya. 1989. *Resources, Values, and Development*. Harvard University Press.

Smith, Adam. 1976. *The Theory of the Moral Sentiments*, ed. D. D. Raphael and A. L. Macfie. Clarendon.

Thoreau, Henry David. 1949. *The Journal of Henry David Thoreau*. vol. 10. Ed. B. Torrey and F. Allen. Houghton Mifflin.

Thoreau, Henry David. 1995. *Walden: Or, Life in the Woods*. Dover.

UN Department of Economic and Social Affairs, Population Division. 2009. World Population Prospects: The 2008 Revision, Highlights, Working paper.

UN Press Release. May 3, 2011. World Population to reach 10 billion by 2100 if Fertility in all Countries Converges to Replacement Level.

US Energy Information Administration. 2012. Annual Energy Outlook 2012 with Projections to 2035. www.eia.gov/forecasts/aeo

Wachtel, Paul. 1994. Consumption, satisfaction, and self-deception. Paper presented at conference on Consumption, Stewardship and the Good Life, University of Maryland.

Whitman, Walt. 1971. *Specimen Days*. Godine.

Wilson, Edward O. 1992. *The Diversity of Life*. Harvard University Press.

World Bank. 2009. Global Economic Prospects. www.climate.nasa.gov/climate_resources www.webofcreation.org

Printed in the USA
CPSIA information can be obtained
at www.ICGtesting.com
LVHW081724230724
786199LV00023B/59

9 781793 519139